countdown to mathematics

Volume 2

Lynne Graham and David Sargent
of the Open University

 ADDISON-WESLEY PUBLISHERS LIMITED

in association with the **OPEN UNIVERSITY PRESS**

Wokingham, England ● Reading, Massachusetts ● Menlo Park, California ●
New York ● Don Mills, Ontario ● Amsterdam ● Bonn ●
Sydney ● Singapore ● Tokyo ● Madrid ● San Juan ●

Published in 1981 by Addison-Wesley Publishers Limited.

Copyright © 1981 The Open University

Cartoons by David Farris
Typeset by Allset Composition, London
Printed in Great Britain by Hollen Street Press Limited,
Slough, Berkshire.

First printed in 1981
Reprinted in 1982 (twice), 1983 (twice), 1984, 1985, 1986,
1987 (twice), 1988 (twice), 1989, 1990, 1991 and 1992

ISBN 201 13731 3

CONTENTS

Introduction   v

MODULE 5
5.1 Circles and Angular Measure   3
5.2 Angle Properties   14
5.3 Similar Triangles   28
5.4 More About Triangles   40
5.5 Shape, Areas and Volumes   52
Solutions   63

MODULE 6
6.1 Factors   73
6.2 Quadratics of the Form $x^2 + bx + c$ 80
6.3 Quadratics of the Form $ax^2 + bx + c$ 91
6.4 Algebraic Fractions   98
6.5 Equations and Formulas   108
Solutions   119

MODULE 7
7.1 Straight Lines   131
7.2 Quadratics   139
7.3 Other Curves   148
7.4 Solving Equations   159
7.5 Algebraic Methods of Solving Linear   168
     Simultaneous Equations
Solutions   176

MODULE 8
8.1 Sines and Cosines   193
8.2 The Trigonometric Ratios and Right   203
     Angled Triangles
8.3 Finding the Angle   213
8.4 Right Angled Triangles   225
8.5 Investigations   235
Solutions   238

MODULE 9

9.1	Indices	253
9.2	Logarithms	262
9.3	Square Roots	272
9.4	Indices (II)	281
9.5	Factorisation	289
Solutions		297

Countdown to Mathematics on Radio

A series of BBC radio programmes, designed to support the study of *Countdown to Mathematics Volume 2*, is broadcast each year, as follows.

December
- Programme 1 Introduction – *Start Countdown*
- Programme 2 Module 5 – *Countdown to Angles*
- Programme 3 Module 6 – *Countdown to Algebra*

following January
- Programme 4 Module 7 – *Countdown to Graphs*
- Programme 5 Module 8 – *Countdown to Trig*
- Programme 6 Module 9 – *Countdown to Logs*

There may be a second broadcast of the programmes in May/June.
Exact broadcast dates and times may be obtained from the
Centre for Mathematics Education (CR), The Open University,
Milton Keynes MK7 6AA.

The series will be accompanied by a booklet containing Radio Notes. All registered students on the Open University *Mathematics Foundation Course* (M101) or *An Introduction to Calculus* (MS284) will be sent this automatically before their study commences, as part of their Preparatory Material. Other listeners may obtain the booklet by sending an A4-sized stamped addressed envelope, to the Centre for Mathematics Education at the above address.

Introduction

This is the second volume of *Countdown to Mathematics* and is
primarily aimed at students who intend to study a mathematics course at
the Open University. It follows on from Volume I in that it continues the
development of skills and techniques in algebra and graphical work. In
addition, we introduce some of the basic ideas in geometry and trigonometry. We have found that many students lack the ability to manipulate
symbols. Consequently much of the book is devoted to such manipulation.
We have included as many examples and exercises as space permits as we
feel it is only by constant repetition of the techniques that confidence
will be increased. Evidence collected in the Open University over the
last ten years suggests that students not only lack confidence in mathematical skills and techniques but they also lack the study skills necessary
for learning in isolation. Thus *Countdown to Mathematics* has been
designed both to brush up mathematical skills and to develop skills for
self-study. The style is informal and the approach follows the learning
strategies adopted by many Open University courses. Although the
emphasis is on preparation for the Open University we feel that many
other students face the same problems. Consequently we hope that
Countdown to Mathematics will appeal to a wider audience.

HOW TO USE THIS BOOK
Volume 2 of *Countdown to Mathematics* is broken down into five
Modules covering geometry, graphs, trigonometry and algebra (two
Modules). Each Module is itself divided into five sections. (See Contents
Page)

Studying on your own requires a special discipline. We hope that
breaking down the book into small sections helps you to organise a study
routine which you feel you can follow. You may not need to work
through all the book. To help you identify which sections you can omit
and which sections you should read carefully we have prefaced each
section with some diagnostic questions: *TRY THESE QUESTIONS FIRST.*
Then turn the page and check your answers. These direct you to the
appropriate subsection. You may feel sufficiently confident to omit the
section, or you may want to read through it quickly just for extra
reassurance. However, if you experience any difficulty with the diagnostic
questions then we advise you to work through the section carefully.

You will find that each section contains plenty of exercises which you
should work through thoroughly in order to gain most benefit. Full
solutions are provided at the end of each Module. When reading mathematics at any level you should have a pencil and paper handy and expect

to use them! Each section concludes with a summary and some supplementary exercises should you want some extra practice.

ASSUMED KNOWLEDGE
In Volume 2 we assume that you are confident in using all the techniques discussed in Volume I. In particular we assume that you
   (i) can use a calculator to perform arithmetic calculations involving positive and negative numbers (whole numbers and decimals),
  (ii) can estimate an answer and round the answer to a required level of accuracy (to a given number of decimal places or significant figures),
 (iii) can manipulate numerical fractions, ratio and proportion,
  (iv) can simplify algebraic expressions by collecting like terms,
   (v) can solve linear equations,
  (vi) can change the subject of an equation or formula,
 (vii) can substitute numerical values into algebraic expressions,
(viii) can plot a graph from a table of values, choosing suitable scales for the axes,
  (ix) can plot the graph of a linear equation and interpret the gradient and intercept in terms of the equation.

CALCULATOR
We also assume that you have a scientific calculator. Many of the concepts are developed through calculator investigation. In order to perform these investigations we encourage you to become familiar with how *your* calculator works, by suggesting preliminary activities which you can check by hand. We usually leave you to determine an appropriate key sequence so you will frequently need to refer to the Maker's Handbook. Several exercises involve complex numbers and, without a calculator, the working will be very complicated, involving the use of log tables, square root tables and trigonometric tables. A calculator removes the drudgery from such calculations so it is desirable that you should use one whenever possible.

Finally we hope that you will find the book readable. After working through *Countdown to Mathematics* we hope that you can go on to use the skills and techniques in your future studies with confidence.

MODULE ⑤

5.1 Circles and Angular Measure

5.2 Angle Properties

5.3 Similar Triangles

5.4 More About Triangles

5.5 Shape, Areas and Volumes

5.1 Circles and Angular Measure

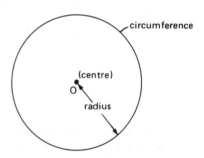

5.1(i) CIRCLES

A circle is defined as the set of all points which are a fixed distance from a fixed point. This fixed point is called the *centre* of the circle and is often indicated with the letter O.

The fixed distance is called the *radius* of the circle and the distance around the circle, or the perimeter, is called the *circumference.*

The term circumference is often used to refer to the circle itself.

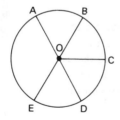

A straight line joining two points on the circumference and which passes through the centre of the circle is called a *diameter.*

For example, in this circle, OA, OB, OC, OD, and OE are all radii and AD and BE are diameters. The points A, B, C, D and E all lie on the circumference.

The plural of radius is radii.

CHECK YOUR ANSWERS

1 $C = 2\pi r$ Section 5.1(i)

   so $C = 2 \times \pi \times 7 \cdot 8 = 49 \cdot 01$ cm.

2 $A = \pi r^2$ Section 5.1(ii)

   so $A = \pi \times (7 \cdot 8)^2 = 191 \cdot 13$ cm^2.

3 1 radian is the angle subtended at the centre of a circle by an arc   Section 5.1(iii)
   equal in length to the radius of the circle.

4 (i) $220° \, 32' = 220 \cdot 53° = 220 \cdot 53 \times \dfrac{2\pi}{360} = 3 \cdot 85$ rad.   Section 5.1(iv)

   (ii) $\dfrac{3\pi}{5}$ radians $= \dfrac{3\pi}{5} \times \dfrac{360}{2\pi} = 108°$.

The circle below has radius 1 cm and diameter 2 cm.

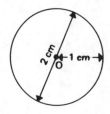

This diagram illustrates that the diameter is twice the radius.

More generally, if d stands for the diameter of a circle and r stands
for the radius, then

   $d = 2r.$

Constructing a circle

The best way to construct (or draw) a circle of a given radius is to
use a pair of compasses. Using a ruler set the distance from the
point of the compasses to the tip of the pencil to the desired radius.
Place the point on the paper at the position where you want the
centre of the circle to be and carefully rotate the compasses on the
point so that the pencil marks out the required circle.

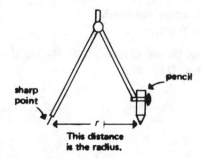

sharp
point

pencil

r

This distance
is the radius.

Measuring the circumference

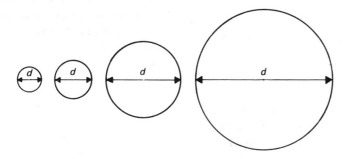

These circles indicate that as the diameter of a circle increases so does the circumference. What is less obvious is that there is a specific relationship between the circumference and diameter.

In fact the circumference is directly proportional to the diameter. So if C stands for the circumference and d for the diameter,

$$C = kd$$

or

$$\frac{C}{d} = k.$$

See Module 2, Section 2.5.

k is the constant of proportionality.

The following investigation enables you to confirm this result for yourself.

Investigation

Collect a number of objects having a circular base or lid.

jam jar   cup and saucer   bowl   bottle

Measure the circumference of each object using a tape measure and record your answer in the table below. Then measure the diameter. This is a bit more difficult. The diameter always passes through the centre of the circle but it's often very difficult to find the centre. However, you should be able to obtain a reasonably accurate measurement by measuring the longest distance from one side of the circle to the other.

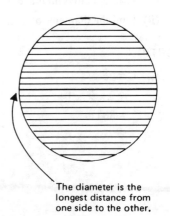

The diameter is the longest distance from one side to the other.

Object	C cm	d cm	$k = \dfrac{C}{d}$
Mug	25·8	8·2	3·15
Sellotape	28·7	9·1	3·15
Dustbin	182	57	3·19

We have used centimetres as the unit of measurement. Of course you can use any unit, as long as both distances are given in the same units.

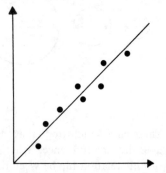

You will probably find that there is some variation in the values of k as a result of inaccurate measurement. However, if you have taken reasonable care you should find that k lies somewhere between 3·0 and 3·2.

You may like to draw a graph of your results. You should get a straight line passing through the origin and the gradient of this line gives the constant of proportionality.

The actual value of k is denoted by π (pronounced pi). A calculator gives π as

$$\pi \doteq 3{\cdot}1415926536.$$

Your calculator may have a $\boxed{\pi}$ key.

Notice that even this value of π is only approximate. It is impossible to give an exact value of π; it's a rather special number.

A useful fraction approximation to π is $\frac{22}{7}$. As a decimal it is often remembered as 3·142. In calculations, any of these approximations may be used, although you'll probably find it easier just to use the π key on your calculator.

The circumference and diameter are therefore related by the formula

$$\frac{C}{d} = \pi$$

which is usually remembered as

$$\boxed{C = \pi d \ \text{ or } \ C = 2\pi r.}$$

Remember, $d = 2r$.

EXAMPLE

   (i) Find the circumference of a circle of radius 14 cm.

   (ii) Find the diameter of a circle of circumference 35 m.

SOLUTION

   (i) $C = 2\pi r$

$$\doteq 2 \times \tfrac{22}{7} \times 14$$

$$= 88 \text{ cm}$$

In this example we have approximated π by $\frac{22}{7}$.

(ii) $C = \pi d$.

Rearranging the formula

$$d = \frac{C}{\pi},$$

so $d = \dfrac{35}{\pi}$

$\simeq 11 \cdot 140846$

$\simeq 11 \cdot 141$ m (correct to three decimal places).

Here, we used the π key.

Remember to give the answer in terms of the appropriate units.

TRY SOME YOURSELF

1(i) Find the circumference of a circle of radius 7 cm.
(ii) Find the diameter of a circle whose circumference is 44 m.

Give your answers correct to two decimal places.

5.1(ii) AREA OF A CIRCLE

Any diameter divides a circle into two equal parts, called semicircles.

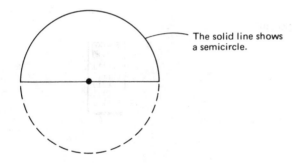

The solid line shows a semicircle.

Since the curved part is half a circle its length is half the circumference of the circle. The length of the curved part is therefore

$\dfrac{\pi d}{2}$ or πr.

This circle has radius r. It has been divided up into equal 'slices' or *sectors*, the shaded sectors being labelled a, b, c, d. The eight sectors can be cut out and re-arranged into the shape below.

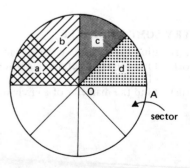

sector

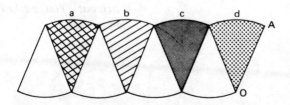

The area of this shape is equal to the area of the circle.

The length of the top side (measured along the curved edges) is equal to the length of the sectors a + b + c + d, which is just the length of the semicircle, πr. OA is the radius r.

Dividing the circle into 16 sectors gives the following shape.

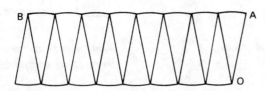

Again, the area is equal to the area of the original circle.

Again the length of the curved path (AB) is πr and OA = r. Dividing the circle into more divisions produces a shape which is even closer to a rectangle with length πr, and width r.

Rearranging the sectors does not affect the area, so ultimately, the area of the circle, A, is given by the area of this rectangle.

The area of a circle is therefore given by the formula

$$\boxed{A = \pi r^2.}$$

Area of rectangle
 = length x width
 = $\pi r \times r$
 = πr^2.

EXAMPLE

Find the radius of a circle whose area is 100 cm^2.

SOLUTION

$$A = \pi r^2$$

Rearranging the formula, $r^2 = \dfrac{A}{\pi}$. Thus

$$r = \sqrt{\frac{A}{\pi}}$$

$$= \sqrt{\frac{100}{\pi}}$$

= 5·64 cm (correct to two decimal places).

Remember to include the units in the answer.

TRY SOME YOURSELF

2(i) Find the area of a circle of radius 7 cm.
(ii) Find the radius of a circle whose area is 616 m^2.
       (Take $\pi = \frac{22}{7}$.)
(iii) Find the diameter of a circle of area 15 cm^2.

Where necessary, give your answer correct to two decimal places.

Watch out! You're asked for the diameter here.

5.1(iii) ANGLES AND ANGULAR MEASURE

What is meant by 'angle'? The *Oxford English Dictionary* defines it as:

> 'space between two meeting lines or planes, inclination of two lines to each other'.

An angle can be pictured as a corner between two straight lines.

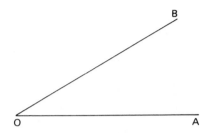

The word 'angle' comes from the Latin 'angulus' meaning corner.

The mathematical term for corner is vertex.

More precisely, the angle is the amount of rotation required to take one of the lines to the other, but even this definition is ambiguous because rotation may be clockwise or anticlockwise.

The diagram opposite shows that if OA is rotated anticlockwise a small rotation is all that is required to bring it to OB. However if OA is rotated clockwise it needs to move through almost a complete circle before it reaches OB.

Think of O as a pivot and move OA until it lies exactly on top of OB.

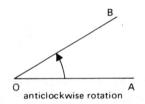

anticlockwise rotation

To overcome this ambiguity angles are always measured using anticlockwise rotations. Thus the angle between OA and OB is the amount of *anticlockwise* rotation which takes OA to OB.

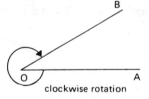

clockwise rotation

Angles are often labelled with Greek letters and sometimes an arrow is used to indicate whether an angle is positive or negative. If the arrow points in an anticlockwise direction the angle is positive; if it points in a clockwise direction the angle is said to be negative.

For example, in the figure opposite the angle between OA and OB is θ, whereas the angle between OA and OC is $-\alpha$.

Some examples of Greek letters are α (pronounced alpha) and θ (pronounced theta).

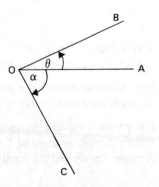

TRY SOME YOURSELF

3   Determine whether each of the following angles is positive or
negative.

β is pronounced beta.
φ is pronounced phi.
γ is pronounced gamma.

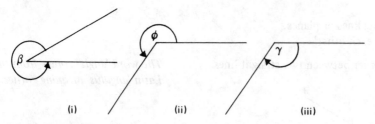

(i)   (ii)   (iii)

Angular measurement

Angles may be measured in radians or degrees.

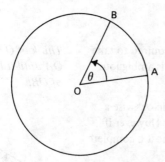

The part of the circumference between A and B is called the *arc* AB.
Joining A and B to the centre of the circle, O, produces an angle, θ.
This angle is called the angle subtended by the arc AB.

*The angle subtended at the centre of a circle by an arc equal in
length to the radius of the circle is defined to be one radian.*

*Strictly speaking there are two
arcs between A and B; a short
arc corresponding to the angle θ,
and a longer arc produced by
moving from A to B in the
opposite direction.*

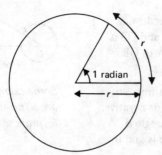

This definition can be used to find the number of radians corresponding to a complete revolution.

In a complete revolution A moves anticlockwise around the
circumference back to its original position, moving a distance $2\pi r$.

Every time A moves a distance r around the circumference it
rotates through an angle of 1 radian, so in one complete revolution
A moves $2\pi r$ around the circumference, rotating through 2π radians.

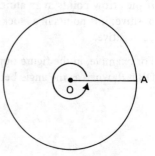

circumference = $2\pi r$

Thus a complete revolution corresponds to an angle of 2π radians, and fractions of a revolution correspond to angles which are fractions of 2π.

2π radians is often written as 2π rad or just 2π.

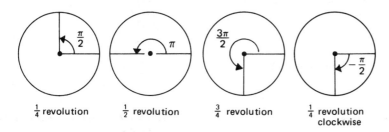

Alternatively, angles may be measured in degrees. A complete revolution is defined to correspond to rotation through an angle of 360 degrees (written $360°$), and fractions of a revolution correspond to angles which are fractions of $360°$.

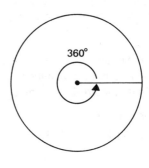

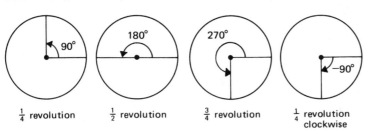

TRY SOME YOURSELF

4   Draw rough diagrams to indicate each of the following angles. Label the angle in both degrees and radians:
(i) 1/3 revolution   (iii) −1/6 revolution
(ii) 1/6 revolution   (iv) −1/12 revolution

5.1(iv) CONVERTING FROM RADIANS TO DEGREES (AND VICE VERSA)

Since

$$2\pi \text{ radians} = 360°,$$

$$1 \text{ radian} = \frac{360°}{2\pi} \text{ and}$$

$$\boxed{x \text{ radians} = x \times \frac{360°}{2\pi}.}$$

Since 2π and $360° = 1$ revolution.

Given the radian measurement, we can convert to degrees.

Similarly,

$$1° = \frac{2\pi}{360} \text{ radians, and}$$

$$\boxed{y° = \left(y \times \frac{2\pi}{360} \right) \text{ radians.}}$$

Given the angle in degrees, we can convert to radians.

EXAMPLE

Convert 113·5° to radians.

SOLUTION

$$113\cdot5° = \left(113\cdot5 \times \frac{2\pi}{360}\right) \text{ radians}$$

$$= 1\cdot98 \text{ radians (correct to two decimal places).}$$

TRY SOME YOURSELF

5(i) Convert each of the following to radians:
    (a) 54°   (b) 125°   (c) −67·18°

(ii) Convert each of the following to degrees:
    (a) 2π/7   (b) 1 radian   (c) −0·5 radians.

Give your answers correct to two decimal places.

In the examples above, angles measured in degrees are given as decimals, but it is common to measure angles in degrees and minutes, where 1° = 60 minutes = 60′.

This is similar to measuring time in hours, minutes, and seconds.

For example

$$113\cdot5° = 113° \ 30′.$$

EXAMPLE

Rewrite 42·295° in degrees and minutes.

SOLUTION

$$42\cdot295° = 42° + 0\cdot295°$$

Since 1° = 60′,

$$0\cdot295° = (60 \times 0\cdot295)′ = 18′.$$

Thus 42·295° = 42° 18′.

We have rounded to the nearest minute.

TRY SOME YOURSELF

6(i) Rewrite each of the following angles in degrees and minutes:
    (a) 51·38°   (b) −62·22°   (c) 115·65°.

(ii) Rewrite each of the following angles in decimal notation:
    (a) 79°52′   (b) 125° 45′   (c) −213° 23′.

Give your answers correct to two decimal places.

To convert an angle measured in degrees to radians, you must ensure that it is first expressed in decimal form.

EXAMPLE

Convert 31°17′ to radians.

SOLUTION

$$31° \ 17' = 31° + 17'$$
$$= 31° + \left(\tfrac{17}{60}\right)°$$
$$= 31\cdot28°$$

$$31\cdot28° = \left(31\cdot28 \times \frac{2\pi}{360}\right) \text{ radians,}$$

$$= 0\cdot55 \text{ radians (correct to two decimal places).}$$

TRY SOME YOURSELF

7   Convert each of the following to radians:
(i) 63° 14′   (ii) 295° 51′   (iii) −12° 46′.

Give your answers correct to two decimal places.

After you have worked through this section you should be able to

a   Identify the radius, diameter and circumference of a circle
b   Find the circumference of a circle using the formula $C = 2\pi r$ or $C = \pi d$
c   Find the area of a circle using the formula $A = \pi r^2$
d   Write down the definition of 1 radian
e   Draw a rough diagram to represent a fraction of revolution, and label the corresponding angle in both degrees and radians
f   Convert an angle from degree measurement to radian measurement, and vice versa

---

Finally here are some exercises if you want more practice.

TRY SOME MORE YOURSELF

8(i)   (a) Find the circumference of the Earth around the equator, given that the radius of the Earth is 6378 km.
(b) A wire is placed around the equator. How much extra wire would be needed to lift the wire 6 cm off the ground all the way round? Have a guess first before working this out.

(ii)   (a) Find the area of a circle of radius 3 cm.
(b) What is the area of a semicircle of radius 3 cm?
(c) A circle has area 50 in.^{2}. What is its radius?

(iii)   Draw rough diagrams to represent each of the following angles. Label the angle in both degrees and radians:
(a) $-\tfrac{2}{3}$ revolution   (b) $\tfrac{5}{6}$ revolution   (c) $\tfrac{5}{12}$ revolution.

(iv)   Convert each of the following angles to radians:
(a) 36°   (b) −175·3°   (c) 14° 24′   (d) 215° 36′.

(v)   Convert each of the following angles to degrees:
(a) $\tfrac{\pi}{8}$ radians   (b) 2 radians   (c) $-\tfrac{\pi}{5}$ radians   (d) −0·2 radians.

5.2 Angles Properties

TRY THESE QUESTIONS FIRST

1 (i)   Relabel α using an alternative notation.

   (ii) Measure α using a protractor.

   (iii) What type of angle is α?

2 Find θ in $\triangle ABC$ without using a protractor.

3 (i)   Mark the side adjacent to the angle α on $\triangle XYZ$.

   (ii) What is the value of α?

4 (i)   Find α in the figure below.

   (ii) Show that FG and EH are parallel.

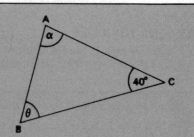

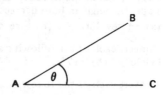

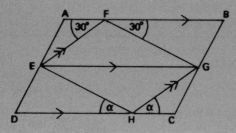

5.2(i) ANGLES: NOTATION AND MEASUREMENT

In the previous section we indicated that an angle has both size and direction (anticlockwise or clockwise), but sometimes you only need to know the size; the direction doesn't matter. In this section we consider some angle properties which involve only the size.

First we introduce some alternative notation for angles. We've already used Greek letters together with arrows to denote size. If the direction is not needed then the arrow may be omitted.

Alternatively an angle may be labelled by the vertex with a hat on it.

For example, $\theta = \hat{A}$.

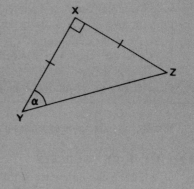

$\hat{A}$ is pronounced A hat. The $^\wedge$ indicates an angle.

However this notation can be ambiguous if several angles meet at the same vertex.

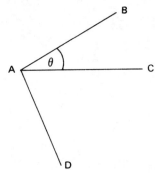

To avoid confusion, it is sometimes necessary to give some additional information.

For example, $\theta = \hat{BAC}$ or $\theta = \angle BAC$.

Here, the middle letter indicates the vertex, and the two outer letters identify the 'arms' of the angle.

Again, the $\frown$ or $\angle$ indicates an angle and both $\hat{BAC}$ and $\angle BAC$ are pronounced the angle BAC.

TRY SOME YOURSELF

1   Relabel each of the following angles in the figure opposite using an alternative notation:
(i) α (ii) β (iii) θ.

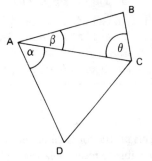

Measuring and drawing angles

The definition of angular measurement does not help in drawing or measuring angles. In practice you will need to use a protractor. This is a mathematical instrument which is used to measure angles in degrees.

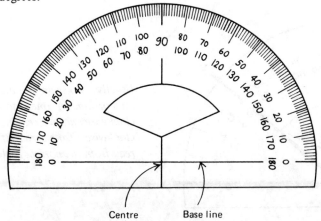

Notice that the base line for the protractor is not usually the bottom edge.

Centre   Base line

CHECK YOUR ANSWERS

1 (i) $\alpha = \hat{A} = B\hat{A}C = \angle BAC$ *Section 5.2(i)*
   (ii) $\alpha = 80°$
   (iii) α is an acute angle since it is less than 90°.

2 $A\hat{B}C + B\hat{A}C + A\hat{C}B = 180°$ (angle sum property)   *Section 5.2(ii)*
   $\theta + 80° + 40° = 180°$,
   so $\theta = 60°$.

3 (i) XY is the side adjacent to α.   *Section 5.2(iii)*
   (ii) $\triangle XYZ$ is isoceles and $X\hat{Y}Z$ and $X\hat{Z}Y$ are base angles. Therefore
         $X\hat{Y}Z = X\hat{Z}Y = \alpha$.
             $90° + 2\alpha = 180°$ (angle sum property)
             so $2\alpha = 90°$ and $\alpha = 45°$.

4 Using the alternate angle property,   *Section 5.2(iv)*
   (i) AB and EG are parallel, so $F\hat{E}G = A\hat{F}E = 30°$.
        EF and HG are parallel, so $H\hat{G}E = F\hat{E}G = 30°$.
        DC and EG are parallel, so $\alpha = C\hat{H}G = H\hat{G}E = 30°$.
   (ii) AB and EG are parallel, so $E\hat{G}F = G\hat{F}B = 30°$.
         EG and DC are parallel, so $G\hat{E}H = E\hat{H}D = \alpha = 30°$.
         Thus $H\hat{E}G = E\hat{G}F = 30°$. $H\hat{E}G$ and $E\hat{G}F$ are alternate angles,
         so EH and FG are parallel.

This protractor is tabulated to measure angles from 0° to 180°. It is
possible to measure larger angles by turning the protractor over. It is
also possible to buy circular protractors which measure angles from
0° to 360°.

The following diagram indicates how the protractor should be
positioned in order to measure an angle.

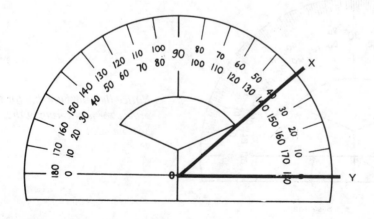

*Usually, two scales are indicated
on a protractor, one reading anticlockwise and one reading
clockwise. Take care that you
read from the correct scale.*

Place the base line of the protractor on one arm of the angle with the centre, O, on the vertex. The angle can then be read straight from the scale. Thus XÔY = 40°. In this example, one of the arms of the angle is horizontal. However, you may find that you need to position the protractor in an awkward position in order to measure the angle.

Here the angle is less than 90°, so we read off the value from the outside scale.

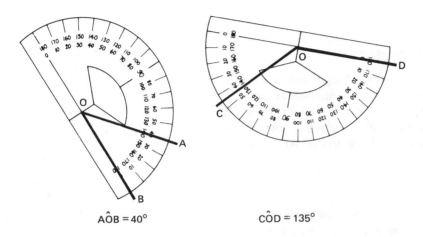

AÔB = 40°   CÔD = 135°

TRY SOME YOURSELF

2(i)   Use a protractor to measure all the marked angles in each of the following figures:

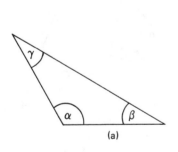

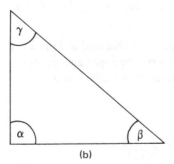

You may need to extend the arms of the angles so that you can read off values from your protractor.

(a)   (b)

(ii)   Use a protractor to draw each of the following angles:
        (a) 37°   (b) 110°   (c) 170°   (d) 230°.

230° = 180° + 50°. Draw a straight line, then turn the protractor upside down.

Depending on its size an angle is described as acute, right, obtuse or reflex.

An acute angle is an angle less than 90°.

A right angle is an angle of 90°.

Notice that a right angle is usually indicated with a square in the vertex.

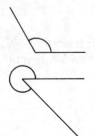

An obtuse angle is greater than 90° but less than 180°.

A reflex angle is greater than 180° but less than 360°.

5.2(ii) TRIANGLES AND THEIR PROPERTIES

A triangle is a figure bounded by three straight lines. These lines, which are called the sides of the triangle, form three angles (hence the name — triangle). The vertices are usually labelled with capital letters and are used to identify the triangle. For example, the triangle in the margin is referred to as triangle ABC, which may be written as △ABC.

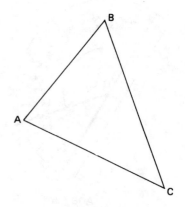

Angle sum property

In Exercise 2(i) we invited you to measure the angles of two triangles. You may have noticed that in each case the sum of the angles was 180°. In fact this is so for any given triangle. This property can be demonstrated in two ways. The first, which you have already experienced, involves measuring the angles with a protractor and adding them up. Alternatively, try the following experiment.

Draw any triangle on a piece of paper or thin card and mark each angle with a different symbol. Cut off the angles and arrange them side by side touching one another as shown below.

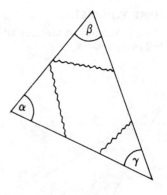

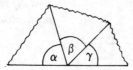

You should find that with all the vertices at a fixed point the pieces of paper form a straight line. A straight line represents an angle of 180°, so this experiment shows that

$$\alpha + \beta + \gamma = 180°$$

or

> the sum of the angles of a triangle is 180°.

The next example illustrates how this property is used to find the third angle of a triangle, given two angles.

It doesn't matter what triangle you choose or which order you re-arrange the angles; you should still get a straight line.

This is often referred to as the angle sum property of a triangle.

EXAMPLE

Find α, β and θ in the figure opposite.

SOLUTION

Consider $\triangle ABD$. $A\hat{B}D = 90°$ and $B\hat{A}D = 20°$.

Thus $\alpha + 20° + 90° = 180°$ (angle sum property), and $\alpha = 70°$.

CDB is a straight line.

$\qquad \theta + \alpha = C\hat{D}B = 180°$,

$\qquad$ so $\theta = 180° - \alpha = 180° - 70° = 110°$.

Now consider $\triangle ADC$. $A\hat{C}D = 30°$ and $C\hat{D}A = \theta = 110°$.

Thus $\beta + 30° + 110° = 180°$ (angle sum property) and $\beta = 40°$.

Remember that ⌐ denotes a right angle or $90°$.

Check for yourself that the angles of $\triangle ABC$ also add up to $180°$.

TRY SOME YOURSELF

3(i) Find the missing angles (marked with Greek letters) in each of the following figures:

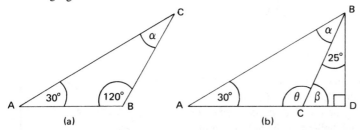

(a)   (b)

(ii) ABCD is a four sided figure. Such a figure is called a *quadrilateral*.

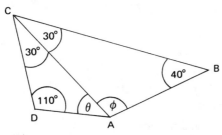

(a) Find θ and ϕ.

(b) Find the sum of all the angles of the quadrilateral ABCD
(that is, find $A\hat{B}C + B\hat{C}D + C\hat{D}A + D\hat{A}B$).

(c) Show that the sum of the angles of any quadrilateral is always
the same.

Notice that ABCD is split into two triangles by drawing the diagonal AC.

19

5.2(iii) SPECIAL TRIANGLES

Some triangles have particular properties and consequently have special names.

Right angled triangles

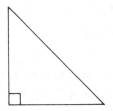

One special triangle, which you have already met, is a *right-angled triangle*. This is a triangle in which one angle is 90°. The right angle is usually clearly identified as the following examples illustrate.

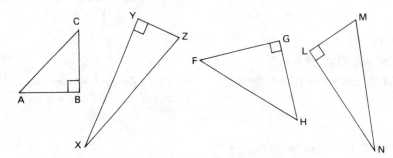

The sides of a right angled triangle are often referred to by special names.

The side opposite the right angle is called the *hypotenuse*.

If one of the angles is labelled α, the side at the vertex of α which is not the hypotenuse, is called the side *adjacent to* α (sometimes just called the *adjacent side*). The other side is called the *side opposite to* α (or just the *opposite side*). The labelling of the adjacent and opposite sides depends upon which angle is specified.

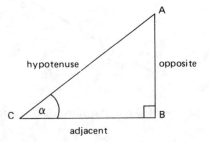

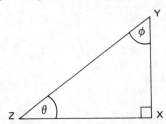

For example, in $\triangle XYZ$, XZ is the side adjacent to θ and the side opposite to ϕ; YX is the side opposite to θ and the side adjacent to ϕ.

EXAMPLE

Label the hypotenuse, adjacent and opposite sides in $\triangle LMN$.

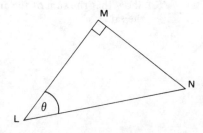

SOLUTION

The hypotenuse is LN.

The side adjacent to θ is LM.

The side opposite θ is MN.

TRY SOME YOURSELF

4   In each of the following triangles label the hypotenuse, the side
     adjacent to and the side opposite the angle α:

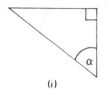   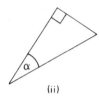   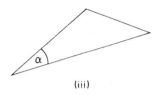

(i)   (ii)   (iii)

Isosceles triangles

*A triangle having two sides of equal length is called an isosceles
triangle.*

The two sides are usually marked with a cross mark. The third side
is called the *base*. For example, in $\triangle ABC$, AB = AC and BC is the
base. Use a protractor to measure the angles α and β. You should
find that $\alpha = \beta = 70°$. These angles are called *base angles*. In any
isosceles triangle the base angles are equal. These angles are often
marked with the same symbol to indicate equality.

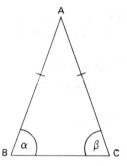

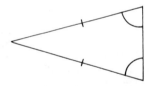

*A quadrilateral like ABCD, in
which AB = AD and CB = CD, is
called a kite.*

EXAMPLE

Find the missing angles in the figure below.

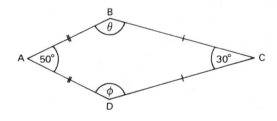

SOLUTION

Draw in the diagonal BD to get two isosceles triangles, $\triangle ABD$ and
$\triangle CBD$.

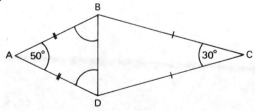

Countdown to Mathematics

In △ABD AB = AD and so $A\hat{B}D = A\hat{D}B$ since they are base angles of an isosceles triangle.

$50° + A\hat{B}D + A\hat{D}B = 180°$ (angle sum property),

so $50° + 2A\hat{B}D = 180°$

and $A\hat{B}D = \dfrac{130°}{2} = 65°$.

Similarly in △CBD CB = CD and $C\hat{B}D = C\hat{D}B$.

$30° + C\hat{B}D + C\hat{D}B = 180°$ (angle sum property)

so $30° + 2C\hat{B}D = 180°$

and $C\hat{B}D = \dfrac{150°}{2} = 75°$.

Now $\theta = A\hat{B}D + C\hat{B}D = 65° + 75° = 140°$

and $\phi = A\hat{D}B + C\hat{D}B = A\hat{B}D + C\hat{B}D = 140° = \theta$.

TRY SOME YOURSELF

5   Find the missing angles in each of the following figures:

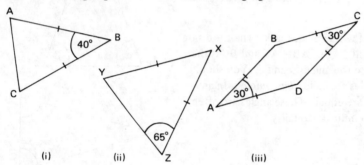

(i)   (ii)   (iii)

*A quadrilateral like ABCD, in which all the sides are equal, is called a **rhombus**.*

Equilateral triangles

A triangle having all three sides the same length is called an equilateral triangle.

The angles of an equilateral triangle are all 60°. This can be proved as follows.

Consider △ABC.

AB = AC and α and β are base angles.

So $\alpha = \beta$.

Also, CA = CB and α and γ are base angles.

So $\alpha = \gamma$.

Thus $\alpha = \beta = \gamma$.

Now $\alpha + \beta + \gamma = 180°$ (angle sum property),

so $3\alpha = 180°$ and $\alpha = 60°$.

Hence $\alpha = \beta = \gamma = 60°$.

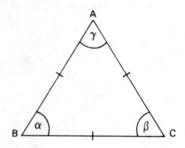

Scalene triangle

Finally we include an 'unspecial triangle', an ordinary triangle, whose sides are unequal. Such a triangle is commonly called a *scalene triangle*.

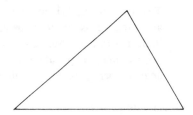

5.2(iv) PARALLEL LINES

In the last part of this section we discuss some angle properties associated with intersecting straight lines.

In this diagram we've labelled the intersecting lines *l* and *m*, and the four angles are α, θ, β and ϕ. Notice that the angles α and β are opposite each other; more precisely they are said to be *vertically opposite*. Similarly, θ and ϕ are vertically opposite angles. In fact $\alpha = \beta$ and $\theta = \phi$.

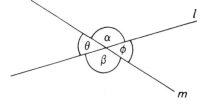

This can be proved using the fact that *l* and *m* are straight lines.

$\alpha + \theta = 180°$ since *l* is a straight line.

Similarly,

$\theta + \beta = 180°$ since *m* is a straight line.

Hence

$\alpha + \theta = \theta + \beta$ *Subtract θ from both sides.*

so $\alpha = \beta$.

A similar argument proves that $\theta = \phi$.   *Try proving this for yourself.*

Thus, for two intersecting straight lines

> vertically opposite angles are equal.

TRY SOME YOURSELF

6   Find all the remaining angles in each of the following diagrams:

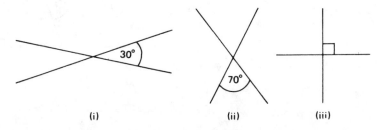

| (i) | (ii) | (iii) |

Thus two intersecting straight lines result in two pairs of equal angles. Generally, two of the angles are acute and two are obtuse (except in the special case where the lines intersect at right angles).

An acute angle is less than 90°; an obtuse angle is greater than 90°.

Countdown to Mathematics

Two straight lines which do not intersect, no matter how far they are extended, as said to be parallel. Pairs of parallel lines are usually indicated with arrows. It's very difficult to determine whether or not two lines are parallel just by inspection. The following two angle properties provide reliable tests.

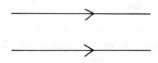

Corresponding angles

The line *l* intersects the two parallel lines *m* and *n*. If you trace one of the intersections and place it over the other you will find that the lines coincide exactly.

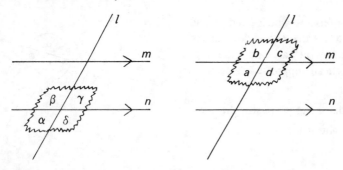

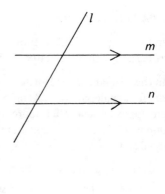

The four angles at each intersection also coincide exactly. The pairs of angles which correspond to each other are called *corresponding angles*. For example, α and *a* are corresponding angles. Because *m* and *n* are parallel, α and *a* coincide exactly. Thus α = *a*. Similarly β = *b*, γ = *c* and δ = *d*.

So, when a line intersects two parallel lines, corresponding angles are equal, and if a line intersects two lines and corresponding angles are *not* equal, then the lines are *not* parallel. This property can therefore be used to determine whether or not two lines are parallel. It can also be used to find missing angles.

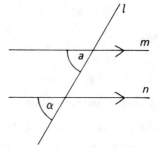

EXAMPLE

Find α and β in the figure opposite.

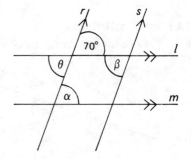

SOLUTION

  r and *s* are parallel lines, indicated by the single arrows;

  l and *m* are also parallel, indicated by the double arrows.

  l is parallel to m,

    so $\alpha = 70°$ (corresponding angles)

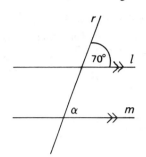

  r is parallel to *s*, indicated by the single arrows,

    so $\theta = \beta$ (corresponding angles).

  But $\theta = 70°$ (vertically opposite angles)

    thus $\beta = 70°$.

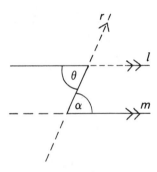

Alternate angles

  The second property is illustrated by the example above. Notice that $\alpha = 70°$ and $\theta = 70°$. These two angles lie within a figure Z, indicated by the solid line in the diagram opposite. Such angles are called *alternate angles*. So, when a line intersects two parallel lines, alternate angles are equal, and if a line intersects two lines and alternate angles are *not* equal, then the lines are *not* parallel. Again, this property can be used to prove whether or not two lines are parallel as well as to find missing angles.

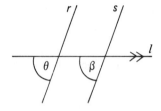

Of course, the figure Z may be reversed Ƨ.

EXAMPLE

  Find α and β in the figure opposite.

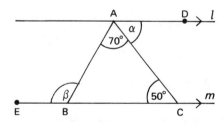

SOLUTION

  l is parallel to *m*, so DÂC = AĈB (alternate angles).

  Thus α = DÂC = 50°.

  Now, BÂD = BÂC + DÂC

     = 70° + 50° = 120°

  and EB̂A = BÂD (alternate angles).

  Thus β = EB̂A = 120°.

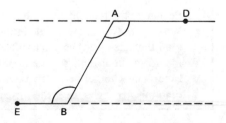

25

TRY SOME YOURSELF

7(i) In each of the following figures determine whether or not the lines l and m are parallel:

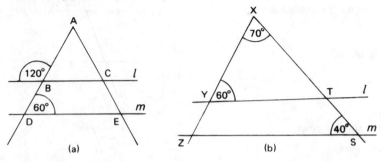

(a) (b)

(ii) Find α and β in each of the following figures:

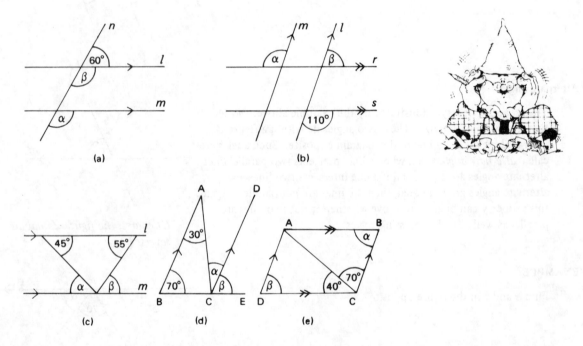

(a) (b) (c) (d) (e)

After you have worked through this section you should be able to

a Recognise the following notations used to label angles: α, $\hat{B}$, $A\hat{B}C$, $\angle ABC$
b Measure or draw a given angle using a protractor
c Find the missing angles in a triangle using the angle sum property
d Identify right angled, isosceles, equilateral and scalene triangles
e Determine whether or not two straight lines are parallel by examining corresponding or alternate angles
f Find missing angles using the corresponding angle and alternate angle properties of parallel lines

Finally, here are some exercises if you want more practice.

TRY SOME MORE YOURSELF

8(i) (a) Measure each of the labelled angles in the figure below.

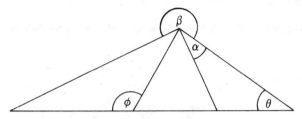

   (b) In each case describe whether the angle is acute, obtuse or reflex.

(ii) Find the labelled angles in the figure below.

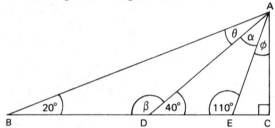

(iii) ABCD is a square. ABE and BFC are equilateral triangles. Find AÊF (you will need to use the angle sum property and the properties of equilateral and isosceles triangles).

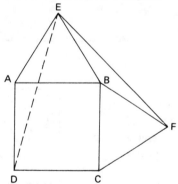

(iv) Find α and β in each of the following figures:

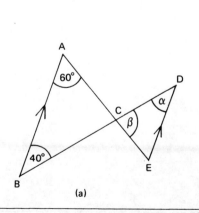

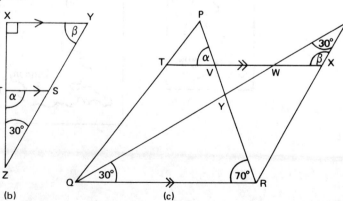

(a)   (b)   (c)

5.3 *Similar Triangles*

TRY THESE QUESTIONS FIRST

1 (i) Determine whether or not △LMN and △PQR are similar.

   (ii) In △ABC, AB = 4 cm, BC = 3·5 cm and AC = 7 cm.
         In △XYZ, XY = 7 cm, XZ = 6 cm and YZ = 12 cm.
         Are these two triangles similar?

2 Find the length of AB in the figure below.

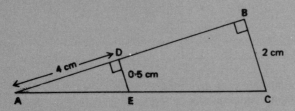

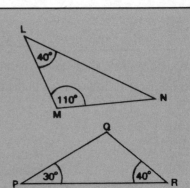

3 Triangle ABC is equilateral. AD is the perpendicular bisector of BC.
   Write down the value of BÂD.

5.3(i) SIMILAR TRIANGLES

If a photograph is enlarged then the original picture and the enlargement are identical but for size. Any shape in one photograph
appears as an identical shape in the other; the only difference is the
size. Similarly, the two maps below have the same shape but
different sizes.

The maps have been drawn to a different scale but the shapes are the same. If a model is made of a railway engine then the original engine and the model have the same shape but are of different sizes. In each of these examples the shapes are said to be *similar*.

In this section we investigate *similar triangles*, that is, triangles of the same shape but different sizes.

Testing for similarity

It is difficult to determine whether or not two triangles are similar just by inspection. For example, △ABC and △XYZ look similar but are they *exactly* the same shape? It's hard to tell from the diagram. However, there are routine tests for similarity, as the following experiment demonstrates.

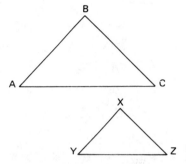

This means that △ABC and △A'B'C' are similar.

In the diagram below △A'B'C' is an enlargement of △ABC.

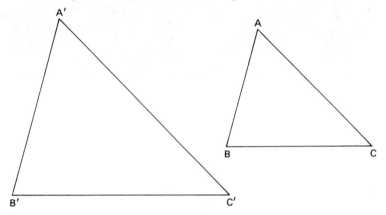

Use a ruler and protractor to measure the angles and lengths of sides of the two triangles. Record your results in the table below.

Â =	Â' =
B̂ =	B̂' =
Ĉ =	Ĉ' =
AB =	A'B' =
AC =	A'C' =
BC =	B'C' =

*Â is the angle **corresponding** to Â' because it is in the same position. Similarly A'B' is the side which corresponds to AB. Notice that we are now using the word 'corresponding' in a slightly different sense to the way we used it in Section 5.2(iv).*

You should find that $\hat{A} = \hat{A}'$, $\hat{B} = \hat{B}'$ and $\hat{C} = \hat{C}'$. Thus corresponding angles are equal.

The lengths of corresponding sides are clearly not the same but they *are* related. Compare the table below to find the *ratios* of corresponding sides.

CHECK YOUR ANSWERS

1 (i) $\hat{L} = \hat{R} = 40°$; $\hat{M} = \hat{Q} = 110°$; $\hat{N} = \hat{P} = 30°$.   *Section 5.3(i)*

Corresponding angles are equal, so $\triangle$LMN and $\triangle$RQP are similar.

(ii) $\dfrac{AC}{YZ} = \dfrac{7}{12}$ $\dfrac{AB}{XY} = \dfrac{4}{7}$ $\dfrac{BC}{XZ} = \dfrac{3{\cdot}5}{6}$.

These ratios are not the same, so triangles ABC and XYZ are not similar.

2 $A\hat{D}E = A\hat{B}C = 90°$ *Section 5.3(ii)*

$\hat{A}$ is common to both triangles and so $\triangle$ADE and $\triangle$ABC are similar.

Now $\dfrac{AD}{AB} = \dfrac{DE}{BC} = \dfrac{0{\cdot}5}{2} = \dfrac{1}{4}$,

so $\dfrac{4}{AB} = \dfrac{1}{4}$ and AB = 16 cm.

3 AD bisects $B\hat{A}C$, so $B\hat{A}D = 30°$.   *Section 5.3(iii)*

$\dfrac{AB}{A'B'} =$

$\dfrac{AC}{A'C'} =$

$\dfrac{BC}{B'C'} =$

You should find that

$$\frac{AB}{A'B'} = \frac{AC}{A'C'} = \frac{BC}{B'C'}.$$

There may be a little discrepancy due to inaccurate measurement.

In other words, corresponding sides are in the same ratio or proportion.

This experiment suggests a more precise definition of similarity.

> Two triangles are similar if
> (i) corresponding angles are equal, and
> (ii) the ratios of corresponding sides are the same.

In fact each of these properties implies the other. If the corresponding angles are equal then the ratios of corresponding sides are the same and if the ratios of corresponding sides are the same then corresponding angles are equal.

TRY SOME YOURSELF

1(i) (a) Draw two lines BC and EF of lengths 3 cm and 5 cm, respectively.

*The process of drawing a triangle accurately using a ruler and protractor is known as **constructing a triangle**.*

   (b) At B and E draw an angle of 40° and at C and F draw an angle of 60°, as shown below.

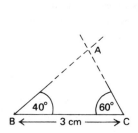
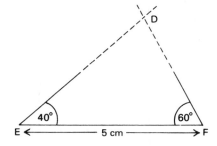

   (c) Complete △ABC and △DEF by extending the lines until they intersect.

(ii) Complete the table below.

$\hat{A} =$	$\hat{D} =$	
$\hat{B} =$	$\hat{E} =$	
$\hat{C} =$	$\hat{F} =$	
AB =	DE =	$\dfrac{AB}{DE} =$
AC =	DF =	$\dfrac{AC}{DF} =$
BC =	EF =	$\dfrac{BC}{EF} =$

Here, you constructed two triangles in which corresponding angles were equal. The exercise shows that, if corresponding angles are equal, then the ratios of corresponding sides are the same. This shows that the first property of similarity implies the second property. The converse can be verified by a similar construction.

The diagrams on the next page show how △A′B′C′ can be constructed from △ABC so that

$$\frac{A'B'}{AB} = \frac{A'C'}{AC} = \frac{B'C'}{BC} = \frac{3}{2}.$$

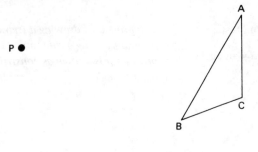

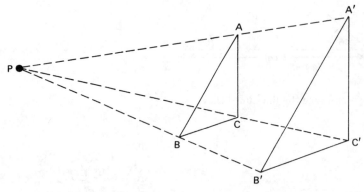

Think of P as a slide projector, △ABC as a triangular 'slide' and △A'B'C' as the image on the screen. By moving the screen backwards and forwards the size of the image can be selected according to requirements.

Choose a point P outside △ABC and measure the distances PA, PB and PC.

Now let PA' = $\frac{3}{2}$ PA, PB' = $\frac{3}{2}$ PB and PC' = $\frac{3}{2}$ PC.

This gives △A'B'C'.

TRY SOME YOURSELF

2(i)   Check for yourself that

$$\frac{A'B'}{AB} = \frac{A'C'}{AC} = \frac{B'C'}{BC} = \frac{3}{2}$$

by measuring the lengths in the diagram above.

(ii)   Use a protractor to measure $\hat{A}$, $\hat{A}'$, $\hat{B}$, $\hat{B}'$, $\hat{C}$, $\hat{C}'$.

You may find that the ratios are not exactly the same. This is due to errors in measurement.

Thus to test for similarity it is sufficient to test only one of the properties. Either

   (i)   show that corresponding angles are equal, or

   (ii)   show that the ratios of corresponding sides are the same.

TRY SOME YOURSELF

3   In each of parts (i) and (ii) determine whether or not △ABC and △XYZ
    are similar by measuring corresponding angles.

*Both pairs of triangles look
similar, so you will need to
measure accurately.*

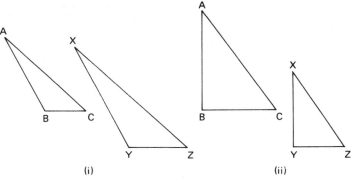

(i)   (ii)

Up till now all the similar triangles which we have considered have
had the same orientation, so corresponding angles have always had
the same relative position on the page, but this is not always the
case.

EXAMPLE

Show that △ABC and △DEF are similar.

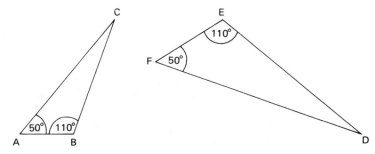

SOLUTION

We need only show that corresponding angles are equal. The way to
do this is to compare the largest angle of one triangle with that of
the other, then to compare the two middle sized angles and finally
the smallest angles.

$\hat{B} = \hat{E} = 110°$

$\hat{A} = \hat{F} = 50°$.

$\hat{A} + \hat{B} + \hat{C} = 180°$, so $\hat{C} = 20°$.

$\hat{E} + \hat{F} + \hat{D} = 180°$, so $\hat{D} = 20°$.

Thus $\hat{C} = \hat{D} = 20°$.

*This shows that
$\hat{B}$ corresponds to $\hat{E}$,
$\hat{A}$ corresponds to $\hat{F}$,
and $\hat{C}$ corresponds to $\hat{D}$.*

Hence △ABC is similar to △FED.

Notice that the letters are rearranged so that the vertices correspond. This is useful if the triangles are to be referred to again.

△ABC

↕↕↕

△FED

Countdown to Mathematics

TRY SOME YOURSELF

4 Determine whether or not each of the following pairs of triangles are similar.

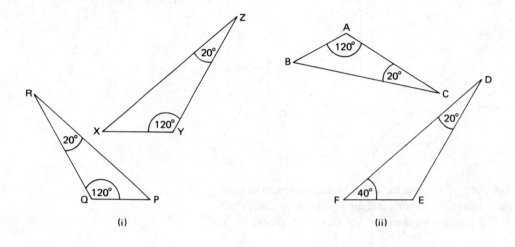

(i)   (ii)

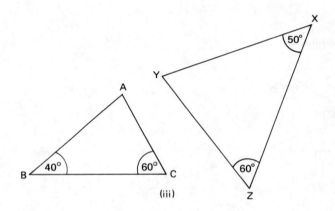

(iii)

EXAMPLE

Show that △XYZ and △DEF are similar.

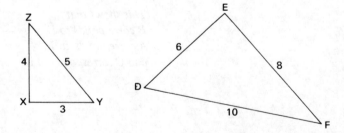

SOLUTION

Since the lengths of the sides are given we need to show that the ratios of corresponding sides are the same.

The way to do this is to look at the ratio of the lengths of the longest sides, then to look at the ratio of the lengths of the shortest sides and finally find the ratio of the remaining sides.

ZY and DF are the longest sides and $\dfrac{ZY}{DF} = \dfrac{5}{10} = \dfrac{1}{2}$.

XY and DE are the shortest sides and $\dfrac{XY}{DE} = \dfrac{3}{6} = \dfrac{1}{2}$.

XZ and EF are the remaining sides and $\dfrac{XZ}{EF} = \dfrac{4}{8} = \dfrac{1}{2}$.

Thus $\dfrac{ZY}{DF} = \dfrac{XY}{DE} = \dfrac{XZ}{EF} = \dfrac{1}{2}$,

so △XYZ is similar to △EDF.

Notice that $\hat{X}$ and $\hat{E}$ (corresponding angles) are both opposite the longest side, and $\hat{Z}$ and $\hat{F}$ (again corresponding angles) are both opposite the shortest side.

Notice again that the letters are ordered so that it is easy to identify corresponding vertices.

$$\triangle XYZ$$
$$\updownarrow\updownarrow\updownarrow$$
$$\triangle EDF$$

You may find it helpful to draw rough sketches of the triangles.

TRY SOME YOURSELF

5   Determine whether or not each of the following pairs of triangles are similar:
(i)   △ABC in which AB = 4, BC = 5 and AC = 6;
     △XYZ in which XZ = 8, XY = 12 and YZ = 10.
(ii)   △ABC in which AB = 3, BC = 6 and AC = 8;
     △XYZ in which XY = 9, XZ = 12 and YZ = 4.

5.3(ii) FINDING UNKNOWN SIDES

If two triangles are known to be similar the ratio property of corresponding sides can be used to find an unknown side in one of the triangles.

EXAMPLE

(i)   Show that △AXY is similar to △ABC.

(ii)   Find the length of AC.

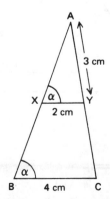

SOLUTION

(i)   The diagram indicates that $A\hat{X}Y = A\hat{B}C = \alpha$.

$\hat{A}$ is common to both triangles.

So, by the angle sum property $A\hat{Y}X = A\hat{C}B$.

Hence △AXY and △ABC are similar.

$\hat{A} + A\hat{X}Y + A\hat{Y}X = 180°$
and $\hat{A} + A\hat{B}C + A\hat{C}B = 180°$.

(ii) The ratios of corresponding sides are the same. Thus

$$\frac{AB}{AX} = \frac{AC}{AY} = \frac{BC}{XY}.$$

$△ABC$

$\updownarrow\updownarrow\updownarrow$

$△AXY$

XY = 2 cm, BC = 4 cm, so $\dfrac{BC}{XY} = \dfrac{4}{2} = 2$.

Now, $\dfrac{AC}{AY} = \dfrac{BC}{XY} = 2$.

But AY = 3 cm, so

$$\frac{AC}{3} = 2$$

and AC = 6 cm.

TRY SOME YOURSELF

6   Show that each of the following pairs of triangles are similar and in each case find the length of AC.

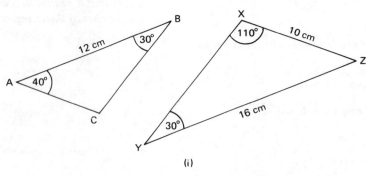

(i)

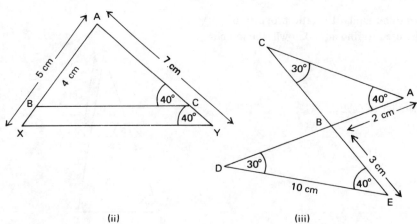

(ii)   (iii)

5.3(iii) TWO COMMON EXAMPLES

Finally we include two examples which rely on the properties introduced in Section 5.2(iii) and (iv). Such examples are quite common and you will probably meet them again several times.

EXAMPLE

(i) Show that △ADE and △ABC are similar.

(ii) Find AC and DE.

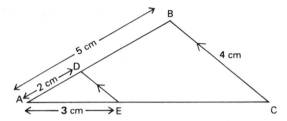

DE and BC are parallel which suggests that we can use the angle properties of parallel lines.

SOLUTION

(i) DE is parallel to BC .

So $A\hat{D}E = A\hat{B}C$ (corresponding angles)

and $A\hat{E}D = A\hat{C}B$ (corresponding angles)

$D\hat{A}E = B\hat{A}C$ (same angle).

So △ADE is similar to △ABC.

Strictly speaking, we need only show that two angles are equal. The angle sum property ensures that the third angles are equal.

(ii) The ratios of corresponding sides are the same. Thus

$$\frac{AD}{AB} = \frac{AE}{AC} = \frac{DE}{BC}.$$

AD = 2 cm and AB = 5 cm, so $\dfrac{AD}{AB} = \dfrac{2}{5}$.

AE = 3 cm, so $\dfrac{3}{AC} = \dfrac{2}{5}$

and AC = $\dfrac{3 \times 5}{2}$ = 7·5 cm.

BC = 4 cm, so $\dfrac{DE}{4} = \dfrac{2}{5}$ and DE = 1·6 cm.

EXAMPLE

(i) Show that △ABD and △ADC are similar.

(ii) Show that BD = DC.

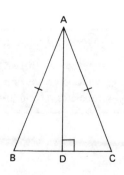

SOLUTION

   (i) △ABC is isosceles, so $A\hat{B}D = A\hat{C}D$ (base angles).

      AD is at right angles to BC, so $A\hat{D}B = A\hat{D}C = 90°$.

      Hence △ABD and △ACD are similar.

  (ii) The ratios of corresponding sides are the same. Thus

$$\frac{AB}{AC} = \frac{AD}{AD} = \frac{BD}{DC}.$$

But $\dfrac{AD}{AD} = 1$,

so $\dfrac{BD}{DC} = 1$ and BD = DC.

Also AB = AC since △ABC is isosceles. Notice that

$$\frac{AB}{AC} = 1.$$

AD is called the *perpendicular bisector* of BC since it is at right angles to BC and bisects BC.

Notice too that since △ABD and △ACD are similar, $B\hat{A}D = C\hat{A}D$. Thus AD also bisects $B\hat{A}C$.

TRY SOME YOURSELF

7(i) (a) Show that △BCD and △ACE are similar.
      (b) Find CE.

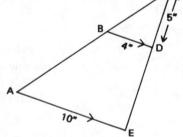

 (ii) (a) Show that △XTW and △XYZ are similar.
      (b) Find XZ and TW.

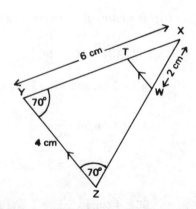

After you have worked through this section you should be able to

a Determine whether or not two given triangles are similar by comparing corresponding angles

b Determine whether or not two given triangles are similar by comparing the ratios of corresponding sides

c Use these properties to find unknown sides in similar triangles

Finally, here are some exercises if you want more practice.

TRY SOME MORE YOURSELF

8(i) Determine which of the following pairs of triangles are similar.
(a) $\triangle$DEF, in which $\hat{D} = 25°$ and $\hat{E} = 70°$;
$\triangle$PQR in which $\hat{P} = 70°$ and $\hat{R} = 85°$.
(b) $\triangle$ABC, in which AB = 4 cm, AC = 8 cm and BC = 10 cm;
$\triangle$XYZ, in which XY = 8 m, XZ = 20 m and YZ = 16 m.
(c) $\triangle$LMN, in which LM = 3 cm, LN = 6 cm and MN = 8 cm;
$\triangle$FGH, in which FG = 5·5 cm, GH = 7·5 cm and FH = 12·5 cm.

(ii) Find all the missing sides in the figure below.

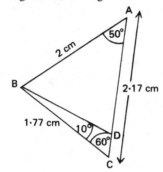

(iii) In the figure below AB = AC and A$\hat{D}$E = A$\hat{B}$C. Find all the missing sides.

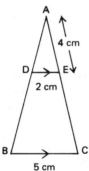

(iv) A rectangle ABCD such that AB = 12 cm, BC = 9 cm and AC = 15 cm is folded over so that A coincides with C. The resulting crease is indicated by EF. Find the length of the crease EF given that EO = OF.

This question is quite hard, so don't worry if you find it difficult.

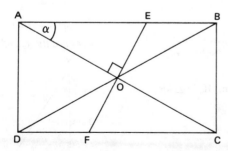

(Hint: since ABCD is a rectangle AB is parallel to DC and AD is parallel to BC.)

5.4 More About Triangles

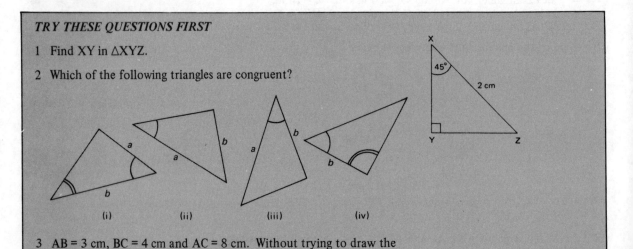
5.4(i) PYTHAGORAS' THEOREM

We start this section by considering one special triangle in more detail, the right angled triangle.

Pythagoras' theorem relates the lengths of the sides of a right angled triangle. It states that

> In any right angled triangle the square on the hypotenuse is equal to the sum of the squares on the other two sides.

In △ ABC for example,

$$c^2 = a^2 + b^2$$

or $AB^2 = BC^2 + AC^2$.

Given the lengths of any two sides of a right angled triangle, the length of the third side can be determined using Pythagoras' theorem.

The converse of Pythagoras' theorem is also true. If, in △ABC

$$AB^2 = BC^2 + AC^2$$

then △ABC is a right angled traingle.

EXAMPLE

Find the length of the remaining side in △XYZ.

We don't prove the theorem here; we merely state it and show how it can be used to find unknown sides.

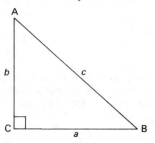

Sometimes the lengths of the sides are indicated by letters.

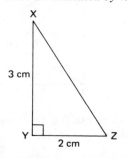

SOLUTION

XZ is the hypotenuse.

Pythagoras' theorem states that

$$XZ^2 = XY^2 + YZ^2$$

so $XZ^2 = 2^2 + 3^2 = 4 + 9 = 13$ and $XZ = \sqrt{13} = 3 \cdot 61$ cm.

Remember to include the unit of measurement if it is indicated on the original figure.

TRY SOME YOURSELF

1(i)   Find the missing sides in each of the following triangles:

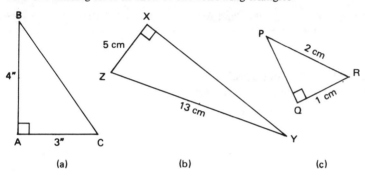

(a)   (b)   (c)

(ii)   Determine which of the following triangles are right angled:
(a) △ABC in which AB = 2, BC = 3 and AC = 4
(b) △XYZ in which XY = 1, YZ = $\sqrt{2}$ and XZ = 1
(c) △PQR in which PQ = 2·1, PR = 3·5 and QR = 4.

We can now introduce two special right angled triangles, which are well worth remembering and which you will meet many times. The first is a right angled triangle in which two sides are equal. In fact AB = BC = 1, so △ABC is isosceles.

Since $B\hat{A}C = A\hat{C}B$ (base angles), and $A\hat{B}C = 90°$,

$2B\hat{A}C = 90°$ (angle sum property).

Thus $B\hat{A}C = A\hat{C}B = 45°$.

AC can be found from Pythagoras' theorem.

$$AC^2 = AB^2 + BC^2$$
$$= 1 + 1 = 2,$$
so $AC = \sqrt{2}$.

This gives the right angled triangle below.

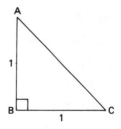

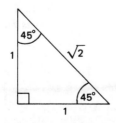

Notice that no units of measurement are indicated. This is quite common in mathematics. Notice, too, that we leave AC as $\sqrt{2}$ rather than giving it as a decimal.

Now consider an equilateral triangle of side 2. Adding AD, the perpendicular bisector of BC, produces two right angled triangles, $\triangle ABD$ and $\triangle ACD$.

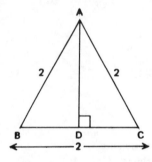

$\triangle ABC$ is equilateral, so $\hat{ABC} = \hat{BAC} = \hat{ACB} = 60°$.

AD bisects BC, so $BD = DC$.

Since $BD + DC = BC = 2$,

   $BD = DC = 1$.

AD also bisects $\hat{BAC}$,

so $\hat{BAD} = \hat{DAC} = 30°$.

AD can be found from Pythagoras' theorem

   $AC^2 = AD^2 + DC^2$

   so $AD^2 = AC^2 - DC^2$

   $= 4 - 1 = 3$,

   and $AD = \sqrt{3}$.

This gives the right angled triangle on the next page.

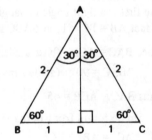

Again, AD is left as $\sqrt{3}$ rather than as a decimal.

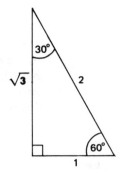

These triangles are useful because they provide visual representations of the angles 30°, 45° and 60°, all common angles.

5.4(ii) CONGRUENT TRIANGLES

If two triangles are similar then the angles correspond exactly. But, although the triangles have the same shape, they need not be exactly the same; one may be bigger than the other. We now consider the case where the triangles are exactly the same.

Two triangles are identical if one can be placed on top of the other and they match exactly. This means that the angles must match exactly *and* the three sides of one triangle must correspond exactly to the three sides of the other. Two triangles which are identical are said to be *congruent*.

Again, it is difficult to tell whether two triangles are identical just by looking at them and routine tests are used to prove congruence. We introduce these tests as investigations, so you will need a ruler, protractor and compasses.

In fact, any two shapes which are identical are called congruent shapes.

Investigation

In this investigation we ask you to construct △ABC in which AB = 7 cm, AC = 3 cm and BC = 6 cm.

Start with the longest side. Draw a line of length 7 cm and label it AB. Set a pair of compasses at 6 cm and draw an arc of radius 6 cm about B.

Now set the compasses at 3 cm and draw an arc of radius 3 cm about A.

The two arcs intersect at a point C. This gives △ABC, where AB = 7 cm, AC = 3 cm and BC = 6 cm.

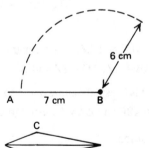

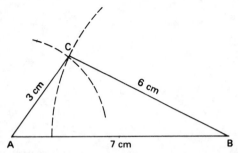

Notice that you could draw this triangle below AB rather than above above AB. But the triangle is exactly the same. Check by placing one on top of the other.

No other triangle is possible. If any other triangle has sides of the same lengths then it must be identical to △ABC.

This shows that it is sufficient to know the lengths of all three sides in order to construct a unique triangle.

This gives the first test of congruence.

However, you will need to be cautious, as the triangle may not exist at all. See Section 5.4(iii).

> If the three sides of one triangle are equal to the corresponding sides of another, then the two triangles are congruent.

This is often abbreviated to

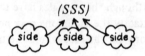

EXAMPLE

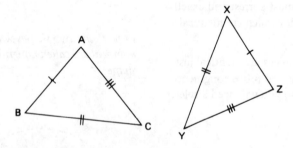

The markings

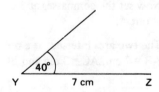

indicate equal sides.

△ABC and △ZXY are congruent since

AB = XZ, AC = YZ and BC = XY.

This is usually abbreviated to

△ABC and △ZXY are congruent   (SSS).

Again, the letters are rearranged so that vertices correspond.

Investigation

In this investigation we ask you to construct △XYZ in which XY = 5 cm, YZ = 7 cm and XŶZ = 40°.

Draw a line of length 7 cm and label it YZ. Use a protractor to draw an angle of 40° at Y. You can now draw YX = 5 cm.

The triangle can be completed by joining X to Z.

*X$\hat{Y}$Z is known as the **included angle** since it is enclosed by the two known sides.*

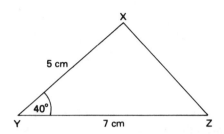

Again, you could draw the triangle below YZ; this produces an identical triangle.

If any other triangle has two corresponding sides of the same length with the same included angle then it must be identical to △XYZ.

This gives the second test of congruence.

This investigation shows that it is sufficient to know the lengths of two sides and the included angle in order to construct a unique triangle.

> If two sides and the included angle of one triangle are respectively equal to two sides and the included angle of another then the two triangles are congruent.

This is often abbreviated to

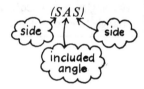

EXAMPLE

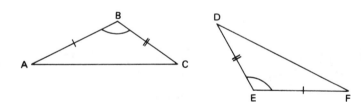

△ABC and △FED are congruent since

AB = FE, BC = ED and A$\hat{B}$C = F$\hat{E}$D.

This is usually abbreviated to

△ABC and △FED are congruent   (SAS).

△*ABC*
$\updownarrow\updownarrow\updownarrow$
△*FED*

Investigation

In this investigation we ask you to construct △ABC in which
BC = 5 cm, A$\hat{B}$C = 80° and A$\hat{C}$B = 30°.

Draw a line of length 5 cm and label it BC. Now use a protractor to draw an angle of 80° at B and an angle of 30° at C.

△ABC can be completed by extending the lines until they intersect.

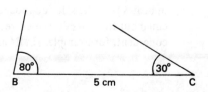

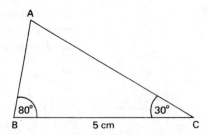

Again you could draw the triangle below BC; this produces an identical triangle. If any other triangle has two angles the same and one corresponding side of the same length as BC, then it must be identical to △ABC.

This investigation shows that it is sufficient to know the length of one side and any two angles in order to construct a unique triangle. Notice that, if two angles are given the third can be deduced from the angle sum property.

This gives the third test of congruence.

> If two angles and a side of one triangle are respectively equal to two angles and the corresponding side of another then the two triangles are congruent.

This may be abbreviated to

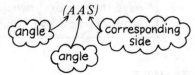

EXAMPLE

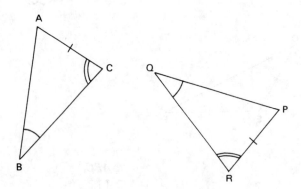

△ABC and △PQR are congruent since
AB̂C = PQ̂R, AĈB = PR̂Q and AC = PR.

This may be abbreviated to
△ABC and △PQR are congruent   (AAS).

Notice that in both triangles the equal sides lie between the un-marked angle and the angle marked with a double band. This indicates that the sides do indeed correspond. If two angles are equal but the sides do *not* correspond then the triangles are *not* congruent, for example △LMN and △ABC are clearly not congruent.

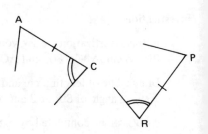

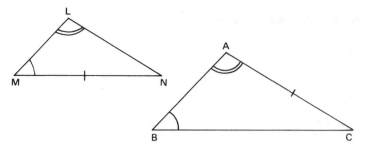

In fact △LMN and △ABC are similar triangles; △ABC is the same shape as △LMN but it is bigger.

Although ML̂N = BÂC, LM̂N = AB̂C and MN = AC, MN and AC are not corresponding sides.

TRY SOME YOURSELF

2(i)   Which of the following triangles are congruent?

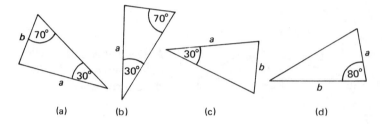

(a)   (b)   (c)   (d)

(ii)   ABCD is a rectangle.
       (a) Show that △AFD and △BFC are congruent.
       (b) Show that AF = FC.

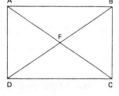

We introduced the three tests of congruence by demonstrating that a unique triangle can be constructed from limited information. But are these the only possible tests of congruence? So far we have demonstrated that a unique triangle can be constructed

       (i)   given the lengths of all three sides, or
       (ii)   given the lengths of two sides and the included angle, or
       (iii) given the length of one side and two angles.

There is another possibility which we now examine. What happens in the case where the lengths of two sides are given together with one angle *other* than the included angle?

Investigation

In this investigation we ask you to construct △ABC, in which AB = 5 cm, BC = 8 cm and AĈB = 30°.

Draw a line of length 8 cm and label it BC. Use a protractor to draw an angle of 30° at C. Now draw an arc of radius 5 cm about B.

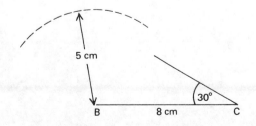

Complete the triangle by extending the line at C until it intersects the arc.

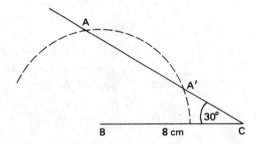

But the line cuts the arc in two places, producing two triangles. Thus △ABC is not unique.

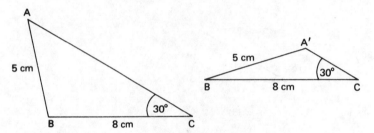

Notice that in △ABC, $A\hat{B}C$ is obtuse, whereas in △A'BC, $A'\hat{B}C$ is acute.

So it is not possible to construct a unique triangle given two sides and an angle other than the included angle. Consequently, for two triangles to be congruent the matching angle *must* be the included angle.

However, there is one special case where this restriction is not needed. The example above illustrates that given two sides and an angle other than the included angle, two triangles are possible; one acute angled and one which includes an obtuse angle. If the triangle is right angled then there is no possibility of one of the other angles being obtuse and this gives the final test of congruence.

Check this yourself by constructing △PQR in which $P\hat{Q}R = 90°$, PQ = 3 cm and PR = 5 cm.

> If two triangles are right angled, and the hypotenuse and one other side of one triangle are respectively equal to the hypotenuse and one other side of the other then the two triangles are congruent.

This is usually written as (right angle, hypotenuse and side).

EXAMPLE

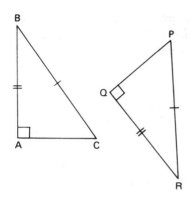

△ABC and △QRP are congruent since

BC = PR = hypotenuse

AB = QR and BÂC = PQ̂R = 90°.

This may be written as
△ABC and △QRP are congruent   (right angle, hypotenuse and side).

TRY SOME YOURSELF

3   Determine whether or not each of the following pairs of triangles
are congruent.

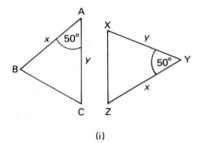

(i)

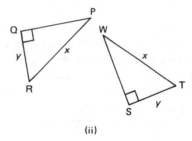

(ii)

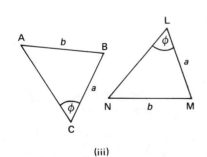

(iii)

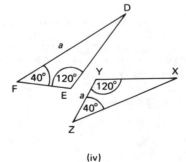

(iv)

5.4(iii) THE TRIANGLE INEQUALITY

We mentioned in Section 5.4(ii) that some caution is needed in the construction of a triangle given all three sides. The following investigation illustrates that the triangle may not even exist.

Investigation

In this investigation we ask you to construct △ABC in which AB = 2 cm, BC = 6 cm and AC = 2 cm.

Start off by drawing the longest side, BC. Now draw an arc of radius 2 cm about B and an arc of radius 2 cm about C.

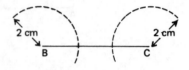

You should find that the arcs do not intersect at all, indicating that △ABC is an 'impossible triangle'.

The next investigation illustrates that the lengths of the sides must satisfy certain conditions for the triangle to exist.

Investigation

Draw any triangle and measure the sides XY, YZ and XZ. Now complete the table below.

XZ =	(XY + YZ) =
XY =	(XZ + YZ) =
YZ =	(XZ + XY) =

Compare the values of both columns.

You should find that in each case the sum of any two sides exceeds the length of the third side. This condition is known as the *triangle inequality*. More generally it states that

> The sum of the lengths of any two sides of a triangle is greater than the length of the other side.

This explains why △ABC in the investigation above is impossible.

TRY SOME YOURSELF

4(i) Without drawing any triangles state whether or not each of the following triangles exists:
    (a) △ABC, in which AB = 4 cm, BC = 7 cm and AC = 5 cm
    (b) △PQR, in which PQ = 3 cm, QR = 10 cm and PR = 6 cm
    (c) △XYZ, in which XY = 3 cm, YZ = 10 cm and XZ = 7 cm.

(ii) In △ABC, AB = 5 cm, BC = 7 cm and AC = 9 cm. Without drawing the triangle accurately, write down
    (a) the smallest angle
    (b) the largest angle.

You might find it helpful to draw a rough sketch.

After you have worked through this section you should be able to

a Find the third side of a right angled triangle using Pythagoras' theorem

b Determine whether or not two triangles are congruent by applying the following tests:
two triangles are congruent if

(i) the three sides of one triangle are equal to the three sides of the other (SSS)

(ii) two sides and the included angle of one triangle are equal to two sides and the included angle of the other (SAS)

(iii) two angles and one side of one triangle are equal to two angles and the corresponding side of the other (AAS)

(iv) the triangles are right angled and the hypotenuse and one side of one triangle are equal to the hypotenuse and one side of the other

c Determine whether or not a given triangle exists by applying the triangle inequality

Finally here are some exercises if you want more practice.

TRY SOME MORE YOURSELF

5(i) Find the missing sides in each of the following triangles:

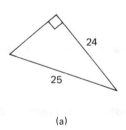

(a)

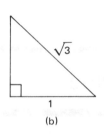

(b)

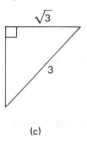

(c)

(ii) Which of the following triangles are congruent?

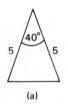

(a)

(b)

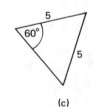

(c)

(d)

(e)

(f)

(iii)   In the rectangle ABCD, AB = 12 cm and BC = 9 cm.

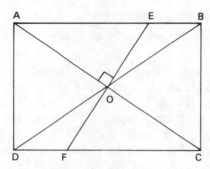

(a) Find AC.
(b) Show that △EOB and △DOF are congruent.

(iv)   Without drawing any triangles, state whether or not each of the following triangles exists. If the triangle does exist write down the largest angle and the smallest angle.
(a) △ABC, in which AB = 1, BC = 1 and AC = 2.
(b) △XYZ, in which XY = 5, YZ = 4 and XZ = 3.

5.5 Shape, Areas and Volumes

TRY THESE QUESTIONS FIRST

1 (i)   Mark all the lines of symmetry and the centre of revolution on the shape opposite.

(ii) State the order of rotational symmetry.

2 Find the area of the triangle below.

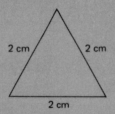

3 The cross-section of the solid shape opposite is a sector of a circle. Find the volume of the solid.

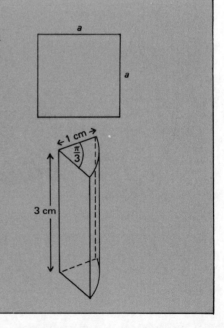

5.5(i) SYMMETRY

Bilateral symmetry

When giving a description of a picture, shape or pattern we often refer to symmetry. In fact symmetry is a mathematical property and you will find that it is very useful to be able to 'spot' whether or not a shape is symmetrical. For example, the graph of $y = x^2$ is symmetrical about the y-axis; one side is the mirror image of the other. You might like to think of this type of symmetry in two ways:

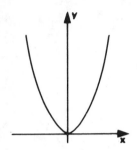

(i) Imagine a mirror placed along the y-axis. The reflection in the mirror gives the other half of the graph.

(ii) Fold the graph of $y = x^2$ along the y-axis. Then one side of the graph lies exactly on top of the other.

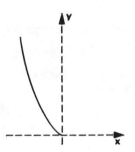

The following shapes are all symmetrical:

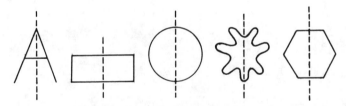

Check for yourself by copying the shapes and folding them along the dashed line.

The dotted lines are called *lines of symmetry*, and each shape is said to be *symmetrical* about this line. A shape can have more than one line of symmetry. For example, a rectangle has two lines of symmetry.

This type of symmetry is called **bilateral symmetry**.

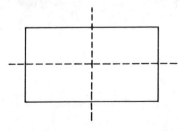

A circle has an infinite number of lines of symmetry since it can be folded about any diameter.

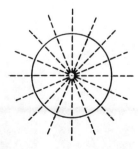

CHECK YOUR ANSWERS

1 (i) The lines of symmetry (there are 4) are indicated below.   *Section 5.5(i)*

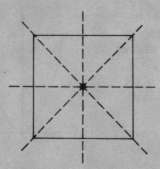

The centre of revolution is the centre of the square.

(ii) The order of rotational symmetry is 4.

2 The triangle is equilateral and can be divided into two right angled   *Section 5.5(ii)*
triangles.

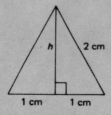

$h^2 = 4 - 1 = 3,$

so $h = \sqrt{3}.$

Area $= \frac{1}{2} \times$ base $\times$ height

$= \frac{1}{2} \times 2 \times \sqrt{3} = \sqrt{3}$ or 1·73 cm^2.

3 Area of sector $= \dfrac{1}{2} \times \dfrac{\pi}{3} \times 1^2$ *Section 5.5(iii)*

$= \dfrac{\pi}{6}$ cm^2.

Volume of solid $= \dfrac{\pi}{6} \times 3 = \dfrac{\pi}{2}$ or 1·57 cm^3.   *Section 5.5(iv)*

TRY SOME YOURSELF

1　Mark the lines of symmetry on each of the following shapes. For each shape state the total number of lines of symmetry.

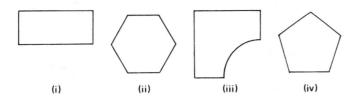

(i)　　　　　(ii)　　　　　(iii)　　　　　(iv)

Rotational symmetry

A shape may also have *rotational symmetry*. Imagine a pin through the centre of this square. If the square is rotated through 90° or $\pi/2$ radians the shape looks exactly the same. The vertices of the square have been labelled to illustrate this property; the shape looks the same but the vertices have been moved round one place. The centre point, which acts as a pivot, is called the *centre of revolution*.

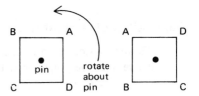

The square occupies exactly the same position.

The shape looks the same if it is rotated through another $\pi/2$. Again the vertices move around one place. If the process is repeated the square will eventually end up in the starting position with the vertex A in the top right hand corner. The diagram below illustrates what happens.

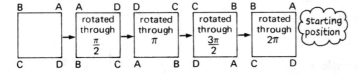

Remember, an angle of 2π corresponds to a complete revolution.

A square is said to have *rotational symmetry of order* 4 because after $\frac{1}{4}$ of a revolution the shape looks exactly the same and lies in the same position.

The shape opposite has rotational symmetry of order 3 because after $\frac{1}{3}$ of a revolution $\left(\dfrac{2\pi}{3}\right)$ the shape looks exactly the same and lies in the same position.

TRY SOME YOURSELF

2(i)　Mark the centre of revolution on each of the following and for each shape state the order of rotational symmetry.

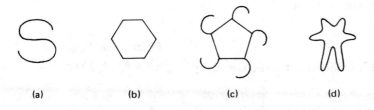

(a)　　　　　(b)　　　　　(c)　　　　　(d)

(ii)   Describe the symmetry of each of the following shapes. In each
        case mark the lines of symmetry and the centre of revolution,
        and state the order of rotational symmetry.

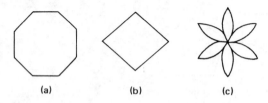

(a)   (b)   (c)

5.5(ii) AREA OF A TRIANGLE

We first consider the area of a right angled triangle. This is easy to
derive since every right angled triangle is exactly half a rectangle.

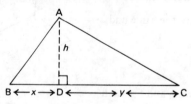

The area of each right angled triangle is exactly half the area of the
corresponding rectangle.

The area of the rectangle ABCD = AB × BC,

so the area of △ABC = $\frac{1}{2}$ × AB × BC.

Area of a rectangle is
length x width.

Similarly the area of △XYZ = $\frac{1}{2}$ × XY × YZ.

Thus the area of a right angled triangle is

   $\frac{1}{2}$ × base × height.

Not every triangle is right angled but the formula can be adapted
to apply to *all* triangles since any triangle can be divided into
two right angled triangles, as shown below.

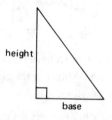

height

base

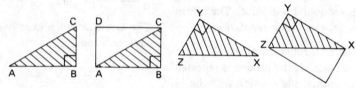

Area of △ABC = Area of △ADB + Area of △ADC,

   $= \frac{1}{2}xh + \frac{1}{2}yh$

   $= \frac{1}{2}h(x+y).$

But $(x + y)$ is just the length of BC, so the area of △ABC is given by

   $\frac{1}{2}$ BC × AD.

Check by multiplying,
$\frac{1}{2}h(x+y) = \frac{1}{2}hx + \frac{1}{2}hy.$

The 'bottom' side of the triangle (BC) is called the *base*.

AD is the perpendicular distance from the base to the opposite vertex, called the *perpendicular height* or just the height. This gives the general formula for the area of a triangle.

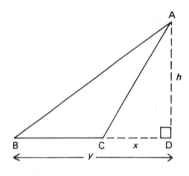

Area of a triangle = $\frac{1}{2}$ × base × perpendicular height

It is not always easy to identify the 'base' of a triangle if it does not have a horizontal side, but the beauty of the formula is that it works no matter which side is designated as the base. The area of this triangle can be evaluated in three ways.

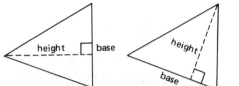 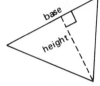

We now look at an obtuse angled triangle. If the longest side is taken as the base then it's quite straightforward. But the formula also holds if one of the other sides is designated as the base. This time the perpendicular distance AD lies outside the original triangle.

Area of △ABC = Area of △ABD − Area of △ACD

$= \frac{1}{2}yh - \frac{1}{2}xh$

$= \frac{1}{2}h(y - x)$

$= \frac{1}{2}$ × BC × AD

$= \frac{1}{2}$ × base × perpendicular height.

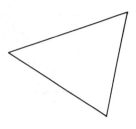

The length of BC is $(y - x)$.

TRY SOME YOURSELF

3   Find the area of each of the following triangles:

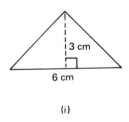

(i)

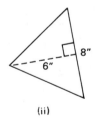

(ii)

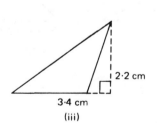

(iii)

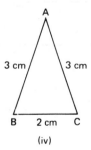

(iv)

A *parallelogram* is a four sided figure (quadrilateral) with opposite sides parallel. In fact opposite sides are also equal. This can be proved by showing that △ABD and △CBD are congruent.

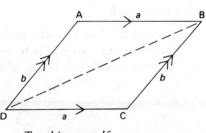

Try this yourself.

The area of this parallelogram can be found by splitting it into two triangles.

Try this yourself.

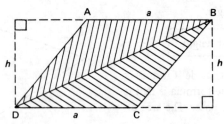

Area of ABCD = Area of $\triangle$ABD + Area of $\triangle$BCD

$$= \tfrac{1}{2}ah + \tfrac{1}{2}ah$$

$$= ah.$$

Thus

The height, *h*, is the perpendicular distance between the parallel lines. Notice that the area does not depend on the length of the other side.

> the area of a parallelogram = base × height.

TRY SOME YOURSELF

4 Find the area of each of the following shapes:

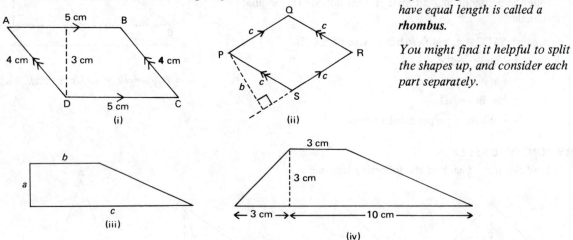

A parallelogram in which all sides have equal length is called a **rhombus**.

You might find it helpful to split the shapes up, and consider each part separately.

5.5(iii) CIRCLES

In Section 5.1 we showed that the circumference of a circle is given by $2\pi r$ and the area is given by πr^2. We now consider the length of an arc of a circle and the area of a sector.

See Section 5.1(iii).

The arc AB subtends an angle of θ at the centre of the circle and the sector has been traced out by rotating OB through an angle θ.
Since an angle of 2π radians corresponds to a complete revolution,

θ corresponds to a fraction of a revolution, $\dfrac{\theta}{2\pi}$.

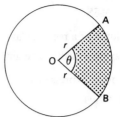

Or if θ is measured in degrees, θ corresponds to $\dfrac{\theta}{360}$.

If θ is measured in radians

the length of the arc AB is given by

$$\frac{\theta}{2\pi} \times 2\pi r = \theta r,$$

and the area of the sector AOB is given by

$$\frac{\theta}{2\pi} \times \pi r^2 = \frac{\theta}{2}r^2.$$

$\dfrac{\theta}{2\pi}$ is a fraction of a revolution;

the arc length is the same fraction of the circumference and the area of the sector is the same fraction of the area of the circle.

If θ is measured in degrees

the length of the arc AB is given by

$$\frac{\theta}{360} \times 2\pi r,$$

and the area of the sector AOB is given by

$$\frac{\theta}{360} \times \pi r^2.$$

TRY SOME YOURSELF

5(i) Find each of the shaded areas marked on the circles below.

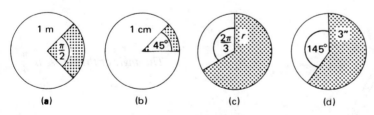

(a) (b) (c) (d)

(ii) Find the length of the arc ACB in each of the circles below.

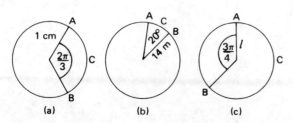

(a) (b) (c)

The point C indicates which arc is intended.

5.5(iv) VOLUMES

The volume of a rectangular box is given by

length × width × height.

This is often expressed as a formula,

$V = lwh$.

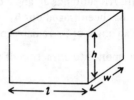

However the volume can be expressed in a slightly different form which is more generally applicable. Notice that

$V = lwh$

$= (lw) \times h$

$= (\text{area of a rectangle}) \times (\text{height})$.

The units of measurement are cm^3 or m^3–cubic units.

If the box is sliced parallel to the base, the cut face will be a rectangle. No matter where the box is cut, the cut face will be the same shape, and will have the same area. The area of the cut face is called the *cross-sectional area*. A solid is said to have *uniform cross-sectional area* if the cross-sectional area is the same throughout the solid.

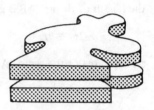

Thus the volume of any solid, of uniform cross-sectional area is given by

$V = (\text{cross-sectional area}) \times (\text{height})$.

This formula can be used to deduce the volume of a cylinder, radius r and height h.

The cross-sectional area is πr^2, so

$V = \pi r^2 \times h = \pi r^2 h$.

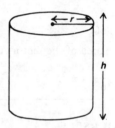

EXAMPLE

The wedge illustrated below has been cut from a cylinder of radius r. Find its volume.

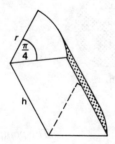

The angle at the centre is $\dfrac{\pi}{4}$.

SOLUTION

Each cross-section is a sector of a circle, so

$$\text{cross-sectional area} = \frac{\theta}{2} \times r^2$$
$$= \frac{\pi}{8} \times r^2.$$

volume = (cross-sectional area) × (height)

$$= \frac{\pi}{8} \times r^2 \times h = \frac{\pi r^2 h}{8}$$

Check this: the area of the sector is 1/8 area of the circle, and the volume of the wedge is 1/8 volume of the cylinder.

TRY SOME YOURSELF

6(i)   Find the volume of each of the following:

Remember to include the units of measurement.

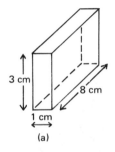
3 cm
8 cm
1 cm
(a)

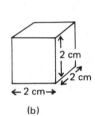
2 cm
2 cm
← 2 cm →
(b)

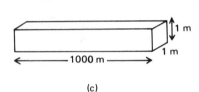
1 m
1 m
← 1000 m →
(c)

(ii)   Find the volume of the triangular wedge opposite.
(iii) Find the volume of each of the following:
       (a) a cylinder of radius 2 cm and height 6 cm
       (b) a cylinder of radius *r* and height *r*
       (c) a triangular wedge, illustrated below.

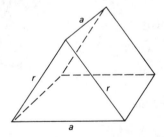
a
r
r
a

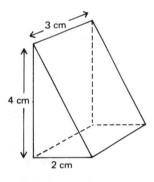
3 cm
4 cm
2 cm

After you have worked through this section you should be able to

a Recognise bilateral and rotational symmetry
b State the number of lines of symmetry and order of rotational symmetry of a given shape
c Find the area of a triangle given the base and perpendicular height
d Find the area of a parallelogram given the base and height
e Find the length of an arc of a circle
f Find the area of a sector of a circle
g Find the volume of a solid of uniform cross-sectional area

Countdown to Mathematics

Finally here are some exercises if you want more practice.

TRY SOME MORE YOURSELF

7(i) On each of the following shapes indicate the lines of symmetry and the centre of revolution. In each case state the order of rotational symmetry.

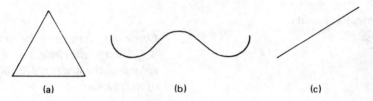

(a)   (b)   (c)

(ii) Find the area of each of the following:

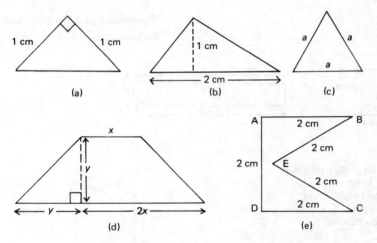

(iii) A bicycle tyre has size $28 \times 1\frac{1}{2}''$. This means that, when properly inflated, the tyre behaves like a wheel $28''$ in diameter. Calculate how far the bicycle moves when the wheel rotates half way round.

(iv) A circular cake of diameter $8''$ is cut into 16 pieces. The height of the cake is $2''$. What is the volume of each slice?

(v) Each of the solids below has uniform cross-sectional area. Find the volume of each solid.

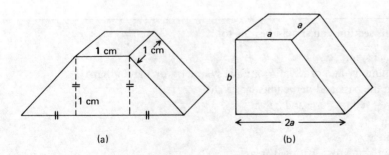

(a)   (b)

Section 5.1 Solutions

1

(i) $C = 2\pi r = 2\pi \times 7 \simeq 43 \cdot 98$ cm

(ii) $C = \pi d$, so $d = \dfrac{C}{\pi} = \dfrac{44}{\pi} \simeq 14 \cdot 01$ m

2

(i) $A = \pi r^2 = \pi \times 7^2 \simeq 153 \cdot 94$ cm^2

(ii) $A = \pi r^2$, so $r^2 = \dfrac{A}{\pi}$

$$\text{and } r = \sqrt{\dfrac{A}{\pi}}$$

$$= \sqrt{\dfrac{616}{\pi}} = \sqrt{\dfrac{616 \times 7}{22}} = 14 \text{ m.}$$

(iii) $A = \pi r^2$, so $r = \sqrt{\dfrac{A}{\pi}}$

$$= \sqrt{\dfrac{15}{\pi}} \simeq 2 \cdot 185 \text{ cm}$$

$$\text{and } d = 2r \simeq 4 \cdot 37 \text{ cm.}$$

3

(i)   Positive because it is an anticlockwise rotation.

(ii) Positive because it is an anticlockwise rotation.

(iii) Negative because it is a clockwise rotation.

4

(i)
$\dfrac{2\pi}{3}$ radians
or 120°

(ii)
$\dfrac{\pi}{3}$ radians
or 60°

(iii)
$-\dfrac{\pi}{3}$ radians
or −60°

(iv)
$-\dfrac{\pi}{6}$ radians
or −30°

5

(i)   (a) $54° = \left(54 \times \dfrac{2\pi}{360}\right)$ radians

$$= \dfrac{3\pi}{10} \text{ or } 0 \cdot 94 \text{ radians}$$

(b) $125° = \left(125 \times \dfrac{2\pi}{360}\right)$ radians

$$= \dfrac{25\pi}{36} \text{ or } 2 \cdot 18 \text{ radians}$$

(c) $-67 \cdot 18° = \left((67 \cdot 18) \times \dfrac{2\pi}{360}\right)$ radians

$$= -1 \cdot 17 \text{ radians}$$

(ii) (a) $\dfrac{2\pi}{7} = \dfrac{2\pi}{7} \times \dfrac{360}{2\pi}$

$$= 51 \cdot 43°$$

(b) 1 radian $= 1 \times \dfrac{360}{2\pi}$

$$= 57 \cdot 30°$$

(c) $-0 \cdot 5$ radians $= (-0 \cdot 5) \times \dfrac{360}{2\pi}$

$$= -28 \cdot 65°$$

6

(i)   (a) $51 \cdot 38° = 51° + 0 \cdot 38°$

$$= 51° + (60 \times 0 \cdot 38)'$$

$$= 51° \ 23' \text{ (rounded to the nearest minute).}$$

(b) $-62 \cdot 22° = -(62° + 0 \cdot 22°)$

$$= -(62° + (0 \cdot 22 \times 60)')$$

$$= -62° \ 13'$$

(c) $115 \cdot 65° = 115° + 0 \cdot 65°$

$$= 115° + (0 \cdot 65 \times 60)'$$

$$= 115° \ 39'$$

(ii) (a) $79° \ 52' = 79° + 52'$

$$= 79° + \left(\tfrac{52}{60}\right)°$$

$$= 79 \cdot 87°$$

(b) $125° \ 45' = 125° + 45'$

$$= 125° + \left(\tfrac{45}{60}\right)°$$

$$= 125 \cdot 75°$$

(c) $-213° \ 23' = -(213° + 13')$

$$= -(213° + \left(\tfrac{13}{60}\right)°)$$

$$= -213 \cdot 38°$$

7

(i) $63° 14' = 63·23°$

$$= 63·23 \times \frac{2\pi}{360}$$

$$= 1·10 \text{ radians}$$

(ii) $295° 51' = 295·85°$

$$= 295·85 \times \frac{2\pi}{360}$$

$$= 5·16 \text{ radians}$$

(iii) $-12° 46' = -12·77°$

$$= (-12·77) \times \frac{2\pi}{360}$$

$$= -0·22 \text{ radians}$$

8

(i) (a) 40 074 km (b) 37·7 cm

(ii) (a) 28·27 cm² (b) 14·14 cm² (c) 3·99″

(iii)

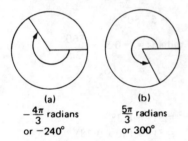

(a)
$-\dfrac{4\pi}{3}$ radians
or $-240°$

(b)
$\dfrac{5\pi}{3}$ radians
or $300°$

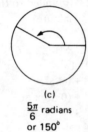

(c)
$\dfrac{5\pi}{6}$ radians
or $150°$

(iv) (a) 0·63 rad (b) −3·06 rad (c) 0·25 rad
(d) 3·76 rad

(v) (a) 22·5° or 22° 30′ (b) 114·59° or 114° 35′
(c) −36° (d) −11·46° or −11° 28′

Section 5.2 Solutions

1

(i) $\alpha = $ CÂD or DÂC or $\angle$CAD or $\angle$DAC.
(ii) $\beta = $ BÂC or CÂB or $\angle$CAB or $\angle$BAC.
(iii) $\theta = $ AĈB or BĈA or $\angle$ACB or $\angle$BCA.

2

(i) (a) $\alpha = 120°, \beta = 30°, \gamma = 30°$.
(b) $\alpha = 90°, \beta = 40°, \gamma = 50°$.

(ii)

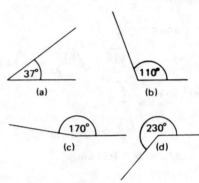

(a)   (b)

(c)   (d)

3

(i) (a) $120° + 30° + \alpha = 180°$, so $\alpha = 30°$.
(b) Consider $\triangle$BCD.
$\beta + 25° + 90° = 180°$, so $\beta = 65°$.
ACB is a straight line, so $\theta = 180° - \beta$.
$= 180° - 65°, = 115°$.
Now consider $\triangle$ABC.
$\alpha + 30° + 115° = 180°$, so $\alpha = 35°$.

(ii) (a) In $\triangle$ABC, $30° + 40° + \phi = 180°$, so $\phi = 110°$.
In $\triangle$ADC, $30° + 110° + \phi = 180°$, so $\theta = 40°$.
(b) AB̂C + BĈD + CD̂A + DÂB
$= 40° + 60° + 110° + 150°$
$= 360°$.
(c) A quadrilateral has 4 sides.

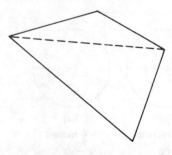

Drawing in a diagonal splits the quadrilateral into two triangles. The sum of the angles of the quadrilateral is therefore equal to the sum of the angles of the two triangles.
Thus the sum of the angles $= 180° + 180°$
$= 360°$.

4

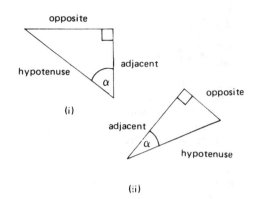

(i)

(;i)

(iii) As this triangle has no right angle the terms do not apply.

5

(i) △ABC is isosceles with AB = BC.
So Â = Ĉ.
Â + Â + 40° = 180° (angle sum property),
thus Â = 70°.

(ii) △XYZ is isosceles with YX = XZ.
So Ŷ = Ẑ = 65°
65° + 65° + X̂ = 180°.
Thus X̂ = 50°.

(iii) Joining B to D gives two isosceles triangles.

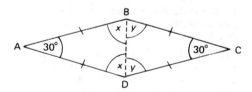

In △ABD, 30° + 2x = 180° (angle sum property),
so x = 75°.
In △CBD, 30° + 2y = 180° (angle sum property),
so y = 75°.
Hence AB̂C = AD̂C = x + y = 150°.

6

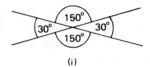

(i)

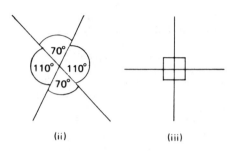

(ii)   (iii)

7

(i) (a) *l* is a straight line. AB̂C + 120° = 180°, so
AB̂C = 60°.
AB̂C and BD̂E are equal corresponding
angles, so *l* and *m* are parallel.

(b) Consider △XYT.
XT̂Y + 70° + 60° = 180°, so XT̂Y = 50°.
XT̂Y and TŜZ are corresponding angles but
they are not equal. Thus *l* and *m* are not
parallel.

(ii) (a) β = 180° − 60° = 120° (since *n* is a straight
line).
α = β = 120° (corresponding angles).

(b)

γ = 180° − 110° = 70° (since *l* is a straight
line).
β = γ = 70° (corresponding angles).
Similarly α = 180° − 70° = 110°.

(c) α = 45° (alternate angles).
β = 55° (alternate angles).

(d) α = 30° (alternate angles).
β = 70° (corresponding angles).

(e) BÂC = 40° (alternate angles).
α + 40° + 70° = 180° (angle sum property
for △ABC).
Thus α = 70°.
Similarly, DÂC = 70° (alternate angles).
β + 70° + 40° = 180° (angle sum property
for △ADC).
Thus β = 70°.

Countdown to Mathematics

8

(i) (a) $\alpha = 30°$, $\theta = 35°$, $\phi = 120°$, $\beta = 240°$.
   (b) α is acute, θ is acute, ϕ is obtuse, β is reflex.

(ii) $\alpha = 30°$, $\beta = 140°$, $\theta = 20°$, $\phi = 20°$.

(iii) $\hat{AEF} = \hat{AEB} + \hat{BEF}$.
$\hat{AEB} = 60°$, since $\triangle AEB$ is equilateral.
$\triangle EBF$ is isosceles, since
  $EB = AB$ ($\triangle ABE$ equilateral),
  $BF = BC$ ($\triangle BFC$ equilateral),
and
  $AB = BC$ (ABCD is a square).
Thus $EB = BF$ and $\hat{BEF} = \hat{BFE}$.
Now, $\hat{ABC} = 90°$, $\hat{EBA} = 60°$ and $\hat{FBC} = 60°$.
$\hat{EBF} + 90° + 60° + 60° = 360°$, so $\hat{EBF} = 150°$.
In $\triangle EBF$,
$\hat{EBF} + \hat{BEF} + \hat{BFE} = 180°$, so $\hat{BEF} = 15°$.
So $\hat{AEF} = 60° + 15° = 75°$.

(iv) (a) $\beta = 80°$ (angle sum property,
         vertically opposite angles).
      $\alpha = 40°$ (alternate angles).
   (b) $\alpha = 90°$ (corresponding angles).
      $\beta = 60°$ (angle sum property).
   (c) $\alpha = 70°$ (corresponding angles).
      $\hat{SWX} = 30°$ (corresponding angles).
      so $\beta = 120°$.

Section 5.3 Solutions

1

(i)

(ii) Your table should look roughly like the one below. The accuracy depends on the level of accuracy in your drawing and measuring.

$\hat{A}$ =	80°	$\hat{D}$ =	80°		
$\hat{B}$ =	40°	$\hat{E}$ =	40°		
$\hat{C}$ =	60°	$\hat{F}$ =	60°		
AB =	2·6 cm	DE =	4·4 cm	AB/DE =	0·59
AC =	2·0 cm	DF =	3·3 cm	AC/DF =	0·61
BC =	3 cm	EF =	5 cm	BC/EF =	0·6

2

(i) $\dfrac{A'B'}{AB} = \dfrac{4\cdot7}{3\cdot2} = 1\cdot5$

$\dfrac{A'C'}{AC} = \dfrac{3\cdot3}{2\cdot2} = 1\cdot5$

$\dfrac{B'C'}{BC} = \dfrac{2\cdot6}{1\cdot7} = 1\cdot5$

All the answers above are given correct to one decimal place. The accuracy of the answers will depend upon the accuracy of your measurement.

(ii) $\hat{A} = \hat{A'} = 30°$.
$\hat{B} = \hat{B'} = 40°$.
$\hat{C} = \hat{C'} = 110°$

3

(i) $\hat{A} = \hat{X} = 20°$
$\hat{B} = \hat{Y} = 120°$
$\hat{C} = \hat{Z} = 40°$
Thus corresponding angles are equal and $\triangle ABC$ and $\triangle XYZ$ are similar.

(ii) $\hat{A} = 38°$, $\hat{X} = 35°$
$\hat{B} = \hat{Y} = 90°$
$\hat{C} = 52°$, $\hat{Z} = 55°$
Thus corresponding angles are not equal and $\triangle ABC$ and $\triangle XYZ$ are not similar.

4

(i) $\hat{Q} = \hat{Y} = 120°$
$\hat{R} = \hat{Z} = 20°$
By the angle sum property $\hat{P} = \hat{X} = 40°$.
Hence $\triangle PQR$ and $\triangle XYZ$ are similar.

(ii) $\hat{C} = \hat{D} = 20°$
In $\triangle ABC$, $\hat{B} = 40°$ (angle sum property).
In $\triangle DEF$, $\hat{E} = 120°$ (angle sum property).
So $\hat{A} = \hat{E} = 120°$ and $\hat{B} = \hat{F} = 40°$.
Hence $\triangle ABC$ and $\triangle EFD$ are similar.

(iii) In $\triangle ABC$, $\hat{A} = 80°$ (angle sum property).
In $\triangle XYZ$, $\hat{Y} = 70°$ (angle sum property).
So although $\hat{C} = \hat{Z}$ the other corresponding angles are not equal and so $\triangle ABC$ and $\triangle XYZ$ are not similar.

66

5

(i) AC and XY are the longest sides and
$$\frac{AC}{XY} = \frac{6}{12} = \frac{1}{2}.$$
AB and XZ are the shortest sides and
$$\frac{AB}{XZ} = \frac{4}{8} = \frac{1}{2}.$$
BC and YZ are the other sides and
$$\frac{BC}{YZ} = \frac{5}{10} = \frac{1}{2}.$$
The ratios of corresponding sides are the same, so △ABC and △XZY are similar.

(ii) AC and XZ are the longest sides and
$$\frac{AC}{XZ} = \frac{8}{12} = \frac{2}{3}.$$
AB and YZ are the shortest sides and
$$\frac{AB}{YZ} = \frac{3}{4}.$$
Since these ratios are not the same △ABC and △XYZ are not similar. (There is no need to work out the third ratio.)

6

(i) In △ABC, $\hat{C} = 110°$ and in △XYZ, $\hat{Z} = 40°$. Since corresponding angles are equal △ABC and △ZYX are similar. The ratios of corresponding sides are the same, so
$$\frac{AB}{ZY} = \frac{AC}{ZX} = \frac{BC}{YX}.$$
Hence $\frac{AC}{10} = \frac{12}{16} \left(= \frac{AB}{ZY}\right)$
and AC = $\frac{15}{2}$ or 7·5 cm.

(ii) Since $\hat{BAC} = \hat{XAY}$ and $\hat{ACB} = \hat{AYX}$, △ABC and △AXY are similar.
The ratios of corresponding sides are the same, so
$$\frac{AB}{AX} = \frac{AC}{AY} = \frac{BC}{XY}.$$
Hence $\frac{AC}{7} = \frac{4}{5} \left(= \frac{AB}{AX}\right)$
and AC = $\frac{28}{5}$ or 5·6 cm.

(iii) Since $\hat{A} = \hat{E}$ and $\hat{C} = \hat{D}$, △ABC and △EBD are similar.
The ratios of corresponding sides are the same, so
$$\frac{AB}{EB} = \frac{AC}{ED} = \frac{BC}{BD}.$$
Hence $\frac{AC}{10} = \frac{2}{3} \left(= \frac{AB}{EB}\right)$
and AC = $\frac{20}{3}$ or 6·67 cm.

7

(i) (a) Since BD and AE are parallel,
CB̂D = CÂE (corresponding angles).
and
CD̂B = CÊA (corresponding angles).
Hence △BCD and △ACE are similar.
(b) $\frac{BC}{AC} = \frac{BD}{AE} = \frac{CD}{CE}.$
Hence $\frac{5}{CE} = \frac{4}{10} \left(= \frac{BD}{AE}\right)$
and CE = $\frac{5 \times 10}{4} = 12·5''.$

(ii) (a) Since TW and YZ are parallel,
XT̂W = XŶZ
and
XŴT = XẐY
Hence △XTW and △XYZ are similar.
(b) $\frac{XT}{XY} = \frac{XW}{XZ} = \frac{TW}{YZ}.$
Since △XYZ is isosceles, XZ = XY = 6 cm.
Hence $\frac{TW}{4} = \frac{2}{6} \left(= \frac{XW}{XZ}\right)$
and TW = $\frac{8}{6}$ = 1·33 cm.

8

(i) (a) △DEF and △QPR are similar.
(b) △ABC and △YXZ are similar.
(c) △LMN and △FGH are not similar.

(ii) AD = 1·84 cm; DC = 0·33 cm, BD = 1·63 cm.

(iii) AD = 4 cm, AC = 10 cm, AB = 10 cm.

(iv) △AOE and △ABC are similar since
AÔE = AB̂C = 90° and Â is common to both triangles.
Hence $\frac{AO}{AB} = \frac{OE}{BC} = \frac{AE}{AC}.$
When A is folded over to C, O lies on the crease, so O is halfway between A and C.
Thus AO = $\frac{15}{2}$ cm.
Now, $\frac{OE}{BC} = \frac{AO}{AB} = \frac{15/2}{12}.$
So OE = $\frac{15/2}{12} \times 9 = 5·625$ cm.
Hence EF = 11·25 cm.

Section 5.4 Solutions

1
(i) (a) $BC^2 = AB^2 + AC^2 = 16 + 9 = 25$
         Hence $BC = \sqrt{25} = 5''$.
     (b) $YZ^2 = XY^2 + XZ^2$
         So $XY^2 = YZ^2 - XZ^2 = 169 - 25 = 144$.
         Hence $XY = \sqrt{144} = 12$ cm.
     (c) $PR^2 = PQ^2 + QR^2$
         So $PQ^2 = PR^2 - QR^2 = 4 - 1 = 3$.
         Hence $PQ = \sqrt{3} = 1\cdot73$ cm.

(ii) The hypotenuse is the longest side, so we need
      to compare the square of the longest side with
      the sum of the squares of the other two sides.
      (a) $AB^2 + BC^2 = 4 + 9 = 13$
          $AC^2 = 16$.
          Hence $\triangle ABC$ is not right angled.
      (b) $XY^2 + XZ^2 = 1 + 1 = 2$
          $XY^2 = 2$
          Hence $\triangle XYZ$ is right angled.
      (c) $PQ^2 + PR^2 = (2\cdot1)^2 + (3\cdot5)^2 = 16\cdot6$
          $QR^2 = 16$.
          Hence $\triangle PQR$ is not right angled.

2
(i) $\triangle$(a) and $\triangle$(b) are congruent (AAS). Two
     angles are equal and in both triangles a is the
     side between the angle marked $30°$ and the
     unmarked angle.
     $\triangle$(a) and $\triangle$(d) are congruent (SAS). In $\triangle$(a)
     the third angle is $80°$. So two sides are
     equal and the included angle in each case is $80°$.

(ii) (a) ABCD is a rectangle so $AD = BC$
          $F\hat{A}D = F\hat{C}B$ (alternate angles).
          and $F\hat{D}A = F\hat{B}C$ (alternate angles).
          Hence $\triangle AFD$ and $\triangle BFD$ are congruent
          (AAS).
      (b) Since the triangles are congruent corres-
          ponding sides are equal. Hence $AF = FC$
          and $DF = FB$.

3
(i) $\triangle ABC$ and $\triangle YZX$ are congruent (SAS).
      ($AB = YZ = x$; $AC = YX = y$ and
      $B\hat{A}C = X\hat{Y}Z = 50°$).
(ii) $\triangle PQR$ and $\triangle WST$ are congruent (right angle,
      hypotenuse and side).
(iii) $\triangle ABC$ and $\triangle LMN$ are not congruent, since the
      equal angle is not the included angle.
(iv) $\triangle DEF$ and $\triangle XYZ$ are not congruent.
      Although $\hat{F} = \hat{Z} = 40°$ and $\hat{E} = \hat{Y} = 120°$, FD
      and YZ are not corresponding sides.

4
(i) (a) $\triangle ABC$ does exist since
         $AB + BC = 11$ cm and $AC = 5$ cm
         $AB + AC = 9$ cm and $BC = 7$ cm
         $BC + AC = 12$ cm and $AB = 4$ cm.
     (b) $\triangle PQR$ does not exist since, although
         $PQ + QR = 13$ cm and $PR = 6$ cm and
         $QR + PR = 16$ cm and $PQ = 3$ cm
         $PQ + PR = 9$ cm but $QR = 10$ cm.
     (c) $\triangle XYZ$ does not exist since
         $XY + XZ = 10$ cm and $YZ = 10$ cm.
         Hence $XY + XZ = YZ$.
         But for the triangle to exist $XY + XZ$ must
         be *greater* than YZ.

(ii) Draw a rough sketch as a guide.

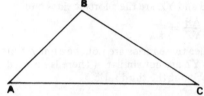

      Notice that the largest side is opposite the
      largest angle and the smallest side is opposite
      the smallest angle.
      (a) The smallest angle is therefore $A\hat{C}B$
          (opposite AB).
      (b) The largest angle is $A\hat{B}C$ (opposite AC).

5
(i)   (a) 7   (b) $\sqrt{2}$ or $1\cdot41$ (c) $\sqrt{6}$ or $2\cdot45$
(ii) $\triangle$(a) and $\triangle$(d) (both isosceles, equal sides of
      length 5)
      $\triangle$(b) and $\triangle$(c) (both equilateral, sides of
      length 5)
      $\triangle$(a) and $\triangle$(f) (SAS)
      $\triangle$(d) and $\triangle$(f) (AAS)
      Hence $\triangle$(a), $\triangle$(d) and $\triangle$(f) are all congruent.
(iii) (a) $AC = 15$ cm (Pythagoras' theorem)
      (b) $E\hat{B}O = O\hat{D}F$ (alternate angles)
          $E\hat{O}B = D\hat{O}F$ (vertically opposite)
          $OB = DO$ (half diagonal: See Exercise
                       5.4, 2(ii))
          Hence $\triangle OEB$ and $\triangle OFD$ are congruent.
(iv) (a) $\triangle ABC$ does not exist.
      (b) The largest angle is $X\hat{Z}Y$, the smallest angle
          is $X\hat{Y}Z$.

Section 5.5 Solutions

1

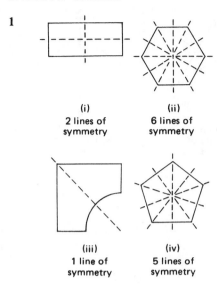

(i)
2 lines of
symmetry

(ii)
6 lines of
symmetry

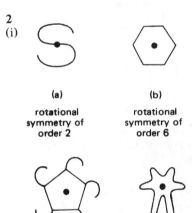

(iii)
1 line of
symmetry

(iv)
5 lines of
symmetry

2
(i)

(a)
rotational
symmetry of
order 2

(b)
rotational
symmetry of
order 6

(c)
rotational
symmetry of
order 5

(d)
rotational
symmetry of
order 1

(ii)

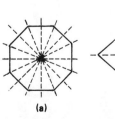 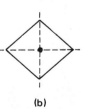 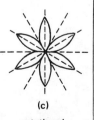

(a)
rotational
symmetry of
order 8

(b)
rotational
symmetry of
order 2

(c)
rotational
symmetry of
order 6

3
(i)   Area = $\frac{1}{2} \times 6 \times 3 = 9$ cm^2.
(ii)   Area = $\frac{1}{2} \times 8 \times 6 = 24$ in^2.
(iii)   Area = $\frac{1}{2} \times 3 \cdot 4 \times 2 \cdot 2 = 3 \cdot 74$ cm^2.
(iv)   △ABC is isosceles. The perpendicular bisector,
       AD, bisects BC.

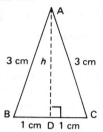

Now $h^2 = 9 - 1 = 8$, so $h = \sqrt{8}$ cm.
Hence area = $\frac{1}{2} \times \sqrt{8} \times 2 = \sqrt{8}$ or $2 \cdot 83$ cm^2.

4
(i)   ABCD is a parallelogram.
       Area = base × height = 5 × 3 = 15 cm^2.
(ii)   PQRS is a parallelogram.
       Area = base × height = $c \times b = cb$.
(iii)   Split the shape up into two parts, a rectangle
       and a triangle.

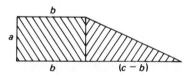

Total area = area of rectangle + area of triangle
$$= ab + \tfrac{1}{2}(c - b)a$$
$$= ab + \tfrac{1}{2}ac - \tfrac{1}{2}ab$$
$$= \frac{ab}{2} + \frac{ac}{2} = \frac{a}{2}(b + c).$$

(iv)   Split the shape up as illustrated below.

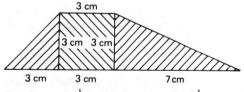

Total area = $(\frac{1}{2} \times 3 \times 3) + (3 \times 3) + (\frac{1}{2} \times 3 \times 7)$
           = 24 cm^2.

5

(i) (a) Area $= \frac{1}{2} \times \frac{\pi}{2} \times 1^2 = \frac{\pi}{4}m^2 = 0\cdot79$ m².

(b) Area $= \frac{45}{360} \times \pi \times 1^2 = 0\cdot39$ cm².

(c) The angle subtended at the centre in the *shaded* sector is $\left(2\pi - \frac{2\pi}{3}\right) = \frac{4\pi}{3}$.

The area of the shaded sector is therefore
$\frac{1}{2} \times \frac{4\pi}{3} \times r^2 = \frac{2\pi r^2}{3}$.

(d) The angle subtended at the centre of the *shaded* sector is $(360° - 145°) = 215°$.

The area of the shaded sector is therefore

$\frac{215}{360} \times \pi \times 3^2 = 16\cdot89$ in².

(ii) (a) Length of ACB $= \frac{2\pi}{3} \times 1 = \frac{2\pi}{3}$ cm.

(b) Length of ACB $= \frac{20}{360} \times 2 \times \pi \times 14 = 4\cdot89$ m.

(c) The angle subtended at the centre is
$2\pi - \frac{3\pi}{4} = \frac{5\pi}{4}$.

The length of ACB is therefore
$\frac{5\pi}{4} \times l = \frac{5\pi l}{4}$.

6

(i) $V = lwh$
(a) $V = 1 \times 8 \times 3 = 24$ cm³
(b) $V = 2 \times 2 \times 2 = 8$ cm³
(c) $V = 1000 \times 1 \times 1 = 1000$ m³

(ii) Cross-sectional area $= \frac{1}{2} \times 2 \times 4 = 4$ cm².
Volume = cross-sectional area × height
$\qquad = 4 \times 3 = 12$ cm³.

(iii) (a) Volume $= \pi r^2 h$
$\qquad = \pi \times 2^2 \times 6 = 75\cdot40$ cm³.
(b) Volume $= \pi \times r^2 \times r = \pi r^3$.
(c) The perpendicular height of the triangle is given by Pythagoras :

$$h^2 = r^2 - \left(\frac{a}{2}\right)^2 = r^2 - \frac{a^2}{4}$$

and

$$h = \sqrt{r^2 - \frac{a^2}{4}}.$$

Cross-sectional area $= \frac{1}{2} \times$ base × height

$$= \frac{1}{2}a \times \sqrt{r^2 - \frac{a^2}{4}}.$$

$$\text{Volume} = a \times \frac{1}{2}a \sqrt{r^2 - \frac{a^2}{4}}$$

$$= \frac{a^2}{2}\sqrt{r^2 - \frac{a^2}{4}}.$$

7

(i)

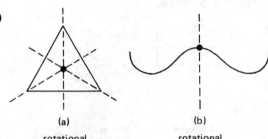

(a)
rotational
symmetry of
order 3

(b)
rotational
symmtery of
order 1

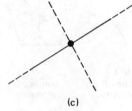

(c)
rotational
symmetry of
order 2

(ii) (a) $\frac{1}{2}$ cm²   (b) 1 cm²

(c) $\frac{1}{2}a\sqrt{\frac{3a^2}{4}} \left(= \frac{\sqrt{3}}{4}a^2\right)$

(d) $\frac{1}{2}y^2 + xy + \frac{1}{2}yx = \frac{3}{2}xy + \frac{1}{2}y^2$

(e) Area of square ABCD = 4 cm².
Area of $\triangle$BEC $= \frac{1}{2} \times 2 \times \sqrt{3} = 1\cdot73$ cm².
Hence area of ABECD $= 4 - 1\cdot73 = 2\cdot27$ cm².

(iii) 14π or $43\cdot98''$.

(iv) $6\cdot28$ in³.

(v) (a) Volume $= (\frac{1}{2} \times 1 \times 1 \times 1) + (1 \times 1 \times 1)$
$\qquad + (\frac{1}{2} \times 1 \times 1 \times 1) = 2$ cm³.
(b) Volume $= (a \times b \times a) + (\frac{1}{2} \times a \times b \times a)$
$\qquad = \frac{3}{2}a^2b$.

MODULE 6

6.1 Factors

6.2 Quadratics of the Form $x^2 + bx + c$

6.3 Quadratics of the Form $ax^2 + bx + c$

6.4 Algebraic Fractions

6.5 Equations and Formulas

6.1 Factors

6.1(i) HIGHEST COMMON FACTORS

You probably remember that a whole number which divides a given number exactly is called a factor of that number. For example, 4 is a factor of 24 but 7 is not.

Module 1, Section 1.4(ii)

A whole number which divides two or more given numbers exactly is a *common factor* of those numbers. For example,

　　2 is a common factor of 24 and 32

　　4 is also a common factor of 24 and 32

　　8 is also a common factor of 24 and 32.

8 is the largest number which divides both given numbers. It is called the *highest common factor*.

Highest common factor is often abbreviated to
　　h.c.f.

You may be able to spot all the factors of a given number by inspection. For larger numbers you will probably need to be a bit more systematic. Try dividing by 2 first, then 3, then 4 and so on. A whole number whose only factors are itself and 1 is called a *prime number*. For example 2, 3, 5, 7, 11, 13, 17, 19, 23, 29, 31, 37, 41, 43, 47, . . . are all prime numbers.

4 is not a prime number, since its factors are 4, 1 and 2.

The same method can be used to find the highest common factor of two or more given numbers. Look at the smallest number and identify all its factors. Then check which of these factors are also factors of the other numbers.

1 divides every number exactly. It is called a trivial factor and is usually omitted when listing the factors of a given number. Similarly, the number itself is a trivial factor.

EXAMPLE

Find the highest common factor of 24, 30 and 54.

SOLUTION

24 is the smallest number. Its factors are 2, 3, 4, 6, 8 and 12. Now check which of these factors are also factors of 30 and 54.

2, 3 and 6 are all common factors. The other numbers (4, 8 and 12) do not divide either 30 or 54.

The highest common factor is therefore 6.

First look at the smallest number and list the factors either by inspection or by trying successive numbers.

TRY SOME YOURSELF

1(i) Find all the factors of each of the following numbers:
     (a) 18 (b) 48 (c) 60 (d) 81.

(ii) Find all the prime factors of each of the following numbers:
     (a) 48 (b) 36 (c) 105.

(iii) Find the highest common factor of each of the following:
     (a) 4, 6 (b) 6, 15 (c) 18, 54 (d) 12, 30, 51.

We started this section by looking at common factors of numbers but the same principle applies to common factors of algebraic terms. For example, consider the terms

     $12a^2$ and $4ab$.

2 and 4 divide both terms exactly, so they are common factors. $12a^2$ and $4ab$ have the letter a in common, so a is also a common factor. In fact

     $12a^2 = 4a \times 3a$

and

     $4ab = 4a \times b$

so that $4a$ is the highest common factor. Notice that the highest common factor, $4a$, is obtained by multiplying together the highest number factor, 4, and the symbol, a.

The following are all factors of $4ab$, since each divides $4ab$ exactly: 2, 4, a, b, 2a, 2b, 4a, 4b, ab, 2ab.

This suggests a method for finding the highest common factor of two or more algebraic terms. First look at the coefficients and find the highest common factor of those numbers. Then consider the symbols. Find the highest factor involving each individual letter. The highest common factor is then the product of all these factors.

EXAMPLE

Find the highest common factor of $12a^3b^2$ and $28a^2b^3$.

SOLUTION

First consider the coefficients: the highest common factor of 12 and 28 is 4.

Now look at the symbol a. The first term contains a^3 and the second term contains a^2. The highest factor is the lower power, a^2. Similarly, the highest factor involving b is b^2.

a divides both $12a^3b^2$ and $28a^2b$ exactly. So does a^2. But a^3 does not divide $28a^2b$.

Thus the highest common factor of $12a^3b^2$ and $28a^2b^3$ is $4 \times a^2 \times b^2$, which is $4a^2b^2$.

Check:
$$12a^3b^2 = 4a^2b^2 \times 3a$$
$$28a^2b^3 = 4a^2b^2 \times 7b.$$

TRY SOME YOURSELF

2   Find the highest common factor of each of the following:
(i) $2ab, 3ax$ (ii) a^2b, a^3b^2 (iii) $9x^2y^2, 12x^3y^2, 6x^3y$.

6.1(ii) FACTORISING ALGEBRAIC EXPRESSIONS

We have shown that $12a^2$ and $4ab$ have $4a$ as the highest common factor. Each term can therefore be written as the product of the highest common factor and another factor. Thus

$$12a^2 = 4a \times 3a$$

and

$$4ab = 4a \times b.$$

Now consider the expression $12a^2 + 4ab$. This can be rearranged as follows

$$12a^2 + 4ab = (4a \times 3a) + (4a \times b)$$
$$= 4a(3a + b).$$

The expression has thus been rewritten as the product of the highest common factor, $4a$, and another algebraic expression $(3a + b)$ in which the terms have no common factors. This process is called *factorisation*. More precisely it is known as *taking out the highest common factor*.

Check that this is the same expression by multiplying out the brackets.

We discuss other forms of factorisation later in this module.

EXAMPLE

Factorise $4a^2b - 6ac - 2a^2$.

SOLUTION

First find the highest common factor of $4a^2b$, $6ac$ and $2a^2$. By inspection, it is $2a$. Now write each term as a product of the highest common factor and another factor to get

$$4a^2b - 6ac - 2a^2 = (2a \times 2ab) - (2a \times 3c) - (2a \times a)$$

$$= 2a(2ab - 3c - a).$$

If all the terms are negative it's best to take the negative sign outside the brackets first.

Take care when the expression involves negative signs. It's always a good idea to check your answer by multiplying out the brackets again.

EXAMPLE

Factorise $-ab - ac$.

SOLUTION

$$-ab - ac = -(ab + ac)$$
$$= -(a(b + c))$$
$$= -a(b + c)$$

TRY SOME YOURSELF

3   Factorise each of the following expressions by taking out the highest common factor:
(i) $2ab + 3ax$ (ii) $a^2b - a^3b^2$ (iii) $-12a^3 - 6a^4$
(iv) $9x^2y - 12x^3y^2 + 6x^3y$.

6.1(iii) EXPANDING BRACKETS

In Module 2 we discussed how to multiply two brackets together. This involves multiplying each term in the first brackets by each term in the second.

Module 2, Section 2.3(iii)

For example

$$(x + 2)(x + 3) = x^2 + 3x + 2x + 6$$
$$= x^2 + 5x + 6.$$

This can also be interpreted geometrically.

A rectangle of length $(x + 3)$ and width $(x + 2)$ has area $(x + 2)(x + 3)$.

But the rectangle can be split into separate areas A, B, C and D and the total area is also given by

$$A + B + C + D = x^2 + 3x + 2x + 6$$
$$= x^2 + 5x + 6.$$

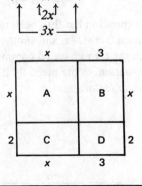

The result can also be obtained by treating $(x + 2)$ as a factor and multiplying each term in the expression $x + 3$ by this factor. Thus

$$\boxed{(x + 2)}(x + 3) = \boxed{(x + 2)}x + \boxed{(x + 2)}3$$
$$= x(x + 2) + 3(x + 2)$$
$$= x^2 + 2x + 3x + 6$$
$$= x^2 + 5x + 6.$$

Remember that order doesn't matter, so that

$$(x + 2)x = x(x + 2)$$

TRY SOME YOURSELF

4 Expand each of the following by multiplying out the brackets and collecting like terms:
(i) $(y + 3)(y + 4)$ (ii) $(t + 4)(t + 1)$ (iii) $(z + 3)(z - 1)$
(iv) $(a - 2)(a - 3)$.

Use whichever method you find easiest.

The expression $(r + s)(r + s)$ is usually written as $(r + s)^2$. From above

$$(r + s)^2 = (r + s)(r + s)$$
$$= r^2 + rs + rs + s^2$$
$$= r^2 + 2rs + s^2.$$

$(r + s)(r + s)$

Any two brackets can be multiplied together in the same way.

Remember that $sr = rs$.

EXAMPLE

Expand $(2x - 3)(x + 5)$.

SOLUTION

$(2x - 3)(x + 5)$

The diagram above shows that the resulting expression should contain four terms indicated by the four pairs of arrows.

Thus

$$(2x - 3)(x + 5) = (2x \times x) + (2x \times 5) + (-3 \times x) + ((-3) \times 5)$$
$$= 2x^2 + 10x - 3x - 15$$
$$= 2x^2 + 7x - 15.$$

TRY SOME YOURSELF

5 Expand each of the following:
(i)   (a) $(x + 2)^2$ (b) $(b - 2)^2$ (c) $(x - a)^2$
(ii) (a) $(2r + 1)(3r + 2)$ (b) $(2x + 5)(x + 2)$ (c) $(3y - 2)(2y + 4)$
      (d) $(3x + 2)^2$
(iii) (a) $(3r + a)(2r + 2a)$ · (b) $(7s + t)(4s - 3t)$ (c) $(2x - 3y)^2$.

Take care with the negative signs.

The same method can be used for brackets containing more than two terms. A little more care is needed as you may well appreciate after studying the diagram in the next example.

EXAMPLE

Expand $(x + 1)(x^2 - 2x + 3)$.

SOLUTION

$$\begin{array}{c}
\overbrace{}^{3x} \\
\overbrace{}^{-2x^2} \\
\overbrace{}^{x^3} \\
(x + 1)(x^2 - 2x + 3) \\
\underbrace{}_{x^2} \\
\underbrace{}_{-2x} \\
\underbrace{}_{3}
\end{array}$$

Notice that the diagram indicates that the resulting expression should contain 6 terms.

Thus $(x + 1)(x^2 - 2x + 3) = x^3 - 2x^2 + 3x + x^2 - 2x + 3$

$$= x^3 - x^2 + x + 3.$$

Simplify the expression by collecting like terms.

Again, each term in the first bracket is multiplied by each term in the second.

TRY SOME YOURSELF

6   Expand each of the following:
   (i) $(a - 1)(2a^2 - 3a + 1)$ (ii) $(2y + 1)(y^2 - 2y + 3)$
   (iii) $(3a - 1)(2a^2 + a - 4)$ (iv) $(2a + 3b)(a - 2b + 3c)$.

You might find it helpful to draw diagrams. Check that you have six terms before simplifying.

6.1(iv) COEFFICIENTS OF QUADRATICS

Expanding $(2x + 5)(x + 2)$ gives

$$2x^2 + 9x + 10.$$

Such an expression is called a *quadratic expression* or just a *quadratic. A quadratic expression always contains a term involving* x^2*. It may also contain a term involving x and a constant term. No other terms are involved.* For example,

Of course, the symbol does not necessarily have to be x. It may be any letter. Notice however that each expression involves only one letter.

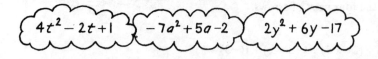

$$4t^2 - 2t + 1 \qquad -7a^2 + 5a - 2 \qquad 2y^2 + 6y - 17$$

are all quadratics whereas $2y + 1$ and $y^3 + 17y^2$ are not.

It is useful to be able to identify the coefficients of a quadratic quickly. For example, in the expression

$$-3x^2 + 2x - 7$$

the coefficient of x^2 is -3, the coefficient of x is 2 and the constant term is -7. The expressions

$$2y^2 - 7 \qquad y^2 + 3y \qquad 7y^2$$

are also quadratics. Notice that the coefficient of y or the constant term may be zero but the coefficient of y^2 must always be non-zero.

If a quadratic is given in the form $(2x - 5)(x + 2)$ it is possible to identify the coefficients without expanding the brackets. Study the following diagram carefully.

$0y^2 + 2y + 1 = 2y + 1$.
This is a linear expression, not a quadratic.

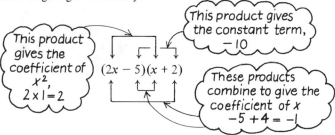

This product gives the coefficient of x^2, $2 \times 1 = 2$

This product gives the constant term, -10

These products combine to give the coefficient of x $-5 + 4 = -1$

$(2x - 5)(x + 2)$

You may well think that it is easier to multiply out the brackets, and in this case it probably is. However the same principle applies if the brackets involve three or more terms and then it *is* easier to use this technique, particularly if you need only identify one coefficient.

EXAMPLE

Find the coefficient of y^2 in the expression $(3y - 4)(4y - 3)$.

SOLUTION

$(3y - 4)(4y - 3)$

The term involving y^2 is obtained by multiplying together the terms involving y. The coefficient is therefore $(3 \times 4) = 12$.

Here, we only need to consider one product, the product giving the term involving y^2.

TRY SOME YOURSELF

7   Without expanding the brackets, find each of the following:
(i)   the coefficient of a^2 in $(2a + 1)(a + 3)$
(ii) the constant term in $(3y - 2)(4y - 3)$
(iii) the coefficient of r^2 in $(2 - r)(3 + 2r)$
(iv) the coefficient of x in $(3x - 4)^2$.

After you have worked through this section you should be able to

a   Find all the prime factors of a given number
b   Find the highest common factor of two or more given numbers
c   Find the highest common factor of two or more algebraic terms
d   Factorise an algebraic expression by taking out the highest common factor
e   Expand brackets of the form $(ax + b)(cx + d)$, and of the form $(ax + b)(cx^2 + dx + e)$ where a, b, c, d and e stand for numbers
f   Identify the coefficients of a quadratic expression given in the form $(ax + b)(cx + d)$ without expanding the brackets

Finally here are some exercises if you want more practice.

TRY SOME MORE YOURSELF

8(i)   Find all the prime factors of each of the following numbers:
(a) 26   (b) 108   (c) 144.

(ii)   Find the highest common factor of each of the following:
(a) 8, 24, 36   (b) 27, 144, 9   (c) 25, 56, 21.

(iii)   Factorise each of the following expressions by taking out the highest common factor:
(a) $6xy - 2xz$ (b) $6x^2y^3z - 3xy^2z^2 + 9y^2z$
(c) $-a^2b - a^3b^2$ (d) $7x^3 + 14x^2 + 21x$ (e) $ax^2 - bx^4$.

(iv)   Expand each of the following:
(a) $(x - 1)(x + 2)$ (b) $(b - 3a)^2$ (c) $(2a - 3)(4a - 7)$
(d) $(4b - 2a)^2$.

(v)   Expand each of the following:
(a) $(2x - 3)(4x^2 + 2x - 1)$ (b) $(1 - 2a)(a^2 + 7a - 1)$
(c) $(3 + 4t)(2 - t - 2t^2)$.

(vi)   Without expanding the brackets find each of the following coefficients:
(a) the coefficient of a in $(6 - a^2)(1 + a)$
(b) the coefficient of x^2 in $(2 + x)(1 - 3x)$
(c) the coefficient of x in $(2x - 3)(4x^2 + 2x - 1)$
(d) the constant term in $(1 - 2a)(a^2 + 7a - 1)$.

6.2 *Quadratics of the Form* $x^2 + bx + c$

TRY THESE QUESTIONS FIRST

1   Factorise $x^2 + 9x + 14$.

2   Factorise $x^2 - 10x + 16$.

3   Factorise $y^2 + 6y - 16$.

4   The expression $x^2 - x - 20$ can be rewritten as $(x + \alpha)(x + \beta)$ where α and β stand for missing numbers. Without finding values for α and β write down the value of (i) $\alpha\beta$ and (ii) $\alpha + \beta$.

5   Solve $x^2 + 6x - 16 = 0$.

6.2(i) FACTORISING QUADRATICS

In the last section we indicated that a quadratic expression always has the form

$$ax^2 + bx + c$$

where a, b, c stand for any numbers and a is not equal to zero. This section is concerned with quadratic expressions in which the coefficient of x^2 is equal to one, that is expressions of the form

$$x^2 + bx + c$$

where b and c stand for any numbers. We now investigate how to rewrite such an expression as the product of two factors. For example, how to rewrite

$$x^2 - 3x + 2 \text{ as } (x - 1)(x - 2).$$

This is another form of factorisation; it is the reverse process to expanding brackets. The method depends to a large extent on trial and error, so it can take a long time at first. However, with practice it becomes easier to 'spot' the required form, which suggests that you should try as many examples as you can. It is worth pointing out at this stage that not all quadratics *can* be factorised. You will discover this for yourself as you work through the section.

b and c may be zero.

b and c may be positive or negative.

Check by multiplying out the brackets.

Quadratics with positive coefficients

We begin by investigating the expression $x^2 + 4x + 3$. We wish to write this as a product of the form

$$(x + \square)(x + \square)$$

where the squares are to be replaced by whole numbers. These missing numbers can be deduced by examining each of the coefficients.

The coefficient of x^2 in the original expression is one. We first need to check that the coefficient of x^2 in the product $(x + \square)(x + \square)$ is also equal to one. The diagram opposite indicates that the coefficients do agree.

The constant term of the original expression is 3 and this provides a clue to the missing numbers since the product of the two numbers should also be equal to 3. This suggests that we need to look at the factors of 3. We want two numbers which multiply together to give 3. The only possible factors are 1 and 3 which suggests that the product should be

$$(x + 1)(x + 3).$$

This can now be checked by examining the coefficient of x. In the original expression the coefficient is 4. In the product $(x + 1)(x + 3)$ the coefficient of x is given by

First we consider examples where b and c are both positive.

Provided the coefficients are positive whole numbers we are looking for positive whole numbers to replace the squares.

x^2

$(x + \square)(x + \square)$

$x^2 + 4x + 3$

$(x + \square)(x + \square)$

$x^2 + 4x + 3$

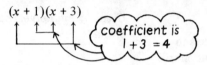

Hence
$$x^2 + 4x + 3 = (x + 1)(x + 3).$$

The quadratic expression has thus been factorised into a product of two factors. The method can be summarised as follows:

> 1 Check the coefficient of x^2
>
> 2 Look at the constant term and consider the possible factors
>
> 3 Check by comparing the coefficient of x

This last stage is particularly important, especially when there are several possibilities. Of course, as an extra check, you can multiply out the brackets and compare the answer with the original expression.

In the next example the process is not quite so straightforward, although the same method is used.

EXAMPLE

Factorise $x^2 + 5x + 6$.

SOLUTION

Consider the product $(x + \square)(x + \square)$.

1 *Check the coefficient of x^2.* $1x^2 + 5x + 6$
   In $(x + \square)(x + \square)$ the coefficient of x^2 is also one.

2 *Look at the constant term.* $x^2 + 5x + 6$
   We need to find two numbers which multiply together to give 6; there are two possibilities

   $(x + 1)(x + 6)$ or $(x + 2)(x + 3)$.

Look at the factors of 6:
$1 \times 6 = 6$, and
$2 \times 3 = 6$.

In both cases the product is 6 as required. By examining the coefficient of x we can determine which is correct.

3 *Check the coefficient of x.*
The coefficient of x in the original expression is 5. Now consider the two possible products.

$x^2 + $▨$x + 6$

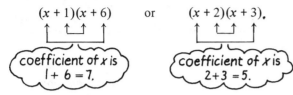

or

This shows that the right hand product is correct.

Hence
$$x^2 + 5x + 6 = (x + 2)(x + 3).$$

This example shows what we mean by trial and error since there are two possible choices of numbers which multiply together to give 6. The correct product is determined by comparing the coefficients of x.

TRY SOME YOURSELF

1 Factorise each of the following expressions:
(i) $x^2 + 3x + 2$ (ii) $x^2 + 6x + 5$ (iii) $x^2 + 5x + 4$
(iv) $x^2 + 8x + 12$ (v) $x^2 + 13x + 30$

In part (iv) you will need to consider all the possible factors of 12.

Not all quadratics can be factorised in this way. This can also be revealed by examination of the coefficients.

EXAMPLE

Show that $x^2 + 4x + 2$ cannot be written in the form $(x + \square)(x + \square)$ where the squares represent whole numbers.

SOLUTION

Try $(x + \square)(x + \square)$.

1 The coefficient of x^2 is one as required.

2 The constant term must be 2, so the only possible missing numbers are 2 and 1 which suggests that the product should be
$(x + 1)(x + 2)$.

$x^2 + 4x + $▨.

The only factors of 2 are 2 and 1.

3 Check the coefficient of x. This should be 4 but in $(x + 1)(x + 2)$ the coefficient is 3 which does not agree.

This shows that the expression $x^2 + 4x + 2$ cannot be written in the required form.

It can be tempting to conclude that a quadratic equation cannot be factorised after trying only one possible product. Remember that you must consider all possibilities before deciding that factorisation is impossible.

TRY SOME YOURSELF

2   Try to factorise each of the following expressions:
(i) $x^2 + x + 1$ (ii) $x^2 + 7x + 10$ (iii) $x^2 + 5x + 5$
(iv) $x^2 + 11x + 30$.

Section 6.2(i) has illustrated that a quadratic of the form $x^2 + bx + c$, where b and c stand for positive numbers, factorises into the product

$$(x + \alpha)(x + \beta)$$

where α and β are both positive.

*Of course, this refers only to those quadratics which **can** be factorised.*

6.2(ii) QUADRATICS OF THE FORM $x^2 - bx + c$

In Section 6.2(i) we only needed to consider positive numbers. The same method can be used when the coefficient of x is negative, but we now have to look at the sign of each number carefully.

EXAMPLE

Factorise $x^2 - 5x + 6$.

SOLUTION

Consider the product $(x + \square)(x + \square)$.

1 The coefficient of x^2 is one as required.

2 Look at the constant term.
We need to find two numbers which multiply together to give +6.
1 and 6, and 2 and 3 are two possibilities, but if you expand

$$(x + 1)(x + 6) \quad \text{or} \quad (x + 2)(x + 3)$$

you will see for yourself that neither of these arrangements gives a negative coefficient of x. We therefore need to consider negative factors. This gives two further possibilities,

$$(x - 1)(x - 6) \quad \text{or} \quad (x - 2)(x - 3).$$

$x^2 - 5x \boxed{+ 6}$

Remember that
$$(-) \times (-) = (+), \text{ so}$$
$$(-1) \times (-6) = (+6)$$
and
$$(-2) \times (-3) = (+6)$$

3 Check the coefficient of x.
The coefficient of x in the original expression is -5. Now consider the possible products to find which is correct.

$x^2 \boxed{- 5x} + 6$

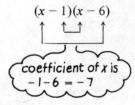

$(x - 1)(x - 6)$ or $(x - 2)(x - 3)$

coefficient of x is
$-1 - 6 = -7$

coefficient of x is
$-2 - 3 = -5$

The right hand product is correct.

Hence
$$x^2 - 5x + 6 = (x - 2)(x - 3).$$

This illustrates that a quadratic of the form $x^2 - bx + c$, where b and c stand for positive numbers, factorises into a product of the form

$$(x - \alpha)(x - \beta)$$

where α and β are both positive.

Notice the form of the product
$(x - \square)(x - \square)$.

TRY SOME YOURSELF

3 Try to factorise each of the following expressions:
(i) $x^2 - 5x + 4$ (ii) $x^2 - 3x + 2$ (iii) $x^2 - x + 2$
(iv) $x^2 - 10x + 16$ (v) $x^2 - 4x + 4$ (vi) $x^2 - 5x + 8$
(vii) $x^2 - 9x + 20$.

Watch out! Not all these
*quadratics **can** be factorised.*

6.2(iii) QUADRATICS WITH A NEGATIVE CONSTANT TERM

We now investigate quadratics of the form

$$x^2 + bx - c \quad \text{and} \quad x^2 - bx - c$$

that is, quadratics in which the constant term is negative and in which the coefficient of x may be positive or negative.

Such quadratics can also be factorised by the same method, as the following examples illustrate.

EXAMPLE

Factorise $x^2 + x - 6$.

SOLUTION

Consider $(x + \square)(x + \square)$.

1 The coefficient of x^2 is one as required.

2 Look at the constant term.
The product of the missing numbers must be -6. This suggests that one factor must be positive and the other negative, giving the following possibilities:

$(x - 1)(x + 6)$ or $(x - 6)(x + 1)$
$(x - 2)(x + 3)$ or $(x - 3)(x + 2)$.

The correct form is determined by comparing the coefficients of x.

$x^2 + x - 6$
Remember that
$(+) \times (-) = (-)$
and
$(-) \times (+) = (-)$.

3 Check the coefficient of x.
In $(x - 1)(x + 6)$ the coefficient of x is $+5$.
In $(x - 6)(x + 1)$ the coefficient of x is -5.
In $(x - 2)(x + 3)$ the coefficient of x is $+1$.
Hence

$$x^2 + x - 6 = (x - 2)(x + 3).$$

$x^2 + 1x - 6$

This gives the correct product.
There is no need to check the
fourth possibility.

EXAMPLE

Factorise $x^2 - 7x - 8$.

SOLUTION

Consider $(x + \square)(x + \square)$.

1 The coefficient of x^2 is one as required.

2 *Look at the constant term.*
This should be -8, so one factor must be positive and the other negative, giving the following possibilities:

$$(x - 1)(x + 8) \quad \text{or} \quad (x - 8)(x + 1)$$
$$(x - 2)(x + 4) \quad \text{or} \quad (x - 4)(x + 2).$$

$x^2 - 7x\ \boxed{-\ 8}$

3 *Check the coefficient of x.*
In $(x - 1)(x + 8)$ the coefficient is $+7$.
In $(x - 8)(x + 1)$ the coefficient is -7.
Hence

$$x^2 - 7x - 8 = (x - 8)(x + 1).$$

$x^2\ \boxed{-\ 7}x - 8$

There is no need to check the other possibilities.

These examples indicate that a quadratic of the form $x^2 + bx - c$ or $x^2 - bx - c$, where b and c stand for positive numbers, factorises into a product of the form

$$(x - \alpha)(x + \beta)$$

where α and β are both positive.

Notice the form of the product $(x - \square)(x + \square)$.

TRY SOME YOURSELF

4   Try to factorise each of the following expressions:
(i) $x^2 - x - 2$ (ii) $x^2 + 2x - 8$ (iii) $x^2 - 9x - 12$
(iv) $x^2 + 2x - 3$ (v) $x^2 + x - 1$ (vi) $x^2 - x - 12$
(vii) $x^2 + 4x - 12$ (viii) $x^2 - 16x - 15$.

Again, not all these quadratics can be factorised.

6.2(iv) A QUICKER METHOD

Having worked through several examples you may well feel confident that you can now spot the factorised product quickly. But you may also find it helpful to analyse the results a little further.

First, consider the following results obtained when the constant term is positive

$$x^2\ \boxed{+}\ 4x\ \boxed{+}\ 3 = (x\ \boxed{+}\ 1)(x\ \boxed{+}\ 3)$$

1 and 3 multiply together to give 3. Their sum is 4.

$$x^2 + 5x + 6 = (x + 2)(x + 3)$$

> 2 and 3 multiply together to give 6. Their sum is 5.

$$x^2 - 8x + 12 = (x - 6)(x - 2).$$

> −6 and −2 multiply together to give 12. Their sum is −8.

This suggests that in each case the product of the missing numbers should correspond to the constant term and the sum of the missing numbers should correspond to the coefficient of x. The next example indicates how to apply this observation.

EXAMPLE

Factorise $x^2 - 9x + 18$.

SOLUTION

We need to find two numbers which multiply together to give 18 and whose sum is -9. This immediately suggests that the numbers are -3 and -6.

You will need to try the possible factors in your head, or on paper.

Hence

$$x^2 - 9x + 18 = (x - 3)(x - 6).$$

A similar pattern emerges when the constant term is negative.

$$x^2 + x - 6 = (x - 2)(x + 3)$$

> −2 and +3 multiply together to give −6. Their sum $((-2) + 3)$ is +1.

$$x^2 - 2x - 3 = (x - 3)(x + 1)$$

> −3 and +1 multiply together to give −3. Their sum $((-3) + 1)$ is −2.

$$x^2 - 7x - 8 = (x - 8)(x + 1)$$

> −8 and +1 multiply together to give −8. Their sum $((-8) + 1)$ is −7.

Again, the product of the numbers corresponds to the constant term and the sum of the numbers corresponds to the coefficient of x. In such cases you will need to take care in determining which factor should be negative and which should be positive.

EXAMPLE

Factorise $x^2 - 3x - 10$.

SOLUTION

We need to find two numbers which multiply together to give -10 and whose sum is -3. This suggests that the numbers are -5 and $+2$.

Hence

$$x^2 - 3x - 10 = (x - 5)(x + 2).$$

TRY SOME YOURSELF

5   Factorise each of the following expressions:
(i) $x^2 + 11x + 28$ (ii) $x^2 - 11x + 30$ (iii) $x^2 - 2x - 24$
(iv) $x^2 + 5x - 24$.

Use whichever method you find easiest.

6.2(v) SOLVING EQUATIONS OF THE FORM $x^2 + bx + c = 0$ BY FACTORISATION

In Module 2 we discussed how to solve *linear equations*, that is equations of the form

$$ax + b = 0$$

where a and b stand for any numbers. A *quadratic equation* has the form

$$ax^2 + bx + c = 0$$

where a, b and c stand for any numbers and a is not equal to zero. We now discuss how to solve equations of the form $x^2 + bx + c = 0$ by factorisation.

You probably remember that a linear equation has only one solution. For example $x = 2$ is the solution to $2x + 3 = 7$.

If a quadratic expression can be factorised it has the form

$$(x + \alpha)(x + \beta).$$

The corresponding quadratic equation is therefore

$$(x + \alpha)(x + \beta) = 0.$$

Now, if the product of two numbers is zero, then one of the numbers must itself be equal to zero. Similarly, if two *factors* multiply together to give zero, then one of the factors must be equal to zero. For example, if

$$(x + 1)(x - 2) = 0$$

then either $(x + 1) = 0$ or $(x - 2) = 0$. This gives two linear equations:

$$x + 1 = 0$$

and $x - 2 = 0$.

Module 2, Section 2.4(iv).

If a is equal to zero, the equation is just

$$bx + c = 0$$

a linear equation.

Not all quadratic expressions can be factorised, so not all quadratic equations can be solved in this way. In Section 6.5(i) and in Module 7, Section 7.4, we discuss more general methods which apply to any quadratic equation.

If ab = 0, then either a = 0 or b = 0.

The solution to the first equation is $x = -1$; the solution to the second equation is $x = 2$.

This shows that if

$$(x + 1)(x - 2) = 0.$$

then $x = -1$ or $x = 2$.

Thus, an equation of the form

$$(x + \alpha)(x + \beta) = 0$$

has two possible solutions.

You can check that $x = -1$ and $x = 2$ are solutions to the original equation by substituting into $(x + 1)(x - 2)$.

TRY SOME YOURSELF

6   Find the values of x which satisfy each of the following:
(i) $(x - 2)(x - 3) = 0$ (ii) $(x - 4)(x + 3) = 0$
(iii) $(x + 5)(x - 2) = 0$ (iv) $x(x - 1) = 0$.

This suggests how to solve a quadratic equation by factorisation. If an equation of the form

$$x^2 + bx + c = 0$$

can be rewritten as the product of two factors

$$(x + \alpha)(x + \beta) = 0$$

then the two possible solutions can be found by equating each factor to zero.

EXAMPLE

Solve the equation $x^2 - 7x - 8 = 0$.

SOLUTION

First consider the left hand side and try to factorise the quadratic expression $x^2 - 7x - 8$.

From the example on page 86, $x^2 - 7x - 8$ factorises into

$$(x - 8)(x + 1).$$

The equation $x^2 - 7x - 8 = 0$ is therefore equivalent to

$$(x - 8)(x + 1) = 0.$$

So, either $(x - 8) = 0$ or $(x + 1) = 0$.

$x - 8 = 0$ has solution $x = 8$ and $x + 1 = 0$ has solution $x = -1$.

The solutions of $x^2 - 7x - 8 = 0$ are therefore $x = 8$ or $x = -1$.

Check by substituting $x = 8$ and $x = -1$ into

$$x^2 - 7x + 8.$$

TRY SOME YOURSELF

7   Solve each of the following equations by factorising:
(i) $x^2 - 3x + 2 = 0$ (ii) $y^2 - y - 12 = 0$ (iii) $a^2 - 8a + 15 = 0$
(iv) $b^2 - 3b - 10 = 0$.

Check your solution by substituting into the original equation.

These exercises suggest that every quadratic equation has two possible solutions, but this is not necessarily the case. For example,

$$x^2 - 4x + 4 = 0$$

is equivalent to

$$(x - 2)(x - 2) = 0.$$

So there is only one solution, $x = 2$.

*In fact there **are** two solutions but they are both equal to 2. Such solutions are said to be **coincident**. See Module 7, Section 7.2 for further explanation.*

TRY SOME YOURSELF

8   Solve each of the following equations by factorisation:
(i) $x^2 + 2x + 1 = 0$ (ii) $x^2 - 6x + 9 = 0$ (iii) $y^2 + 8y + 16 = 0$
(iv) $x^2 + 10x + 25 = 0$.

Check your solutions by substituting into the original equation.

After you have worked through this section you should be able to

a   Factorise a quadratic expression of the form $x^2 + bx + c$ where b and c stand for any positive or negative numbers, or state that it cannot be expressed in the form $(x + \alpha)(x + \beta)$

b   Recognise that if a quadratic expression of the form $x^2 + bx + c$ can be factorised as $(x + \alpha)(x + \beta)$ then the product of α and β is equal to c and the sum of α and β is equal to b

c   Solve a quadratic equation of the form $x^2 + bx + c = 0$ by factorisation

---

Finally here are some exercises if you want more practice.

TRY SOME MORE YOURSELF

9(i)   Try to factorise each of the following expressions:
(a) $x^2 - 10x + 25$ (b) $t^2 + 12t + 35$ (c) $m^2 - 5m - 36$
(d) $c^2 - 22c + 23$ (e) $b^2 - b - 42$ (f) $c^2 - 22c - 23$
(g) $t^2 - 15t + 26$ (h) $y^2 - 28y - 27$.

(ii)   Solve each of the following equations by factorisation:
(a) $y^2 - 2y - 15 = 0$ (b) $m^2 - 5m - 36 = 0$
(c) $t^2 + t - 72 = 0$ (d) $t^2 + 14t - 72 = 0$
(e) $t^2 - 18t + 72 = 0$ (f) $t^2 - 16t + 64 = 0$.

6.3 Quadratics of the Form $ax^2 + bx + c$

TRY THESE QUESTIONS FIRST

1 Factorise $3 + 8y - 16y^2$.

2 Factorise $6t^4 - 17t^2 + 12$.

3 Solve $3a^2 + a - 2 = 0$.

6.3(i) QUADRATICS IN WHICH THE COEFFICIENT OF x^2 IS NOT EQUAL TO ONE

In the last section we discussed how to factorise quadratics of the form

$$x^2 + bx + c.$$

If the coefficient of x^2 is not equal to one then the process is a bit more complicated.

We start this section by investigating how to factorise

$$6x^2 - 23x + 10.$$

There is no point in starting with a product of the form

$$(x + \square)(x + \square)$$

since the coefficient of x^2 must be 6. We must therefore determine $6x^2 - 23x + 10$
the *form* of the product first. There are two possibilities

$$(6x + \square)(x + \square) \quad \text{or} \quad (2x + \square)(3x + \square).$$

The method is then essentially the same.

1 *Check the coefficient of x^2.*
   In both $(6x + \square)(x + \square)$ and $(2x + \square)(3x + \square)$ the coefficient of x^2 is 6 as required.

2 *Look at the constant term.* $6x^2 - 23x \;\boxed{+\,10}$
   The constant term is positive so we need two numbers which
   multiply together to give 10. Since the coefficient of x is $(-1) \times (-10) = 10$
   negative, the numbers must both be negative. There are several $(-2) \times (-5) = 10$
   possible products!

   $$
   \begin{array}{ll}
   (6x - 1)(x - 10) & \text{or} \quad (6x - 10)(x - 1); \\
   (6x - 5)(x - 2) & \text{or} \quad (6x - 2)(x - 5); \\
   (3x - 1)(2x - 10) & \text{or} \quad (3x - 10)(2x - 1); \\
   (3x - 5)(2x - 2) & \text{or} \quad (3x - 2)(2x - 5).
   \end{array}
   $$

   These products have been written down methodically. However it is easy to miss one out.

CHECK YOUR ANSWERS

1 $3 + 8y - 16y^2 = -(16y^2 - 8y - 3)$ *Sections 6.3(i) and 6.3(ii)*

  $= -(4y - 3)(4y + 1)$

  $= (3 - 4y)(4y + 1)$

2 $6t^4 - 17t^2 + 12 = (2t^2 - 3)(3t^2 - 4)$ *Section 6.3(iii)*

3 $3a^2 + a - 2 = 0$ means that $(3a - 2)(a + 1) = 0$. So $a = \frac{2}{3}$ or $a = -1$.   *Section 6.3(iv)*

---

3 *Check the coefficient of x.*
  Checking each product systematically gives

  $$6x^2 - 23x + 10 = (2x - 1)(3x - 10).$$

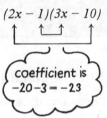

There can be quite a lot of checking to do when there are so many possibilities, and indeed sometimes the situation can appear to be even more complex. But although the method looks complicated it is quite systematic. This is illustrated in the next example. Follow through the solution but don't panic; this is one of the hardest examples that you will meet and we don't expect you to tackle such an exercise on your own at the moment.

EXAMPLE

  Factorise $6x^2 - 11x - 10$.

SOLUTION

1 *Check the coefficient of x^2.*
  This must be 6, so there are two possible forms for the product $6x^2 - 11x - 10.$

  $(6x + \square)(x + \square)$ and $(2x + \square)(3x + \square)$.

2 *Look at the constant term.*
  We need two numbers which multiply together to give -10. This $6x^2 - 11x - 10$
  suggests that one factor must be positive and the other negative.

  $-1 \times 10 = -10$ and $-10 \times 1 = -10$

  $-2 \times 5 = -10$ and $-5 \times 2 = -10$

This leads to the following possibilities!

  $(6x + 1)(x - 10)$ or $(6x + 10)(x - 1)$
  $(6x + 2)(x - 5)$ or $(6x + 5)(x - 2)$

  $(6x - 1)(x + 10)$ or $(6x - 10)(x + 1)$
  $(6x - 2)(x + 5)$ or $(6x - 5)(x + 2)$

  $(3x + 1)(2x - 10)$ or $(3x + 10)(2x - 1)$
  $(3x + 2)(2x - 5)$ or $(3x + 5)(2x - 2)$

  $(3x - 1)(2x + 10)$ or $(3x - 10)(2x + 1)$
  $(3x - 2)(2x + 5)$ or $(3x - 5)(2x + 2)$

We have grouped the expressions into blocks of four to help you differentiate between them. It's quite a formidable list!

3 Check the coefficient of x.

It is very hard to determine which possibility is correct. In fact

$$6x^2 - 11x - 10 = (2x - 5)(3x + 2).$$

Check by multiplying out the brackets.

As we mentioned earlier, don't worry if you think this example looks hard. With practice you will find that you get a 'feel' for the right combination and will not need to work through this rather laborious method.

Again, the *signs* of the coefficients give a clue to the form of the product.

$ax^2 + bx + c$ factorises into a product of the form $(\square + \square)(\square + \square)$

$ax^2 - bx + c$ factorises into a product of the form $(\square - \square)(\square - \square)$

$ax^2 + bx - c$ factorises into a product of the form $(\square - \square)(\square + \square)$

$ax^2 - bx - c$ factorises into a product of the form $(\square - \square)(\square + \square)$

a, b and c are all positive whole numbers.

The following exercises are not as difficult as the previous example. Try them to get some practice.

TRY SOME YOURSELF

1   Factorise each of the following expressions:
   (i) $3x^2 + 7x + 2$ (ii) $4x^2 + 8x + 3$ (iii) $6x^2 - 7x + 2$
   (iv) $4x^2 - 21x + 5$ (v) $6x^2 + 13x + 6$ (vi) $10x^2 + 3x - 1$.

All these expressions can be factorised. If in doubt check your answers by multiplying out the brackets again.

6.3(ii) AN ALTERNATIVE METHOD

There is an alternative method for factorising such quadratics. This is a modification of the method to factorise expressions like $x^2 + bx + c$. It is quite a neat technique, so we ask you to work through it slowly. Consider again the expression

$$6x^2 - 11x - 10.$$

Now, rather than look for two numbers which multiply together to give -10, we need to find two numbers whose product is equal to $6 \times (-10) = -60$. Again the sum of the two numbers must be equal to the coefficient of x, -11.

6 is the coefficient of x^2.
-10 is the constant term.
  $6 \times (-10) = -60$

Trial and error produces the factors (-15) and 4.

  $4 \times (-15) = -60$

Now look at the two pairs of numbers

$$(6, -15) \text{ and } (6, 4).$$

  $4 + (-15) = -11$

The first number in each pair is the coefficient of x^2, 6. The second number is one of the required factors of -60.

Notice that the highest common factor of 6 and -15 is 3 and the highest common factor of 6 and 4 is 2. Divide each pair of numbers by their highest common factor to get

$$(2, -5) \text{ and } (3, 2).$$

The factors can now be written down immediately:

(2, −5) corresponds to the factor $(2x − 5)$

and

(3, 2) corresponds to the factor $(3x + 2)$.

Hence

$$6x^2 − 11x − 10 = (2x − 5)(3x + 2).$$

We have described this method as a technique, and although we have outlined how to apply it we have not explained why it works. Such an explanation requires a higher level of mathematics than this book allows. For the moment you should concentrate on how to *use* the technique. Here is another example.

(2, −5) (3, 2)
↓   ↓ ↓   ↓
(2x − 5)(3x + 2)

Hopefully, if you go on to study higher mathematics you will gain more understanding of the method.

EXAMPLE

Factorise $12x^2 − 83x + 20$.

SOLUTION

We need to find two numbers which multiply together to give $12 \times 20 = 240$ and whose sum is −83.

Trial and error produces the numbers −3 and −80. Now consider the two pairs of numbers

(12, −3) and (12, −80).

The highest common factor of 12 and −3 is 3.

The highest common factor of 12 and −80 is 4.

Dividing each pair by its highest common factor gives

(4, −1) and (3, −20).

These correspond to the factors $(4x − 1)$ and $(3x − 20)$.

Hence

$$12x^2 − 83x + 20 = (4x − 1)(3x − 20).$$

One word of warning. Before applying this method you must ensure that any common factors of the coefficients have been removed first.

For example, you may like to investigate what happens if you apply this method to the expression

$$4x^2 − 14x + 10.$$

Notice however that 2 is a factor of each of the coefficients 4, −14 and 10. This common factor can be removed first to give

$$2(2x^2 − 7x + 5).$$

You can now apply the technique to factorise

$$2x^2 − 7x + 5.$$

Again, the first number in each pair is the coefficient of x^2, and the second number is one of the required factors.

Check by multiplying out the brackets.

You will find that the technique breaks down.

In fact $4x^2 − 14x + 10$ factorises into $2(2x − 5)(x − 1)$.

The process is summarised below.

> To factorise $ax^2 + bx + c$:
>
> 1 Remove any common factors
>
> 2 Look for two numbers whose product is equal to ac and whose sum is equal to b. Suppose these factors are α and β
>
> 3 Write down the two pairs (a, α) and (a, β)
>
> 4 Divide each pair by its highest common factor. Suppose this gives (r, s) and (t, u)
>
> 5 The factors can now be written down immediately to give $(rx + s)(tx + u)$
>
> 6 Check by expanding to ensure that the factorised form is correct

a is a positive number;
b and c may be positive or negative numbers.

α and β may be positive or negative numbers.

r, s, t and u may be positive or negative numbers.

TRY SOME YOURSELF

2 Factorise each of the following expressions:
(i) $6x^2 + 17x - 3$ (ii) $4x^2 - 12x - 27$ (iii) $2x^2 + 21x - 36$
(iv) $9x^2 + 17x + 8$ (v) $4x^2 + 28x - 32$

Check your solutions by multiplying out the brackets again.

If the coefficient of x^2 is negative the easiest way to factorise expression is to take out the common factor of -1 first. This converts the expression to a form which we have already discussed.

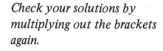

EXAMPLE

Factorise $1 - x - 2x^2$.

SOLUTION

Notice that $1 - x - 2x^2 = -(2x^2 + x - 1)$.

$2x^2 + x - 1$ can now be factorised using the method above.

$$2x^2 + x - 1 = (2x - 1)(x + 1)$$

So

$$-(2x^2 + x - 1) = -(2x - 1)(x + 1).$$

The minus sign can now be put back into one of the brackets to give

$$-(2x^2 + x - 1) = (1 - 2x)(x + 1) \text{ or } (2x - 1)(-x - 1).$$

Check by multiplying out the brackets.

TRY SOME YOURSELF

3 Factorise each of the following expressions:
(i) $1 + 2x - 3x^2$ (ii) $1 + 3x - 10x^2$ (iii) $2 + 3x - 2x^2$
(iv) $8 - 3x - 5x^2$.

Check your solutions by multiplying out the brackets again.

6.3(iii) MORE COMPLICATED QUADRATICS

It is sometimes possible to factorise more complicated expressions by substitution. For example, consider the expression

$$x^4 - 3x^2 + 2.$$

We can substitute $t = x^2$ to get the quadratic

$$t^2 - 3t + 2.$$

This can be factorised to give $(t - 2)(t - 1)$. We can now substitute back to get

$$x^4 - 3x^2 + 2 = (x^2 - 2)(x^2 - 1).$$

You may spot that $x^4 = x^2 \times x^2 = (x^2)^2$, in which case you may not need to substitute, but can just write down the factors immediately.

Check by multiplying out the brackets.

EXAMPLE

Factorise $2y^4 - 5y^2 + 3$.

SOLUTION

Put $t = y^2$ to get

$$2t^2 - 5t + 3.$$

We need to find two numbers which multiply together to give $2 \times 3 = 6$, and whose sum is -5. The required numbers are -2 and -3.

Now consider the pairs $(2, -2)$ and $(2, -3)$. These reduce to $(1, -1)$ and $(2, -3)$, so

$$2t^2 - 5t + 3 = (t - 1)(2t - 3).$$

The highest common factor of 2 and -2 is 2.

Substitute back for t to get

$$2y^4 - 5y^2 + 3 = (y^2 - 1)(2y^2 - 3).$$

TRY SOME YOURSELF

4   Factorise each of the following expressions:
(i) $15a^4 - a^2 - 2$ (ii) $10x^4 + x^2 - 3$ (iii) $2 + 3a^2 - 2a^4$

Check your solutions by multiplying out the brackets again.

6.3(iv) SOLVING EQUATIONS OF THE FORM $ax^2 + bx + c = 0$ BY FACTORISATION

Having discussed how to factorise expressions like $ax^2 + bx + c$, it is an easy step to solving equations by factorisation, as the next examples illustrate. Remember that quadratic equations usually have two solutions.

EXAMPLE

Solve $(x - 3)(2x + 7) = 0$.

SOLUTION

If $(x - 3)(2x + 7) = 0$, then either $(x - 3) = 0$ or $(2x + 7) = 0$.

$x = 3$ is the solution to $x - 3 = 0$; the solution to $2x + 7 = 0$ is $x = -\frac{7}{2}$.   *See Module 2, Section 2.4(iv).*

Hence $(x - 3)(2x + 7) = 0$ has solutions $x = 3$ or $x = -\frac{7}{2}$.   *Check by substitution into*
$(x - 3)(2x + 7)$.

EXAMPLE

Solve $2y^2 - 5y - 3 = 0$.

SOLUTION

First consider the left hand side of the equation and try to factorise   *Again, we remind you that not all*
the quadratic expression $2y^2 - 5y - 3$.   *quadratics can be factorised, so*
you will sometimes need to use
We want two numbers whose product is -6 and whose sum is -5.   *other methods. See Section 6.5(i)*
The required numbers are -6 and 1. This gives the pairs   *and Module 7, Section 7.2.*

$\qquad (2, -6)$ and $(2, 1)$

which reduce to

$\qquad (1, -3)$ and $(2, 1)$.

Hence

$\qquad 2y^2 - 5y - 3 = (y - 3)(2y + 1)$.

The equation $2y^2 - 5y - 3 = 0$ is therefore equivalent to

$\qquad (y - 3)(2y + 1) = 0$.   *The solution to $2y + 1 = 0$ is*
$y = -\frac{1}{2}$.
So, either $(y - 3) = 0$ or $(2y + 1) = 0$.

The solutions of $2y^2 - 5y - 3 = 0$ are therefore $y = 3$ or $y = -\frac{1}{2}$.   *Check by substituting into*
$2y^2 - 5y - 3$.

TRY SOME YOURSELF

5   Solve each of the following equations by factorisation: *Check your solutions by*
    (i) $3x^2 - 11x + 6 = 0$ (ii) $5y^2 - 5y - 30 = 0$ *substituting into the original*
    (iii) $2 + 3x - 2x^2 = 0$ (iv) $4x^2 - 12x - 27 = 0$.   *equation.*

After you have worked through this section you should be able to

a   Factorise any expression of the form $ax^2 + bx + c$ into the product $(rx + s)(tx + u)$, where a, b, c, r, s, t
    and u stand for any numbers and a is non-zero
b   Factorise more complicated quadratics, such as $ax^4 + bx^2 + c$, by substitution
c   Solve equations of the form $ax^2 + bx + c = 0$ by factorisation

Finally here are some exercises if you want more practice.

TRY SOME MORE YOURSELF

6(i) Factorise each of the following expressions:
   (a) $4x^2 + 13x + 3$ (b) $6t^2 - 6t - 12$ (c) $10x^2 + x - 3$
   (d) $2 + a^2 - 15a^4$ (e) $2x(x - 1) - 3(x + 1)$*   (f) $3 - 5x - 2x^2$
   (g) $7x^3 + 14x^2 - 21x$ (h) $36p^2 + 12p - 15$.

(ii) Solve each of the following equations by factorisation.
   (a) $12t^2 - 13t - 4 = 0$ (b) $10x^2 + x - 3 = 0$ (c) $6x^2 + 11x + 3 = 0$
   (d) $4a^2 + 4a - 3 = 0$ (e) $2p^2 - 3p - 2 = 0$ (f) $2y^2 - 2y - 4 = 0$.

* simplify the expression first

6.4 *Algebraic Fractions*

TRY THESE QUESTIONS FIRST

1 Reduce $\dfrac{2pq(p + q)}{4p^2q(q - p)}$ to its simplest form.

2 Simplify $\dfrac{21a^5b^7}{49a^3b^{10}}$.

3 Simplify $\dfrac{4b^2 - 2b - 6}{6b^2 - 15b + 9}$.

4 Simplify

   (i) $\dfrac{9x^2y}{12xyz^3} \div \dfrac{27x^4y}{4y^5z^3}$

   (ii) $\dfrac{2}{x} - \dfrac{1}{x + 2a} - \dfrac{1}{x - a}$.

6.4(i) SIMPLIFYING FRACTIONS

Algebraic fractions are handled in much the same way as numerical fractions although they often look more complicated.

Numerical fractions were discussed in Module 1, Section 1.4.

An algebraic fraction comprises one algebraic expression over another. The expression above the line is the numerator and the expression below the line is the denominator. Some examples are given on the next page.

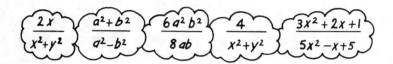

$$\frac{2x}{x^2+y^2} \qquad \frac{a^2+b^2}{a^2-b^2} \qquad \frac{6a^2b^2}{8ab} \qquad \frac{4}{x^2+y^2} \qquad \frac{3x^2+2x+1}{5x^2-x+5}$$

A numerical fraction is simplified by dividing the numerator and denominator by common factors. The fraction is in its simplest form when the numerator and denominator have no further common factors. This process is called *cancelling*. The same process is applied in algebraic fractions.

For example

$$\frac{24}{36} = \frac{24 \div 12}{36 \div 12} = \frac{2}{3}.$$

EXAMPLE

Reduce $\frac{6a}{8b}$ to its simplest form.

SOLUTION

$$\frac{6a}{8b} = \frac{6a \div 2}{8b \div 2} = \frac{3a}{4b}$$

$3a$ and $4b$ have no other common factors so the fraction is now in its simplest form.

2 is a common factor of $6a$ and $8b$, so divide numerator and denominator by 2.

TRY SOME YOURSELF

1 Reduce each of the following fractions to its simplest form:

(i) $\frac{8a}{4x}$ (ii) $\frac{12b}{8c}$ (iii) $\frac{15x}{12}$ (iv) $\frac{-36a}{45b}$.

Reducing an algebraic fraction to its simplest form usually involves cancelling symbols.

EXAMPLE

Reduce $\frac{6x^3y}{8x^3z}$ to its simplest form.

SOLUTION

$$\frac{6x^3y}{8x^3z} = \frac{6x^3y \div 2}{8x^3z \div 2} = \frac{3x^3y}{4x^3z}$$

Now divide numerator and denominator by x^3,

$$\frac{3x^3y}{4x^3z} = \frac{3y}{4z}.$$

$3y$ and $4z$ have no other common factors, so the fraction is now in its simplest form.

Consider the coefficients first, and cancel numerical factors.

x^3 is a common factor of $3x^3y$ and $4x^3z$.

This example suggests a more efficient method for simplifying fractions. Rather than look for each common factor in turn, it is quicker to look for the highest common factor of the numerator and denominator and divide through by this expression. The highest common factor of $6x^3y$ and $8x^3z$ is $2x^3$. Thus

$$\frac{6x^3y}{8x^3z} = \frac{2x^3 \times 3y}{2x^3 \times 4z} = \frac{3y}{4z}.$$

Rewrite the numerator and denominator as the product of the highest common factor and another factor. Now cancel.

EXAMPLE

Simplify $\dfrac{12x^2y^2z}{27x^3yz}$.

SOLUTION

We need to find the highest common factor of $12x^2y^2z$ and $27x^3yz$. By inspection this is $3x^2yz$.

Hence

$$\frac{12x^2y^2z}{27x^3yz} = \frac{(3x^2yz)4y}{(3x^2yz)9x} = \frac{4y}{9x}.$$

Rewrite each expression as a product of the highest common factor and another factor.

It is sometimes easier to cancel each factor by striking a line through the symbols, a technique you probably use already for numerical fractions.

EXAMPLE

Simplify $\dfrac{36ab^2}{8ac}$.

SOLUTION

$$\frac{\overset{9}{\cancel{36}}ab^2}{\underset{2}{\cancel{8}}ac} = \frac{9b^2}{2c}$$

Watch out though that you don't miss anything when writing down the final answer. Here, for example it's easy to omit the 9 or the 2.

TRY SOME YOURSELF

2   Simplify each of the following fractions:

(i) $\dfrac{6ab^2}{3a}$ (ii) $\dfrac{9x^2y^2}{6x^2z^3}$ (iii) $\dfrac{-15a^2b}{9ab^2}$ (iv) $\dfrac{30a^2b^2}{6abc}$ (v) $\dfrac{-14axt}{21x^2y}$.

Use whichever method you find easiest.

6.4(ii) COPING WITH HIGHER POWERS

In Module 2 we indicated that power notation can be used to represent symbols multiplied by themselves. For example,

$a \times a = a^2$

$b \times b \times b \times b \times b = b^5$

and

$\underbrace{z \times z \times \ldots \times z}_{10} = z^{10}.$

Module 2, Section 2.2(iii)

In Module 1 we discussed how to manipulate powers of 10. We showed that to multiply two powers of 10 you need only add the powers. Thus

$10^2 \times 10^5 = 10^{2\,+\,5} = 10^7$

and

$10^4 \times 10^5 = 10^{4\,+\,5} = 10^9.$

Module 1, Section 1.3(???)

Similarly to divide one power of 10 by another you just subtract the second power from the first. Thus

$10^5 \div 10^2 = 10^{5\,-\,2} = 10^3$

and

$10^4 \div 10^5 = 10^{4\,-\,5} = 10^{-1} = \frac{1}{10}.$

These rules can also be applied to powers of symbols.

> To multiply one power by another, add the powers; to divide one power by another, subtract the second power from the first.

Of course the symbol must be the same. $a^2 \times a^5$ can be simplified by this method but not $a^2 \times b^5$.

For example

$a^2 \times a^5 = a^{2\,+\,5} = a^7$

$b^4 \times b^5 = b^{4\,+\,5} = b^9$

$c^5 \div c^2 = c^{5\,-\,2} = c^3$

$d^4 \div d^5 = d^{4\,-\,5} = d^{-1} = \dfrac{1}{d}.$

Check these by multiplying the expressions out. For example

$a^2 \times a^5$

$= (a \times a) \times (a \times a \times a \times a \times a)$

$= a^7.$

This observation is useful when simplifying more complicated fractions. Consider the fraction

$\dfrac{a^5}{a^2}$

Manipulation of powers is discussed more fully in Module 9.

a^2 divides a^5 exactly since $a^5 \div a^2 = a^{5-2} = a^3$. Hence, a^2 is a factor of both the numerator and denominator, and

$$\frac{a^5}{a^2} = \frac{(a^2)(a^3)}{a^2} = a^3.$$

Similarly

$$\frac{a^3}{a^7} = \frac{a^3}{(a^3)(a^4)} = \frac{1}{a^4}.$$

TRY SOME YOURSELF

3   Simplify each of the following fractions:

(i) $\dfrac{x^3}{x^2}$ (ii) $\dfrac{6a^2}{4a^4}$ (iii) $\dfrac{10b}{5b^3}$ (iv) $\dfrac{9c^6}{12c^4}$.

The next example is a bit more complicated.

EXAMPLE

Simplify $\dfrac{4x^2y^4z}{6xy^2z^2}$.

SOLUTION

We can deal with each symbol at the same time by striking lines through the individual factors:

$$\frac{\overset{2\,x\,y^2}{\cancel{4x^2y^4z}}}{\underset{3\quad z}{\cancel{6xy^2z^2}}} = \frac{2xy^2}{3z}$$

Alternatively, $2xy^2z$ is the highest common factor of numerator and denominator, and

$$\frac{(2xy^2z)(2xy^2)}{(2xy^2z)(3z)} = \frac{2xy^2}{3z}.$$

TRY SOME YOURSELF

4   Simplify each of the following fractions:

(i) $\dfrac{2x^5yz^6}{6xy^3z^4}$ (ii) $\dfrac{-12x^2y^4z^5}{15xy^2z^2}$ (iii) $\dfrac{9a^2bc^2}{6a^4bc^3}$ (iv) $\dfrac{x^4y^4z^4}{x^4y^4z^6}$.

6.4(iii) SIMPLIFYING BY FACTORISATION

Up till now we have only considered fractions in which the numerator and denominator are single terms. When two or more terms are involved, it may be possible to simplify the fraction by factorising the expressions first.

EXAMPLE

Simplify $\dfrac{a^2b^2c + abc^2}{a^2b^2}$.

SOLUTION

Factorise the numerator first by taking out the highest common factor

See Section 6.1(iii).

$$a^2b^2c + abc^2 = abc(ab + c).$$

Hence

$$\frac{a^2b^2c + abc^2}{a^2b^2} = \frac{abc(ab + c)}{a^2b^2}$$

$$= \frac{c(ab + c)}{ab}.$$

Now look for factors of the numerator and denominator. Here we can cancel through by ab.

TRY SOME YOURSELF

5   Simplify each of the following fractions:

(i) $\dfrac{6h^2 + 8h}{2h}$ (ii) $\dfrac{2a^2b + 3ab^2}{4b}$ (iii) $\dfrac{8a}{4ab - 4ac}$ (iv) $\dfrac{8y}{6x^3y^2 - 4xy^2}$.

Remember, you must factorise first, before cancelling.

Sometimes it is necessary to factorise both numerator *and* denominator. The next example is quite difficult, so follow through the solution carefully.

EXAMPLE

Simplify $\dfrac{2x^2 + 10x + 12}{4x^2 + 12x + 8}$.

SOLUTION

First consider the numerator, $2x^2 + 10x + 12$.

$$2x^2 + 10x + 12 = 2(x^2 + 5x + 6)$$

Look for common factors first.

There are no more *common* factors but it is possible to factorise $x^2 + 5x + 6$ into a product of two factors. Thus

$$2(x^2 + 5x + 6) = 2(x + 3)(x + 2).$$

If the resulting expression contains a quadratic, try to factorise it. See Sections 6.2 and 6.3.

The same process is now applied to the denominator:

$$4x^2 + 12x + 8 = 4(x^2 + 3x + 2)$$

$$= 4(x + 2)(x + 1).$$

Hence

$$\frac{2x^2 + 10x + 12}{4x^2 + 12x + 8} = \frac{2(x + 3)(x + 2)}{4(x + 2)(x + 1)}$$

$$= \frac{(x + 3)}{2(x + 1)}.$$

Now look for factors of the numerator and denominator. Here, we can cancel through by 2(x + 2).

This solution may look quite complicated, but again the method is systematic. As long as you approach each problem systematically, you should find that the algebra 'drops out'. Of course we can't guarantee that you won't make any mistakes. If you find that an algebraic expression looks *more* complicated after you have tackled it, rather than easier, then that is often an indication that you have made a mistake, and it is a good idea to check your working, or maybe start afresh on a clean piece of paper.

Countdown to Mathematics

Remember that you must factorise expressions *before* cancelling. It's tempting to take short cuts, but this can lead to mistakes such as

$$\frac{\cancel{a}b + c}{\cancel{a}d} = \frac{b + c}{d}$$ wrong

which is nonsense. If fact $\frac{ab + c}{ad}$ cannot be simplified any further.

*a is a factor of the denominator, but it is not a **common** factor of the numerator.*

TRY SOME YOURSELF

6   Simplify each of the following fractions:

(i) $\dfrac{4a^2 + 4ab}{5ab - 5a^2}$ (ii) $\dfrac{x^2 - xy}{x^2 + xy}$ (iii) $\dfrac{c^2 + 8c + 12}{c^2 + 6c + 8}$

(iv) $\dfrac{d^2 + 4d + 3}{3 - 2d - d^2}$ (v) $\dfrac{3x^2 + 3x - 18}{x^2 + 2x - 3}$ (vi) $\dfrac{4x^2 + 14x + 6}{12x^2 + 14x + 4}$.

6.4(iv) ARITHMETIC OF ALGEBRAIC FRACTIONS

Multiplying and dividing

Having discussed how to simplify fractions it is an easy step to multiplying and dividing. The rules are the same as those used for numerical fractions:

(i)   to multiply two fractions multiply the numerators and denominators;

(ii) to divide by a fraction turn it upside down and multiply.

As with numerical fractions you should simplify the answer as much as possible.

For example

$$\frac{a}{b} \times \frac{c}{d} = \frac{a \times c}{b \times d} = \frac{ac}{bd},$$

$$\frac{a}{b} \div \frac{c}{d} = \frac{a}{b} \times \frac{d}{c} = \frac{ad}{bc}.$$

EXAMPLE

Simplify $\dfrac{3a^2 b}{4ac^2} \div \dfrac{bc^2}{6a^3}$.

SOLUTION

$$\frac{3a^2 b}{4ac^2} \div \frac{bc^2}{6a^3} = \frac{3a^2 b}{4ac^2} \times \frac{6a^3}{bc^2} = \frac{18a^5 b}{4abc^4} = \frac{9a^4}{2c^4}$$

Here we have multiplied out the numerator and denominator before cancelling, but you can omit this stage if you want.

TRY SOME YOURSELF

7   Simplify each of the following:

(i) $\dfrac{4ax^2}{b} \times \dfrac{b^3}{9xy^2}$ (ii) $\dfrac{4a^2}{14b} \div \dfrac{2a}{7b^2}$ (iii) $\dfrac{x^2}{y^2} \div \dfrac{x}{y}$ (iv) $x^2 \div \dfrac{1}{x}$.

Adding and subtracting

Again, the rules for adding and subtracting algebraic fractions are the same as those used to add and subtract numerical fractions. Remember that fractions can only be added or subtracted if they have the same denominator.

So $\dfrac{a}{b} + \dfrac{c}{b}$ can be added immediately to give $\dfrac{a+c}{b}$,

but $\dfrac{b}{a} + \dfrac{b}{c}$ cannot be added straight away because the denominators of the two fractions are not the same.

If the denominators are different, the first step is to find a common denominator. One way of doing this is to multiply all the different denominators together. This is probably the easiest way to handle algebraic fractions. For example, consider

$$\frac{2}{b} + \frac{3}{c}.$$

The product of the two denominators is bc. Now, each fraction must be rewritten in terms of this common denominator.

Notice that

$$\frac{2}{b} = \frac{2 \times c}{b \times c} = \frac{2c}{bc}.$$

Similarly

$$\frac{3}{c} = \frac{3 \times b}{c \times b} = \frac{3b}{bc}.$$

Now

$$\frac{2}{b} + \frac{3}{c} = \frac{2c}{bc} + \frac{3b}{bc} = \frac{2c + 3b}{bc}.$$

Just as

$$\frac{2}{17} + \frac{5}{17} = \frac{2+5}{17} = \frac{7}{17}$$

Compare this with

$$\frac{2}{5} + \frac{3}{7}$$

Remember that it is customary to write products of symbols in alphabetical order.

The fractions can now be combined by adding the numerators.

EXAMPLE

Simplify $\dfrac{a}{2x} - \dfrac{b}{3y}$.

SOLUTION

A suitable common denominator is $6xy$.

$$\frac{a}{2x} = \frac{a}{2x} \times \frac{3y}{3y} = \frac{3ay}{6xy}$$

and

$$\frac{b}{3y} = \frac{b}{3y} \times \frac{2x}{2x} = \frac{2bx}{6xy}$$

so

$$\frac{a}{2x} - \frac{b}{3y} = \frac{3ay}{6xy} - \frac{2bx}{6xy} = \frac{3ay - 2bx}{6xy}.$$

Multiply the different denominators to get a common denominator (here, (2x) × (3y) = 6xy); then rewrite each fraction in terms of the common denominator. Finally add or subtract as necessary and simplify the answer as much as possible.

This fraction cannot be simplified any further, but as a general rule you should always reduce the answer to its simplest form.

Notice that any term can be turned into a fraction. For example

$$3 = \frac{3}{1}, \; x = \frac{x}{1}, \; x^2 + 2 = \frac{x^2 + 2}{1}.$$

The next example shows that it is sometimes necessary to turn something into a fraction in order to simplify an expression.

EXAMPLE

Simplify $a - \dfrac{a}{3 + 2b}$.

SOLUTION

The common denominator is $3 + 2b$.

$$a = \frac{a(3 + 2b)}{(3 + 2b)}$$

Since $a = a \times 1$ and
$$\frac{(3 + 2b)}{(3 + 2b)} = 1$$

so $\quad a - \dfrac{a}{3 + 2b} = \dfrac{a(3 + 2b)}{(3 + 2b)} - \dfrac{a}{(3 + 2b)}$

$$= \frac{3a + 2ab - a}{3 + 2b}$$

$$= \frac{2a + 2ab}{3 + 2b} = \frac{2a(1 + b)}{3 + 2b}.$$

TRY SOME YOURSELF

8   Simplify each of the following:

(i) $\dfrac{b}{a} + \dfrac{2}{a}$ (ii) $\dfrac{2a}{b} + \dfrac{4}{d}$ (iii) $\dfrac{a^2}{b} + \dfrac{b^2}{a}$

(iv) $\dfrac{3b}{4c} - \dfrac{d}{5e}$ (v) $1 + \dfrac{2a}{a + c}$ (vi) $y - \dfrac{4y}{2x + 4}$

The next example is more complicated but the method is the same.

EXAMPLE

Simplify $\dfrac{4}{3(x + 2)} - \dfrac{2}{(x + 3)}$.

SOLUTION

A suitable common denominator is $3(x + 2)(x + 3)$.

$$\frac{4}{3(x + 2)} = \frac{4}{3(x + 2)} \times \frac{(x + 3)}{(x + 3)} = \frac{4(x + 3)}{3(x + 2)(x + 3)}$$

Multiply the different denominators together to get a common denominator.

and $\quad \dfrac{2}{(x + 3)} = \dfrac{2}{(x + 3)} \times \dfrac{3(x + 2)}{3(x + 2)} = \dfrac{6(x + 2)}{3(x + 2)(x + 3)}$

so $\quad \dfrac{4}{3(x + 2)} - \dfrac{2}{(x + 3)} = \dfrac{4(x + 3)}{3(x + 2)(x + 3)} - \dfrac{6(x + 2)}{3(x + 2)(x + 3)}$

$$= \frac{4(x + 3) - 6(x + 2)}{3(x + 2)(x + 3)}$$

Simplify the numerator by multiplying out the brackets and collecting like terms.

$$= \frac{4x + 12 - 6x - 12}{3(x + 2)(x + 3)}$$

$$= \frac{-2x}{3(x + 2)(x + 3)}.$$

It's helpful to put brackets around the numerator of a fraction if it contains more than one term. This is particularly important when subtracting fractions.

EXAMPLE

Simplify $x - \dfrac{3x-1}{x-1}$.

SOLUTION

Since $\qquad x = \dfrac{x(x-1)}{x-1}$

$$x - \frac{3x-1}{x-1} = \frac{x(x-1)}{x-1} - \frac{(3x-1)}{x-1}$$

$$= \frac{x(x-1) - (3x-1)}{(x-1)}$$

$$= \frac{x^2 - x - 3x + 1}{x-1}$$

$$= \frac{x^2 - 4x + 1}{x-1}.$$

Putting brackets around $(3x-1)$ ensures that the -1 becomes a $+1$ when the fractions are combined. If you omit the brackets it's easy to forget that $-\dfrac{3x-1}{x-1}$ means $\dfrac{-3x+1}{x-1}$

If the common denominators contain a common factor it's not necessary to take the product of the denominators as the common denominator; you can sometimes spot an easier combination. This is illustrated in the next example.

If you can't spot an easier combination remember that the product of different denominators always works.

EXAMPLE

Simplify $\dfrac{x}{ab} + \dfrac{y}{ac}$.

SOLUTION

One common denominator is obtained by taking the product $(ab)(ac)$ which gives a^2bc. But a is a common factor of ab and ac, which suggests that an easier common denominator is abc. Now

$$\frac{x}{ab} = \frac{x}{ab} \times \frac{c}{c} = \frac{cx}{abc}$$

and $\qquad \dfrac{y}{ac} = \dfrac{y}{ac} \times \dfrac{b}{b} = \dfrac{by}{abc}$

so $\qquad \dfrac{x}{ab} + \dfrac{y}{ac} = \dfrac{cx+by}{abc}.$

ab and ac are both factors of abc. If you like, try working through the same example, taking a^2bc as the common denominator. This illustrates that both approaches work, but the algebraic manipulation is easier with the simpler denominator.

TRY SOME YOURSELF

9   Simplify each of the following:

(i) $\dfrac{4}{x^2} - \dfrac{5}{x}$ (ii) $\dfrac{a}{2y^2} - \dfrac{b}{4yz}$ (iii) $\dfrac{1}{ab} + \dfrac{1}{ac} + \dfrac{1}{bc}$

(iv) $\dfrac{n}{n+1} - \dfrac{n+1}{n+2}$ (v) $2b - \dfrac{b-1}{b-4}$ (vi) $\dfrac{2x-1}{x+2} - \dfrac{x+1}{2x}.$

After you have worked through this section you should be able to

a Reduce an algebraic fraction to its simplest form by cancelling through by the highest common factor of the numerator and denominator
b Simplify an algebraic fraction involving powers of symbols, using the rules for multiplying and dividing powers
c Simplify an algebraic fraction by factorising the numerator and denominator
d Add, subtract, multiply and divide algebraic fractions

Finally, here are some exercises if you want more practice.

TRY SOME MORE YOURSELF

10(i) Reduce each of the following fractions to its simplest form:

(a) $\dfrac{x^3 y^3}{xy}$ (b) $\dfrac{3a^2 b^2}{12a^3 b}$ (c) $\dfrac{5(a + b)}{-(a + b)}$ (d) $\dfrac{c^6 d^3}{c^3 d^3}$ (e) $\dfrac{pq(p + q)}{p^2 q(q - p)}$

(f) $\dfrac{l^2 m(2 - m)}{(m - 2)l^3}$ (g) $\dfrac{y^2 z(x + 1)^4}{y(x + 1)^6 z^2}$

(ii) Simplify each of the following fractions:

(a) $\dfrac{2x^2 + 6x}{3x^2 + 9x}$ (b) $\dfrac{(6x + 3y)(2x - y)}{4x^2 - 2xy}$ (c) $\dfrac{(2a + 8)c^2}{bc(a^2 + 5a + 4)}$

(d) $\dfrac{b(c^2 - bc)}{ab(ac - ab)}$ (e) $\dfrac{12p^2 + 20p + 8}{6p^2 + 7p + 2}$.

(iii) Simplify each of the following fractions:

(a) $\dfrac{2k - 3}{6} - \dfrac{3k + 1}{8}$ (b) $\dfrac{a}{a^2 - ab} - \dfrac{1}{b}$ (c) $\dfrac{a}{ab + b^2} + \dfrac{b}{a^2 + ab}$

(d) $\dfrac{3x^2 - x + 2}{3x^2 - 5x - 2} - \dfrac{x}{x - 2}$ (e) $\dfrac{n}{(n + 1)} - \dfrac{3 - n}{(n + 1)(n - 2)}$.

6.5 Equations and Formulas

TRY THESE QUESTIONS FIRST

1 Solve (i) $3x^2 - 10x + 4 = 0$

(ii) $5x^2 - 2x + 4 = 0$.

Give your answers correct to 2 decimal places.

2 Solve $\dfrac{x}{x - 1} - \dfrac{2}{x} = 6$.

3 Make a the subject of

$$\dfrac{2 - 3a}{a - 1} = \dfrac{2b + 1}{4b} + \dfrac{b}{2}.$$

6.5(i) QUADRATIC EQUATIONS: THE FORMULA METHOD

In Sections 6.2 and 6.3 we discussed how to solve quadratic equations by factorising. If an equation can be manipulated into a form where the product of two factors is equal to zero, then the solutions can be found by equating each factor to zero. But not all quadratics can be factorised so it's not always possible to use this method. However, there is another method which can be used to solve any quadratic equations of the form

$$ax^2 + bx + c = 0$$

where a, b, and c stand for positive or negative numbers. This method takes the form of a formula which gives the solutions in terms of the coefficients a, b and c. The formula is stated below.

The solutions to $ax^2 + bx + c = 0$ are given by

$$x = \frac{-b + \sqrt{b^2 - 4ac}}{2a} \text{ or } x = \frac{-b - \sqrt{b^2 - 4ac}}{2a}.$$

These are often combined into one expression

$$x = \frac{-b \pm \sqrt{b^2 - 4ac}}{2a}.$$

± is a shorthand way of writing + or −.

For the moment you should try and get plenty of practice in applying this formula. As you will need to use a calculator most of the answers will be approximations.

We don't explain how this formula is derived. You may come across the derivation if you go on to study more mathematics.

EXAMPLE

Solve $2x^2 + x - 21 = 0$.

SOLUTION

The formula states that

$$x = \frac{-b \pm \sqrt{b^2 - 4ac}}{2a}.$$

Here, $a = 2$, $b = 1$ and $c = -21$, so

$$x = \frac{-1 \pm \sqrt{(1)^2 - 4(2)(-21)}}{2(2)}$$

$$= \frac{-1 \pm \sqrt{1 + 168}}{4}$$

$$= \frac{-1 \pm \sqrt{169}}{4} = \frac{-1 \pm 13}{4}.$$

Thus $x = \frac{-1 + 13}{4}$ or $\frac{-1 - 13}{4}$

so $x = 3$ or $x = -\frac{7}{2}$.

$2x^2 + 1x - 21$
$\quad a \quad\quad b \quad\quad c$

Substitute straight into the formula.

CHECK YOUR ANSWERS

1 (i) $x = \dfrac{-(-10) \pm \sqrt{100 - 4(3)(4)}}{6}$ *Section 6.5(i)*

$\quad\quad = \dfrac{10 \pm \sqrt{52}}{6}$

$\quad x = 0{\cdot}46$ or $x = 2{\cdot}87$.

(ii) Since $4 - 4(5)(4)$ is less than zero, $5x^2 - 2x + 4 = 0$ has no solutions.

2 $\dfrac{x}{x-1} - \dfrac{2}{x} = 6$ is equivalent to *Section 6.5(ii)*

$\quad\quad 5x^2 - 4x - 2 = 0$

$\quad$ so $x = \dfrac{4 \pm \sqrt{16 + 40}}{10}$.

Hence $x = -0{\cdot}35$ or $x = 1{\cdot}15$.

3 $\dfrac{2 - 3a}{a - 1} = \dfrac{2b + 1 + 2b^2}{4b}$ *Section 6.5(iii)*

Cross multiplying,

$\quad\quad 4b(2 - 3a) = (a - 1)(2b^2 + 2b + 1)$

so

$\quad\quad 8b - 12ab = 2ab^2 + 2ab + a - 2b^2 - 2b - 1$

and

$\quad\quad 8b + 2b^2 + 2b + 1 = 2ab^2 + 2ab + a + 12ab$

which simplifies to

$\quad\quad 2b^2 + 10b + 1 = a(2b^2 + 14b + 1)$.

Hence

$\quad\quad a = \dfrac{2b^2 + 10b + 1}{2b^2 + 14b + 1}$.

In fact this equation can be solved by factorisation since

$\quad\quad 2x^2 + x - 21 = (2x + 7)(x - 3)$.

The solutions are therefore $x = -\frac{7}{2}$ or $x = 3$.

Of course you can always check the solutions by substituting back into the original equation. This is particularly important if you have obtained the answers using a calculator.

This shows that the answers given by the two methods are exactly the same, so if in doubt, use the formula.

EXAMPLE

Solve $2x^2 + 7x + 4 = 0$.

SOLUTION

The formula states that

$$x = \frac{-b \pm \sqrt{b^2 - 4ac}}{2a}.$$

Here $a = 2$, $b = 7$ and $c = 4$, so

$$x = \frac{-7 \pm \sqrt{(7)^2 - (4)(2)(4)}}{4}$$

$$= \frac{-7 \pm \sqrt{49 - 32}}{4}.$$

Thus $x = \frac{-7 + \sqrt{17}}{4}$ or $x = \frac{-7 - \sqrt{17}}{4}$.

This is clearly a situation where a calculator should be used. You should be able to evaluate the expression without writing down any intermediate stages.

$$\frac{-7 + \sqrt{17}}{4} = -0{\cdot}72 \text{ correct to two decimal places,}$$

and

$$\frac{-7 - \sqrt{17}}{4} = -2{\cdot}78 \text{ correct to two decimal places.}$$

You can check for yourself that $x = -0{\cdot}72$ and $x = -2{\cdot}78$ are solutions to $2x^2 + 7x + 4 = 0$ by substituting into $2x^2 + 7x + 4$. However, if you do substitute these values of x you will find that the results are not *exactly* equal to zero. This is because the solutions are approximations, rounded off to two decimal places. Nevertheless the answers should be very close to zero, so it is a useful checking procedure.

Check with the maker's handbook.

Investigate a possible key sequence by considering

$$\frac{-1 + \sqrt{9}}{2}$$

You should get the answer, 1.

For example,
$2(-0{\cdot}72)^2 + 7(-0{\cdot}72) + 4$
$= -0{\cdot}0032$.

TRY SOME YOURSELF

1 Solve each of the following equations:
(i) $x^2 + 4x + 2 = 0$ (ii) $5x^2 + 6x - 3 = 0$ (iii) $5x^2 - 9x + 3 = 0$
(iv) $10y^2 - 6y - 15 = 0$ (v) $3x^2 + 5x - 7 = 0$.

A quadratic equation may have two coincident solutions. For example,

$$x^2 - 4x + 4 = (x - 2)(x - 2)$$

so the solution to $x^2 - 4x + 4 = 0$ is just $x = 2$.

What happens in the formula method?

$a = 1$, $b = -4$ and $c = 4$, so

$$x = \frac{-(-4) \pm \sqrt{(-4)^2 - (4)(1)(4)}}{2(1)}$$

$$= \frac{4 \pm \sqrt{16 - 16}}{2}, = \frac{4 \pm 0}{2}.$$

Thus $x = 2$.

Give your answers correct to two decimal places.

Check your solutions by substituting into the original equations.

For reference, the formula is

$$x = \frac{-b \pm \sqrt{b^2 - 4ac}}{2a}$$

Notice that the expression under the square root sign turned out to be zero. This observation can be generalised. In the formula the expression under the square root sign is

$$b^2 - 4ac$$

so if $b^2 - 4ac = 0$ then the equation has coincident roots.

There is another special situation which is illustrated by the equation $x^2 + 1 = 0$.

Applying the formula

$$x = \frac{-0 \pm \sqrt{0^2 - 4(1)(1)}}{2(1)}$$

$$= \frac{\sqrt{-4}}{2}.$$

$$x = \frac{-b \pm \sqrt{b^2 - 4ac}}{2a}$$

where $a = 1$, $b = 0$ and $c = 1$.

The number under the square root sign is negative and square roots of negative numbers do not exist. We can therefore conclude that $x^2 + 1 = 0$ has no solutions.

Try finding $\sqrt{-4}$ on your calculator; you will get an error message.

This observation can also be generalised; if the expression under the square root sign, $b^2 - 4ac$, is negative, then the equation has no solutions. The three possible situations are summarised below.

If $b^2 - 4ac$ is greater than zero, $ax^2 + bx + c$ has two solutions.

If $b^2 - 4ac$ equals zero, $ax^2 + bx + c$ has coincident solutions.

If $b^2 - 4ac$ is less than zero, $ax^2 + bx + c$ has no solutions.

In Module 7, Section 7.2(iii) we give a graphical interpretation of these results.

EXAMPLE

Solve $3x^2 - 2x + 4 = 0$.

SOLUTION

Notice that $b^2 - 4ac = (-2)^2 - (4)(3)(4)$

$$= 4 - 48 = -44.$$

$a = 3$, $b = -2$, $c = 4$.

Since $b^2 - 4ac$ is less than zero, $3x^2 - 2x + 4 = 0$ has no solutions.

TRY SOME YOURSELF

2   Determine the number of solutions to each of the following equations. (There is no need to find the solutions):
(i) $x^2 - 1\cdot2x + 0\cdot3 = 0$ (ii) $2y^2 - 2y + \frac{1}{2} = 0$
(iii) $x^2 - 3\cdot5x + 7\cdot4 = 0$ (iv) $1 - 2\cdot5t - 6\cdot25t^2 = 0$.

6.5(ii) SOLVING MORE COMPLICATED EQUATIONS

So far we have only considered how to solve quadratic equations expressed in the form

$$ax^2 + bx + c = 0.$$

But equations are not always expressed so neatly and you will often need to perform some preliminary manipulation in order to turn an equation into this standard form before it can be solved using one of the techniques we have already discussed.

The rules used to manipulate quadratic equations are the same as those used in Module 2 to manipulate linear equations. Remember that in order to maintain the balance, whatever is done to one side must also be done to the other.

See Module 2, Section 2.4(ii).

EXAMPLE

Solve $3x^2 - 7x + 1 = 2x^2 - 4x - 1$.

SOLUTION

To get this equation into standard form we take all the terms to the left hand side of the equals sign. Thus

$$3x^2 - 7x + 1 = 2x^2 - 4x - 1$$
$$x^2 - 7x + 1 = -4x - 1 \qquad \text{(subtract } 2x^2 \text{ from both sides)}$$
$$x^2 - 3x + 1 = -1 \qquad \text{(add } 4x \text{ to both sides)}$$
$$x^2 - 3x + 2 = 0. \qquad \text{(add 1 to both sides)}$$

So $(x - 2)(x - 1) = 0$ and $x = 2$ or $x = 1$.

This is an arbitrary choice. We could have taken all terms to the right hand side if we wished.

We dealt with each term separately here. With practice you will find that you can cope with the whole expression at once.

TRY SOME YOURSELF

3 Solve each of the following equations:
(i) $5x^2 - 3x = 4x^2 - 2x + 6$ (ii) $2x^2 + 4 = 7 - 5x$
(iii) $x^2 - 6x + 2 = 7x^2 - 7x - 3$.

It is possible that the equation involves fractions, in which case it is usually best to remove the fractions first.

EXAMPLE

Solve $\dfrac{4}{x + 1} = \dfrac{3}{x - 2}$.

SOLUTION

$$\frac{4}{x + 1} = \frac{3}{x - 2}$$

We first put both fractions over a common denominator

$$\frac{4(x - 2)}{(x + 1)(x - 2)} = \frac{3(x + 1)}{(x + 1)(x - 2)}.$$

Now, since the denominators are equal, the numerators must be equal. But there is one point to consider first. If $x = -1$ or $x = 2$ then the denominators are zero and the fractions are undefined.

See Module 3, Section 3.4(iii); division by zero is not defined.

We can arrange that this is avoided by stating a proviso. Thus providing $x \neq 2$ and $x \neq -1$ the equation can be simplified to

$4(x - 2) = 3(x + 1)$.

≠ means is not equal to.

This is a linear equation and it can now be solved quite easily.

$4x - 8 = 3x + 3$

$x - 8 = 3$

$x = 11$

Multiply out brackets, subtract 3x from both sides and add 8 to both sides.

Since $x = 11$ there is no problem with the denominators. Nevertheless it is good practice to state the proviso—just in case!

You may have noticed a quicker way to solve this equation. The original equation was

$$\frac{4}{x + 1} = \frac{3}{x - 2}$$

which became

$4(x - 2) = 3(x + 1)$.

The overall effect is illustrated by the diagram below.

$$\frac{4}{(x + 1)} \diagup\!\!\!\!\diagdown \frac{3}{(x - 2)}$$

The denominators are moved as directed by the arrows.

This process is called *cross multiplying*.

More generally, if

$$\frac{a}{b} = \frac{c}{d}$$

then $ad = bc$.

$$\frac{a}{b} \diagup\!\!\!\!\diagdown \frac{c}{d}$$

provided $b \neq 0$, $d \neq 0$.

TRY SOME YOURSELF

4   Solve each of the following equations:

(i) $\dfrac{1}{x + 2} = 3$ (ii) $\dfrac{1}{5x - 4} = \dfrac{1}{x}$ (iii) $\dfrac{3}{1 + b} = \dfrac{5}{b + 3}$

(iv) $\dfrac{2}{3d} = \dfrac{1}{2d + 5}$.

In the next example the resulting equation is a quadratic.

EXAMPLE

Solve $\dfrac{3x - 5}{x - 1} = \dfrac{2x + 15}{x + 5}$.

SOLUTION

Provided $x \neq 1$ and $x \neq -5$, cross multiply to get

$$\frac{(3x - 5)}{(x - 1)} \diagup\!\!\!\!\diagdown \frac{(2x + 15)}{(x + 5)}$$

That is $(x - 1) \neq 0$ and $(x + 5) \neq 0$.

or

$$(3x - 5)(x + 5) = (2x + 15)(x - 1).$$

Since

$$(3x - 5)(x + 5) = 3x^2 - 5x + 15x - 25$$

and

$$(2x + 15)(x - 1) = 2x^2 + 15x - 2x - 15$$

the equation becomes

$$3x^2 + 10x - 25 = 2x^2 + 13x - 15.$$

Taking all the terms to the left hand side of the equation gives

$$3x^2 + 10x - 25 - (2x^2 + 13x - 15) = 0$$

Subtract $2x^2 + 13x - 15$ from both sides. Alternatively deal with each term separately.

or

$$x^2 - 3x - 10 = 0.$$

The equation is now in standard form and factorises into

$$(x - 5)(x + 2) = 0.$$

Hence the solutions are $x = 5$ and $x = -2$.

Notice that the solutions do not contravene the initial proviso. Check the solutions if you want, by substituting into the original equation.

TRY SOME YOURSELF

5   Solve each of the following equations. Where necessary give your answers correct to two decimal places.

If you have time, check your solutions by substituting into the original equation.

(i) $x + 1 = \dfrac{2}{x}$ (ii) $\dfrac{a + 2}{a} = \dfrac{a}{2a - 5}$ (iii) $\dfrac{4y + 3}{3y + 5} = \dfrac{2y + 5}{y + 2}$

(iv) $\dfrac{5r + 4}{2r + 4} = \dfrac{4r + 11}{r + 9}$

Notice that you can only cross multiply if the equation has the form

$$\frac{a}{b} = \frac{c}{d}.$$

That is, it must involve only a single fraction on each side. If it is not in this form initially the first step must be to rearrange it so that it is.

EXAMPLE

Solve $\dfrac{3}{x} = \dfrac{4}{2 + x} + 3.$

It's tempting to cross multiply straight away but this would be wrong, since the right hand side is not a single fraction.

SOLUTION

First rearrange the right hand side and express it as a single fraction.

$$\frac{4}{2+x} + 3 = \frac{4}{2+x} + \frac{3(2+x)}{2+x} = \frac{4+6+3x}{2+x} = \frac{10+3x}{2+x}$$

Put everything over a common denominator and simplify.

Now

$$\frac{3}{x} = \frac{10+3x}{2+x}$$

so provided $x \neq 0$ and $x \neq -2$,

$$3(2+x) = x(10+3x)$$

or

$$6 + 3x = 10x + 3x^2.$$

$$\frac{3}{x} \diagup \frac{10+3x}{2+x}$$

cross multiply

This is equivalent to

$$3x^2 + 7x - 6 = 0$$

or

$$(3x - 2)(x + 3) = 0.$$

So $x = \frac{2}{3}$ or $x = -3$.

Subtract $6 + 3x$ from both sides to get the equation in standard form.

TRY SOME YOURSELF

6   Solve each of the following equations:

(i) $\dfrac{x+1}{3x-2} = \dfrac{2}{3} + \dfrac{1}{x}$ (ii) $\dfrac{3}{x+5} = \dfrac{1}{2x+7} + \dfrac{1}{3}.$

Give your answers correct to two decimal places.

6.5(iii) CHANGING THE SUBJECT OF A FORMULA

In Module 2 we discussed how to change the subject of a formula using the strategy for solving equations. We now consider some harder examples.

Module 2, Section 2.5(ii).

Cross multiplication is a quick way of removing fractions. For example, if

$$\frac{a}{x} = \frac{b}{c}$$

then $ac = bx$ and $\dfrac{ac}{b} = x.$

The same principle applies when the algebra is more complicated.

There is no problem in cross multiplying symbols. However, if you need to substitute numbers into a formula you will need to ensure that the denominators are not equal to zero.

EXAMPLE

Make x the subject of $\dfrac{x+a-b}{a+b} = \dfrac{x+b}{a}.$

SOLUTION

Cross multiply to get

$$a(x + a - b) = (a + b)(x + b)$$

so

$$ax + a^2 - ab = ax + bx + ab + b^2.$$

$$\frac{x + a - b}{a + b} \diagdown\!\!\!\!\diagup \frac{x + b}{a}$$

Expand brackets.

Now take all the terms involving x to one side of the equals sign and all the other terms to the other side.

$$ax - ax - bx + a^2 - ab = ab + b^2$$

$$ax - ax - bx = ab + b^2 - a^2 + ab$$

Subtract $(ax + bx)$ from both sides.
Subtract $(a^2 - ab)$ from both sides.

Thus

$$-bx = 2ab + b^2 - a^2$$

$$x = -\frac{(2ab + b^2 - a^2)}{b}$$

$$= \frac{a^2 - b^2 - 2ab}{b}.$$

Divide both sides by $-b$ and simplify.

TRY SOME YOURSELF

7(i)   Make x the subject of $\dfrac{1}{x} = \dfrac{a}{b}$.

(ii)   Make v the subject of $\dfrac{s + t}{45v} = \dfrac{t - s}{45t}$.

(iii)   Make b the subject of $\dfrac{b + c}{b - 2c} = \dfrac{c + a}{c - 2a}$.

(iv)   Make m the subject of $\dfrac{mf - nd}{df} = d - f$.

Again it is sometimes necessary to rearrange the formula before cross multiplying.

EXAMPLE

Make y the subject of $\dfrac{y}{a} - \dfrac{c}{b} = a - b$.

SOLUTION

First express the left hand side as a single fraction

$$\frac{y}{a} - \frac{c}{b} = \frac{by - ac}{ab}.$$

ab is a common denominator:

$$\frac{y}{a} = \frac{by}{ab} \text{ and } \frac{c}{b} = \frac{ac}{ab}.$$

Thus $\dfrac{by - ac}{ab} = (a - b)$.

Now cross multiply to get

$$by - ac = ab(a - b)$$

$$= a^2 b - ab^2.$$

$$\frac{by - ac}{ab} \diagup (a - b)$$

Now take all the terms involving y to one side of the equals sign and all other terms to the other side:

$$by = a^2b - ab^2 + ac \qquad \textit{Add ac to both sides.}$$

$$y = \frac{a^2b - ab^2 + ac}{b}. \qquad \textit{Divide both sides by b.}$$

This can also be written as

$$y = \frac{a(ab - b^2 + c)}{b}. \qquad \textit{Factorise the numerator.}$$

TRY SOME YOURSELF

8(i) Make y the subject of $\dfrac{1}{y} = x - \dfrac{4}{x}$.

(ii) Make c the subject of $\dfrac{m}{c} - \dfrac{a}{y} = y(m - a)$.

(iii) Make m the subject of $\dfrac{1}{m+n} + \dfrac{1}{m+p} = \dfrac{2}{m-n}$.

(iv) Make u the subject of $\dfrac{1}{f} = \dfrac{1}{u} + \dfrac{1}{v}$.

After you have worked through this section you should be able to

a Solve a quadratic equation of the form $ax^2 + bx + c = 0$, using the formula

$$x = \frac{-b \pm \sqrt{b^2 - 4ac}}{2a}$$

b Determine whether a quadratic equation has two, one or zero solutions

c Solve quadratic equations which are not expressed in the standard form, $ax^2 + bx + c = 0$

d Change the subject of a formula, using cross multiplication and algebraic manipulation

---

Finally here are some exercises if you want more practice.

TRY SOME MORE YOURSELF

9(i) Solve each of the following equations using the formula method. Give your answers correct to two decimal places:
(a) $r^2 - 2r - 17 = 0$ (b) $2f^2 + 19f + 10 = 0$ (c) $5x^2 - 3x - 17 = 0$
(d) $f^2 + 3f + 5 = 0$ (e) $4 + 17y - 2y^2 = 0$.

(ii) Solve each of the following equations. Where necessary give your answers correct to two decimal places:
(a) $\dfrac{3-x}{2+x} = \dfrac{1}{7-x}$ (b) $\dfrac{2}{x+5} = \dfrac{7x}{x+5}$ (c) $\dfrac{1}{y} = 3 - \dfrac{4}{2y+1}$

(d) $\dfrac{1}{m+2} + \dfrac{1}{m+3} = \dfrac{2}{m-1}$ (e) $\dfrac{2}{x} - \dfrac{1}{x+2} = \dfrac{2}{x-1}$.

(iii) (a) Make y the subject of $\dfrac{y+x}{xy} = (p+q)^2$.

(b) Make x the subject of $\dfrac{1}{y} = \dfrac{x-4}{x}$.

(c) Make a the subject of $\dfrac{m}{c} - \dfrac{a}{y} = y(m - a)$.

(d) Make m the subject of $\dfrac{m}{c} - \dfrac{a}{y} = y(m - a)$.

Section 6.1 Solutions

1

(i) (a) 18 has factors 2, 3, 6 and 9

(b) 48 has factors 2, 3, 4, 6, 8, 12, 16, 24

(c) 60 has factors 2, 3, 4, 5, 6, 10, 12, 15, 20, 30

(d) 81 has factors 3, 9 and 27

Notice that we haven't included the trivial factor, 1. The number itself is also a trivial factor (for example 18 is a factor of 18); again this is usually omitted. The larger factors can be found by dividing the number by its smaller factors.

(ii) (a) The factors are listed in solution (i)(b) above. 2 and 3 are the only prime factors since 2 is a factor of each of the other factors. In fact, $48 = 2 \times 2 \times 2 \times 2 \times 3 \times 3$.

(b) 36 has factors 2, 3, 4, 6, 9, 12 and 18; the only prime factors are 2 and 3. In fact $36 = 2 \times 2 \times 3 \times 3$.

(c) 105 has factors 3, 5, 7, 15, 21 and 35; the prime factors are 3, 5 and 7. In fact $105 = 3 \times 5 \times 7$.

Notice that every number can be expressed as a product of prime factors. Check this for yourself if you like by trying some more examples.

(iii) (a) 4 has factors 2 and 4. Notice that we have included the number itself as it is possible that this is a factor of the other number. In fact, of these factors, only 2 divides 6 exactly, so the highest common factor is 2.

(b) 6 has factors 2, 3 and 6. Of these, only 3 divides 15 exactly, so the highest common factor is 3.

(c) 18 has factors 2, 3, 6, 9 and 18. All these numbers divide 54 exactly and indeed, the highest common factor is 18.

(d) 12 has factors 2, 3, 4, 6 and 12. Of these, 2, 3 and 6 divide 30 exactly and 3 divides 51 exactly, so the highest common factor is 3.

Notice that each number can be expressed as a product of the highest common factor and another factor. For example,

$4 = 2 \times 2$ and $6 = 2 \times 3$

$6 = 3 \times 2$ and $15 = 3 \times 5$

and so on.

2

(i) The highest common factor of 2 and 3 is 1. Now look at symbol a; the highest factor is a. There are no other common symbols, so the highest common factor is therefore $1 \times a = a$.

(ii) The highest factor involving a is a^2; the highest factor involving b is just b. The highest common factor is therefore $a^2 \times b = a^2b$.

(iii) The highest common factor of 9, 12 and 6 is 3. The highest factor involving x is x^2; the highest factor involving y is y. The highest common factor is therefore $3 \times x^2 \times y = 3x^2y$.

3

(i) $2ab + 3ax = (a \times 2b) + (a \times 3x)$
$= a(2b + 3x)$

(ii) $a^2b - a^3b^2 = (a^2b \times 1) - (a^2b \times ab)$
$= a^2b(1 - ab)$

(iii) $-12a^3 - 6a^4 = -(12a^3 + 6a^4)$
$= -((6a^3 \times 2) + (6a^3 \times a))$
$= -(6a^3(2 + a))$
$= -6a^3(2 + a)$

(iv) $9x^2y - 12x^3y^2 + 6x^3y$
$= (3x^2y \times 3) - (3x^2y \times 4xy) + (3x^2y \times 2x)$
$= 3x^2y(3 - 4xy + 2x)$

4

(i) $(y + 3)(y + 4) = y^2 + 4y + 3y + 12$
$= y^2 + 7y + 12$

(ii) $(t + 4)(t + 1) = t^2 + t + 4t + 4$
$= t^2 + 5t + 4$

(iii) $(z + 3)(z - 1) = z^2 - z + 3z - 3$
$= z^2 + 2z - 3$

(iv) $(a - 2)(a - 3) = a^2 - 3a - 2a + 6$
$= a^2 - 5a + 6$

5

(i) (a) $(x + 2)^2 = (x + 2)(x + 2) = x^2 + 2x + 2x + 4$
$= x^2 + 4x + 4$
(b) $(b - 2)^2 = (b - 2)(b - 2)$
$= b^2 - 2b - 2b + 4 = b^2 - 4b + 4$
(c) $(x - a)^2 = (x - a)(x - a)$
$= x^2 - ax - ax + a^2 = x^2 - 2ax + a^2$
(Remember that $xa = ax$.)

(ii) (a) 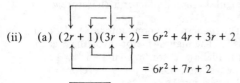 $(2r + 1)(3r + 2) = 6r^2 + 4r + 3r + 2$
$= 6r^2 + 7r + 2$

(b) $(2x + 5)(x + 2) = 2x^2 + 4x + 5x + 10$
$= 2x^2 + 9x + 10$

(c) $(3y - 2)(2y + 4) = 6y^2 + 12y - 4y - 8$
$= 6y^2 + 8y - 8$

(d) $(3x + 2)^2 = (3x + 2)(3x + 2)$
$= 9x^2 + 6x + 6x + 4$
$= 9x^2 + 12x + 4$

(iii) (a) $(3r + a)(2r + 2a) = 6r^2 + 6ar + 2ar + 2a^2$
$= 6r^2 + 8ar + 2a^2$
(Remember that $ra = ar$.)

(b) $(7s + t)(4s - 3t) = 28s^2 - 21st + 4st - 3t^2$
$= 28s^2 - 17st - 3t^2$
(Remember that $ts = st$.)

(c) $(2x - 3y)^2 = (2x - 3y)(2x - 3y)$
$= 4x^2 - 6xy - 6xy + 9y^2$
$= 4x^2 - 12xy + 9y^2$

6

(i) 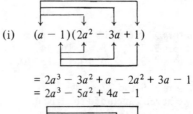 $(a - 1)(2a^2 - 3a + 1)$
$= 2a^3 - 3a^2 + a - 2a^2 + 3a - 1$
$= 2a^3 - 5a^2 + 4a - 1$

(ii) 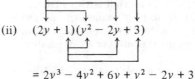 $(2y + 1)(y^2 - 2y + 3)$
$= 2y^3 - 4y^2 + 6y + y^2 - 2y + 3$
$= 2y^3 - 3y^2 + 4y + 3$

(iii) $(3a - 1)(2a^2 + a - 4)$
$= 6a^3 + 3a^2 - 12a - 2a^2 - a + 4$
$= 6a^3 + a^2 - 13a + 4$

(iv) 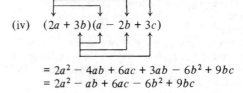 $(2a + 3b)(a - 2b + 3c)$
$= 2a^2 - 4ab + 6ac + 3ab - 6b^2 + 9bc$
$= 2a^2 - ab + 6ac - 6b^2 + 9bc$

7

(i) You need only multiply the terms involving a,
$(2a + 1)(a + 3)$
The coefficient of a^2 is therefore 2.

(ii) You need only multiply the constant terms
$(3y - 2)(4y - 3)$
The constant term is therefore $(-2) \times (-3) = 6$.

(iii) You need only multiply the terms involving r,
$(2 - r)(3 + 2r)$
The coefficient is therefore $(-1) \times (2) = -2$.

(iv) You need to combine the two terms obtained by multiplying together the term involving x and a constant,
$(3x - 4)^2 = (3x - 4)(3x - 4)$.
The coefficient is therefore $(-12 - 12) = -24$.

8

(i)   (a) 2, 13   (b) 2, 3   (c) 2, 3

(ii)   (a) 4   (b) 9   (c) 1

(iii) (a) $2x(3y - z)$ (b) $3y^2z(2x^2y - xz + 3)$
      (c) $-a^2b(1 + ab)$ (d) $7x(x^2 + 2x + 3)$
      (e) $x^2(a - bx^2)$

(iv) (a) $x^2 + x - 2$ (b) $b^2 - 6ab + 9a^2$
      (c) $8a^2 - 26a + 21$ (d) $16b^2 - 16ab + 4a^2$

(v)   (a) $8x^3 - 8x^2 - 8x + 3$
      (b) $-2a^3 - 13a^2 + 9a - 1$
      (c) $-8t^3 - 10t^2 + 5t + 6$

(vi) (a) 6   (b) -3 (c) -8 (d) -1

Section 6.2 Solutions

1

(i)   Try $(x + \square)(x + \square)$.
    1 Coefficient of x^2 is one as required.
    2 The constant term is 2, so there is only one possibility, $(x + 1)(1 + 2)$.
    3 Check coefficient of x.

$$(x + 1)(x + 2)$$

Hence $x^2 + 3x + 2 = (x + 1)(x + 2)$.

(ii)   Try $(x + \square)(x + \square)$.
    1 Coefficient of x^2 is one as required.
    2 The constant term is 5, which suggests $(x + 1)(x + 5)$.
    3 In $(x + 1)(x + 5)$ the coefficient of x is 6 as required.
    Hence $x^2 + 6x + 5 = (x + 1)(x + 5)$.

(iii) Try $(x + \square)(x + \square)$.
    1 Coefficient of x^2 is one as required.
    2 The constant term is 4, so there are two possibilities, $(x + 1)(x + 4)$ or $(x + 2)(x + 2)$.
    3 In $(x + 1)(x + 4)$ the coefficient of x is 5, as required.
    Hence $x^2 + 5x + 4 = (x + 1)(x + 4)$.

(iv) Try $(x + \square)(x + \square)$.
    1 Coefficient of x^2 is one as required.
    2 The constant term is 12 which gives the following possibilities:

$$(x + 1)(x + 12)$$
$$\text{or } (x + 3)(x + 4)$$
$$\text{or } (x + 2)(x + 6).$$

    3 In $(x + 2)(x + 6)$ the coefficient of x is 8 as required.
    Hence $x^2 + 8x + 12 = (x + 2)(x + 6)$.

(v)   Try $(x + \square)(x + \square)$.
    1 Coefficient of x^2 is one as required.
    2 The constant term is 30 which gives the following possibilities:

$$(x + 1)(x + 30)$$
$$\text{or } (x + 2)(x + 15)$$
$$\text{or } (x + 3)(x + 10)$$
$$\text{or } (x + 5)(x + 6).$$

    3 In $(x + 3)(x + 10)$ the coefficient of x is 13 as required.
    Hence $x^2 + 13x + 30 = (x + 3)(x + 10)$.

2

(i)   Try $(x + \square)(x + \square)$.
    1 The coefficient of x^2 is one as required.
    2 The only possibility is $(x + 1)(x + 1)$.
    3 The coefficient of x should be 1, but in $(x + 1)(x + 1)$ it is 2. This indicates that $x^2 + x + 1$ cannot be factorised.

(ii)   Try $(x + \square)(x + \square)$.
    1 The coefficient of x^2 is one.
    2 There are two possibilities,
        $(x + 1)(x + 10)$ or $(x + 2)(x + 5)$.
    3 Checking the coefficient of x gives
        $x^2 + 7x + 10 = (x + 2)(x + 5)$.

(iii) Try $(x + \square)(x + \square)$.
    1 The coefficient of x^2 is one.
    2 The only possibility is $(x + 1)(x + 5)$.
    3 The coefficient of x should be 5, but in $(x + 1)(x + 5)$ it is 6. This indicates that $x^2 + 5x + 5$ cannot be factorised.

(iv) Try $(x + \square)(x + \square)$.
    1 The coefficient of x^2 is one.
    2 The possibilities are:

$$(x + 1)(x + 30)$$
$$(x + 2)(x + 15)$$
$$(x + 3)(x + 10)$$
$$(x + 5)(x + 6).$$

    3 Checking the coefficient of x gives
        $x^2 + 11x + 30 = (x + 5)(x + 6)$.

3   Since the coefficient of x^2 is always 1 we omit step 1 in each of the following solutions.

(i)   Since the coefficient of x is negative you need to consider negative factors of 4. The possibilities are therefore
        $(x - 1)(x - 4)$ or $(x - 2)(x - 2)$.
    Checking the coefficient of x gives
        $x^2 - 5x + 4 = (x - 1)(x - 4)$.

(ii)   The only possibility is $(x - 1)(x - 2)$.
    The coefficient of x is -3 as required, so
        $x^2 - 3x + 2 = (x - 1)(x - 2)$.

(iii) The only possibility is $(x - 1)(x - 2)$.
    In this case the coefficient of x should be -1, but in $(x - 1)(x - 2)$ it is -3. This indicates that $x^2 - x + 2$ cannot be factorised.

(iv) The possibilities are:
$$(x - 1)(x - 16)$$
$$(x - 2)(x - 8)$$
$$(x - 4)(x - 4).$$
Checking the coefficient of x gives
$$x^2 - 10x + 16 = (x - 2)(x - 8).$$

(v) From Part (i), $x^2 - 4x + 4 = (x - 2)(x - 2)$.

(vi) The possibilities are:
$$(x - 1)(x - 8) \text{ or } (x - 2)(x - 4).$$
The coefficient of x should be -5, but in $(x - 1)(x - 8)$ it is -9, and in $(x - 2)(x - 4)$ it is -6. This indicates that $x^2 - 5x + 8$ cannot be factorised.

(vii) The possibilities are:
$$(x - 1)(x - 20)$$
$$(x - 2)(x - 10)$$
$$(x - 4)(x - 5).$$
Checking the coefficient of x gives
$$x^2 - 9x + 20 = (x - 4)(x - 5).$$

4 Since the coefficient of x^2 is always 1 we omit step 1 in each of the following solutions.

(i) The possibilities are:
$$(x - 1)(x + 2) \text{ or } (x - 2)(x + 1).$$
Checking the coefficient of x gives
$$x^2 - x - 2 = (x - 2)(x + 1).$$

(ii) The possibilities are:
$$(x - 1)(x + 8) \text{ or } (x + 8)(x - 1)$$
$$(x - 2)(x + 4) \text{ or } (x - 4)(x + 2).$$
Checking the coefficient of x gives
$$x^2 + 2x - 8 = (x - 2)(x + 4).$$

(iii) The possibilities are:
$$(x - 1)(x + 12) \text{ or } (x - 12)(x + 1)$$
$$(x - 2)(x + 6) \quad \text{or } (x - 6)(x + 2)$$
$$(x - 3)(x + 4) \quad \text{or } (x - 4)(x + 3).$$
Checking the coefficient of x, which should be -9, shows that $x^2 - 9x - 12$ cannot be factorised.

(iv) The possibilities are:
$$(x - 3)(x + 1).$$
Checking the coefficient of x gives
$$x^2 + 2x - 3 = (x - 1)(x + 3).$$

(v) The only possibility is $(x - 1)(x + 1)$. $(x - 1)(x + 3)$ or the coefficient of x, which should be 1, shows that $x^2 + x - 1$ cannot be factorised.

(vi) The possibilities are:
$$(x - 1)(x + 12) \text{ or } (x - 12)(x + 1)$$
$$(x - 2)(x + 6) \quad \text{or } (x - 6)(x + 2)$$
$$(x - 3)(x + 4) \quad \text{or } (x - 4)(x + 3).$$
Checking the coefficient of x gives
$$x^2 - x - 12 = (x - 4)(x + 3).$$

(vii) The possibilities are listed in part (vi) above. In this case
$$x^2 + 4x - 12 = (x - 2)(x + 6).$$

(viii) The possibilities are:
$$(x - 1)(x + 15) \text{ or } (x - 15)(x + 1)$$
$$(x - 3)(x + 5) \quad \text{or } (x - 5)(x + 3).$$
Checking the coefficient of x, which should be -16, shows that $x^2 - 16x - 15$ cannot be factorised.

5

(i) You need to find two numbers whose product is 28 and whose sum is 11.
$4 \times 7 = 28$ and $4 + 7 = 11$, so
$$x^2 + 11x + 28 = (x + 4)(x + 7).$$

(ii) You need to find two numbers whose product is 30 and whose sum is -11.
$(-5) \times (-6) = 30$ and $(-5) + (-6) = -11$, so
$$x^2 - 11x + 30 = (x - 5)(x - 6).$$

(iii) You need for find two numbers whose product is -24 and whose sum is -2.
$(-6) \times 4 = -24$ and $(-6) + 4 = -2$, so
$$x^2 - 2x - 24 = (x - 6)(x + 4).$$

(iv) You need to find two numbers whose product is -24 and whose sum is 5.
$(-3) \times 8 = -24$ and $(-3) + 8 = 5$, so
$$x^2 + 5x - 24 = (x - 3)(x + 8).$$

6

(i) $(x - 2) = 0$ or $(x - 3) = 0$, so $x = 2$ òr $x = 3$.

(ii) $(x - 4) = 0$ or $(x + 3) = 0$, so $x = 4$ or $x = -3$.

(iii) $(x + 5) = 0$ or $(x - 2) = 0$, so $x = -5$ or $x = 2$.

(iv) $x = 0$ or $(x - 1) = 0$, so $x = 0$ or $x = 1$.

7

(i) $x^2 - 3x + 2 = 0$, so $(x - 2)(x - 1) = 0$.
Either $(x - 2) = 0$ or $(x - 1) = 0$, so $x = 2$ or $x = 1$.

(ii) $y^2 - y - 12 = 0$, so $(y - 4)(y + 3) = 0$.
Either $(y - 4) = 0$ or $(y + 3) = 0$, so $y = 4$, or $y = -3$.

(iii) $a^2 - 8a + 15 = 0$, so $(a - 3)(a - 5) = 0$.
Either $(a - 3) = 0$ or $(a - 5) = 0$, so $a = 3$, or $a = 5$.

(iv) $b^2 - 3b - 10 = 0$, so $(b - 5)(b + 2) = 0$.
Either $(b - 5) = 0$ or $(b + 2) = 0$, so $b = 5$ or $b = -2$.

8

(i) $x^2 + 2x + 1 = 0$, so $(x + 1)^2 = 0$, and $x = -1$.

(ii) $x^2 - 6x + 9 = 0$, so $(x - 3)^2 = 0$, and $x = 3$.

(iii) $y^2 + 8y + 16 = 0$, so $(y + 4)^2 = 0$, and $y = -4$.

(iv) $x^2 + 10x + 25 = 0$, so $(x + 5)^2 = 0$, and $x = -5$.

9

(i) (a) $(x - 5)^2$ (b) $(t + 5)(t + 7)$
(c) $(m - 9)(m + 4)$ (d) cannot be factorised
(e) $(b - 7)(b + 6)$ (f) $(c - 23)(c + 1)$
(g) $(t - 13)(t - 2)$ (h) cannot be factorised.

(ii) (a) $y = 5$ or $y = -3$ (b) $m = 9$ or $m = -4$
(c) $t = 8$ or $t = -9$ (d) $t = 4$ or $t = -18$
(e) $t = 6$ or $t = 12$ (f) $t = 8$.

Section 6.3 Solutions

1

(i) *1* Consider factors of the form
$(3x + \square)(x + \square)$.

2 The possibilities are:
$(3x + 1)(x + 2)$ or $(3x + 2)(x + 1)$.

3 Checking the coefficient of x gives
$3x^2 + 7x + 2 = (3x + 1)(x + 2)$.

(ii) *1* Consider factors of the form
$(4x + \square)(x + \square)$ or $(2x + \square)(2x + \square)$.

2 The possibilities are:
$(4x + 1)(x + 3)$ or $(4x + 3)(x + 1)$
$(2x + 1)(2x + 3)$ or $(2x + 3)(2x + 1)$.

3 Checking the coefficient of x gives
$4x^2 + 8x + 3 = (2x + 1)(2x + 3)$.

(iii) The possibilities are:
$(6x - 1)(x - 2)$ or $(6x - 2)(x - 1)$
$(3x - 2)(2x - 1)$ or $(3x - 1)(2x - 2)$.

Checking the coefficient of x gives
$6x^2 - 7x + 2 = (3x - 2)(2x - 1)$.

(iv) The possibilities are:
$(4x - 1)(x - 5)$ or $(4x - 5)(x - 1)$ or
$(2x - 1)(2x - 5)$.

Checking the coefficient of x gives
$4x^2 - 21x + 5 = (4x - 1)(x - 5)$.

(v) The possibilities are:
$(6x + 1)(x + 6)$ or $(6x + 6)(x + 1)$
$(6x + 2)(x + 3)$ or $(6x + 3)(x + 2)$
$(3x + 1)(2x + 6)$ or $(3x + 6)(2x + 1)$
$(3x + 2)(2x + 3)$ or $(3x + 3)(2x + 2)$.

Checking the coefficient of x gives
$6x^2 + 13x + 6 = (3x + 2)(2x + 3)$.

(vi) The possibilities are:
$(10x + 1)(x - 1)$ or $(10x - 1)(x + 1)$
$(5x + 1)(2x - 1)$ or $(5x - 1)(2x + 1)$.

Checking the coefficient of x gives
$10x^2 + 3x - 1 = (5x - 1)(2x + 1)$.

2

(i) The product should be $6 \times (-3) = -18$ and
the sum is 17. This gives 18 and -1. Now
consider the pairs $(6, 18)$ and $(6, -1)$. The
highest common factor of 6 and 18 is 6, so
the numbers reduce to $(1, 3)$ and $(6, -1)$.
Hence $6x^2 + 17x - 3 = (x + 3)(6x - 1)$.

(ii) The product should be $4 \times (-27)$, and the sum
is -12. This gives -18 and 6. Now consider
$(4, -18)$ and $(4, 6)$. These reduce to $(2, -9)$
and $(2, 3)$.
Hence $4x^2 - 12x - 27 = (2x - 9)(2x + 3)$.
Notice that it is not necessary to multiply out
$4 \times (-27)$. If you want you need only
consider different combinations of factors.
For example, $4 \times (-27) = 2 \times (-54)$
$= 6 \times (-18)$ etc.

(iii) The product should be $2 \times (-36)$, and the sum
is 21. This gives 24 and -3. Now consider
$(2, 24)$ and $(2, -3)$. These reduce to $(1, 12)$
and $(2, -3)$.
Hence $2x^2 + 21x - 36 = (x + 12)(2x - 3)$.

(iv) The product should be 9×8, and the sum is
17. This immediately gives the numbers
9 and 8. Now consider $(9, 9)$ and $(9, 8)$.
These reduce to $(1, 1)$ and $(9, 8)$.
Hence $9x^2 + 17x + 8 = (x + 1)(9x + 8)$.

(v) In this case 4 is a common factor of each term,
so remove the common factor first to give
$4x^2 + 28x - 32 = 4(x^2 + 7x - 8)$.
$x^2 + 7x - 8$ factorises into $(x + 8)(x - 1)$.
Hence $4x^2 + 28x - 32 = 4(x + 8)(x - 1)$.

3

(i) $1 + 2x - 3x^2 = -(3x^2 - 2x - 1)$
$= -(3x + 1)(x - 1)$
$= (3x + 1)(1 - x)$

(ii) $1 + 3x - 10x^2 = -(10x^2 - 3x - 1)$
$= -(5x + 1)(2x - 1)$
$= (5x + 1)(1 - 2x)$

(iii) $2 + 3x - 2x^2 = -(2x^2 - 3x - 2)$
$= -(2x + 1)(x - 2)$
$= (2x + 1)(2 - x)$

(iv) $8 - 3x - 5x^2 = -(5x^2 + 3x - 8)$
$= -(5x + 8)(x - 1)$
$= (5x + 8)(1 - x)$

4

(i) Put $t = a^2$ to get $15t^2 - t - 2$. This factorises
into $(5t - 2)(3t + 1)$.
Hence $15a^4 - a^2 - 2 = (5a^2 - 2)(3a^2 + 1)$.

(ii) Put $t = x^2$ to get $10t^2 + t - 3$. This factorises
into $(2t - 1)(5t + 3)$.
Hence $10x^4 + x^2 - 3 = (2x^2 - 1)(5x^2 + 3)$.

(iii) Put $t = a^2$ to give $2 + 3t - 2t^2$, or $-(2t^2 - 3t - 2)$.
This factorises into $-(2t + 1)(t - 2)$, or
$(2t + 1)(2 - t)$.
Hence $2 + 3a^2 - 2a^4 = (2a^2 + 1)(2 - a^2)$.

5

(i) $3x^2 - 11x + 6 = 0$, so $(3x - 2)(x - 3) = 0$.
Either $(3x - 2) = 0$ or $(x - 3) = 0$, so
$x = \frac{2}{3}$ or $x = 3$.

(ii) $5y^2 - 5y - 30 = 0$, so $5(y^2 - y - 6) = 0$,
and $5(y - 3)(y + 2) = 0$.
Either $(y - 3) = 0$ or $(y + 2) = 0$, so
$y = 3$ or $y = -2$.

(iii) $2 + 3x - 2x^2 = 0$, so $-(2x^2 - 3x - 2) = 0$.
The minus sign now makes no difference;
this equation is equivalent to $2x^2 - 3x - 2 = 0$
or $(2x + 1)(x - 2) = 0$.
Either $(2x + 1) = 0$ or $(x - 2) = 0$, so
$x = -\frac{1}{2}$ or $x = 2$.

(iv) $4x^2 - 12x - 27 = 0$, so $(2x - 9)(2x + 3) = 0$.
Either $(2x - 9) = 0$ or $(2x + 3) = 0$, so
$x = \frac{9}{2}$ or $x = -\frac{3}{2}$.

6

(i)   (a) $(4x + 1)(x + 3)$ (b) $6(t - 2)(t + 1)$
(c) $(2x - 1)(5x + 3)$ (d) $(3a^2 + 1)(2 - 5a^2)$
(e) $2x(x - 1) - 3(x + 1) = 2x^2 - 5x - 3$
$\qquad\qquad\qquad\qquad = (2x + 1)(x - 3)$
(f) $(1 - 2x)(x + 3)$
(g) $7x^3 + 14x^2 - 21x = 7x(x^2 + 2x - 3)$
$\qquad\qquad\qquad\qquad = 7x(x + 3)(x - 1)$
(h) $36p^2 + 12p - 15 = 3(12p^2 + 4p - 5)$
$\qquad\qquad\qquad\qquad = 3(2p - 1)(6p + 5)$

(ii)   (a) $t = \frac{4}{3}$ or $t = -\frac{1}{4}$ (b) $x = -\frac{3}{5}$ or $x = \frac{1}{2}$
(c) $x = -\frac{3}{2}$ or $x = -\frac{1}{3}$ (d) $a = -\frac{3}{2}$ or $a = \frac{1}{2}$
(e) $p = -\frac{1}{2}$ or $p = 2$ (f) $y = 2$ or $y = -1$.

Section 6.4 Solutions

1

(i) $\dfrac{8a}{4x} = \dfrac{4 \times 2a}{4 \times x} = \dfrac{2a}{x}$

(ii) $\dfrac{12b}{8c} = \dfrac{3b}{2c}$

(iii) $\dfrac{15x}{12} = \dfrac{5x}{4}$

(iv) $\dfrac{-36a}{45b} = -\dfrac{4a}{5b}$

2

(i) $\dfrac{6ab^2}{3a} = \dfrac{(3a)(2b^2)}{3a} = 2b^2$

(ii) $\dfrac{9x^2y^2}{6x^2z^3} = \dfrac{(3x^2)3y^2}{(3x^2)2z^3} = \dfrac{3y^2}{2z^3}$

(iii) $\dfrac{-15a^2b}{9ab^2} = \dfrac{(3ab)(-5a)}{(3ab)(3b)} = \dfrac{-5a}{3b}$

(iv) $\dfrac{30a^2b^2}{6abc} = \dfrac{(6ab)(5ab)}{(6ab)c} = \dfrac{5ab}{c}$

(v) $\dfrac{-14axt}{21x^2y} = \dfrac{(7x)(-2at)}{(7x)3xy} = \dfrac{-2at}{3xy}$

3

(i) $\dfrac{x^3}{x^2} = \dfrac{(x^2)x}{x^2} = x$

(ii) $\dfrac{6a^2}{4a^4} = \dfrac{(2a^2)3}{(2a^2)(2a^2)} = \dfrac{3}{2a^2}$

(iii) $\dfrac{10b}{5b^3} = \dfrac{(5b)2}{(5b)(b^2)} = \dfrac{2}{b^2}$

(iv) $\dfrac{9c^6}{12c^4} = \dfrac{(3c^4)(3c^2)}{(3c^4)4} = \dfrac{3c^2}{4}$

4

(i) $\dfrac{2x^5yz^6}{6xy^3z^4} = \dfrac{(2xyz^4)(x^4z^2)}{(2xyz^4)(3y^2)} = \dfrac{x^4z^2}{3y^2}$

Alternatively you may have cancelled each
symbol separately as in the next solution.

(ii) $\dfrac{-4 \ x \ y^2 z^3}{\cancel{-1}\cancel{5}\cancel{x}^2\cancel{y}^4\cancel{z}^6}{\ \cancel{5}\cancel{x}\cancel{y}^2\cancel{z}^2} = \dfrac{-4xy^2z^3}{5}$

If you do simplify fractions like this take care
you don't miss a term when writing down the
answer.

(iii) $\dfrac{9a^2bc^2}{6a^4bc^3} = \dfrac{3}{2a^2c}$

(iv) $\dfrac{x^4y^4z^4}{x^4y^4z^6} = \dfrac{1}{z^2}$

5

(i) $6h^2 + 8h = 2h(3h + 4)$,
so $\dfrac{6h^2 + 8h}{2h} = \dfrac{2h(3h + 4)}{2h} = 3h + 4$.

(ii) $2a^2b + 3ab^2 = ab(2a + 3b)$,
so $\dfrac{2a^2b + 3ab^2}{4b} = \dfrac{ab(2a + 3b)}{4b} = \dfrac{a(2a + 3b)}{4}$.

(iii) $\dfrac{8a}{4ab - 4ac} = \dfrac{8a}{4a(b - c)} = \dfrac{2}{(b - c)}$

(iv) $\dfrac{8y}{6x^3y^2 - 4xy^2} = \dfrac{8y}{2xy^2(3x^2 - 2)} = \dfrac{4}{xy(3x^2 - 2)}$

6

(i) $\dfrac{4a^2 + 4ab}{5ab - 5a^2} = \dfrac{4a(a + b)}{5a(b - a)} = \dfrac{4(a + b)}{5(b - a)}$

(ii) $\dfrac{x^2 - xy}{x^2 + xy} = \dfrac{x(x - y)}{x(x + y)} = \dfrac{x - y}{x + y}$

(iii) $\dfrac{c^2 + 8c + 12}{c^2 + 6c + 8} = \dfrac{(c + 6)(c + 2)}{(c + 4)(c + 2)} = \dfrac{c + 6}{c + 4}$

(iv) $\dfrac{d^2 + 4d + 3}{3 - 2d - d^2} = \dfrac{(d + 3)(d + 1)}{(d + 3)(1 - d)} = \dfrac{d + 1}{1 - d}$

(v) $\dfrac{3x^2 + 3x - 18}{x^2 + 2x - 3} = \dfrac{3(x^2 + x - 6)}{x^2 + 2x - 3}$
$\qquad\qquad = \dfrac{3(x + 3)(x - 2)}{(x + 3)(x - 1)} = \dfrac{3(x - 2)}{x - 1}$

(vi) $\dfrac{4x^2 + 14x + 6}{12x^2 + 14x + 4} = \dfrac{2(2x^2 + 7x + 3)}{2(6x^2 + 7x + 2)}$
$\qquad\qquad = \dfrac{2(2x + 1)(x + 3)}{2(2x + 1)(3x + 2)} = \dfrac{x + 3}{3x + 2}$

7

(i) $\dfrac{4ax^2}{b} \times \dfrac{b^3}{9xy^2} = \dfrac{4ax^2b^3}{9bxy^2} = \dfrac{4axb^2}{9y^2}$

(ii) $\dfrac{4a^2}{14b} \div \dfrac{2a}{7b^2} = \dfrac{4a^2}{14b} \times \dfrac{7b^2}{2a} = \dfrac{28a^2b^2}{28ab} = ab$

(iii) $\dfrac{x^2}{y^2} \div \dfrac{x}{y} = \dfrac{x^2}{y^2} \times \dfrac{y}{x} = \dfrac{x^2y}{y^2x} = \dfrac{x}{y}$

(iv) $x^2 \div \dfrac{1}{x} = x^2 \times x = x^3$

8

(i) $\dfrac{b}{a} + \dfrac{2}{a} = \dfrac{b+2}{a}$

(ii) A common denominator is bd

$$\dfrac{2a}{b} = \dfrac{2a \times d}{b \times d} = \dfrac{2ad}{bd}$$

and

$$\dfrac{4}{d} = \dfrac{4 \times b}{d \times b} = \dfrac{4b}{bd}$$

so

$$\dfrac{2a}{b} + \dfrac{4}{d} = \dfrac{2ad + 4b}{bd} = \dfrac{2(ad + 2b)}{bd}.$$

(iii) A common denominator is ab

$$\dfrac{a^2}{b} = \dfrac{a^3}{ab} \text{ and } \dfrac{b^2}{a} = \dfrac{b^3}{ab},$$

so

$$\dfrac{a^2}{b} + \dfrac{b^2}{a} = \dfrac{a^3 + b^3}{ab}.$$

(iv) A common denominator is $20ce$

$$\dfrac{3b}{4c} = \dfrac{15be}{20ce} \text{ and } \dfrac{d}{5e} = \dfrac{4cd}{20ce},$$

so

$$\dfrac{3b}{4c} - \dfrac{d}{5e} = \dfrac{15be - 4cd}{20ce}.$$

(v) $1 = \dfrac{a+c}{a+c}$, so

$$1 + \dfrac{2a}{a+c} = \dfrac{a+c}{a+c} + \dfrac{2a}{a+c} = \dfrac{a+c+2a}{a+c} = \dfrac{3a+c}{a+c}.$$

(vi) $y = \dfrac{y(2x+4)}{(2x+4)}$, so

$$y - \dfrac{4y}{2x+4} = \dfrac{y(2x+4) - 4y}{2x+4} = \dfrac{2xy}{2x+4} = \dfrac{xy}{x+2}.$$

9 In these solutions where appropriate, we use the simplest possible common denominator, although you may have chosen to use the products of all the denominators. However, even though your working may be different, your final answer should be the same as ours.

(i) A common denominator is x^2, and

$$\dfrac{4}{x^2} - \dfrac{5}{x} = \dfrac{4 - 5x}{x^2}.$$

(ii) A common denominator is $4y^2z$, and

$$\dfrac{a}{2y^2} - \dfrac{b}{4yz} = \dfrac{2az - by}{4y^2z}.$$

(iii) A common denominator is abc, and

$$\dfrac{1}{ab} + \dfrac{1}{ac} + \dfrac{1}{bc} = \dfrac{c + b + a}{abc}.$$

(iv) A common denominator is $(n+1)(n+2)$, and

$$\dfrac{n}{n+1} - \dfrac{(n+1)}{n+2} = \dfrac{n(n+2) - (n+1)(n+1)}{(n+1)(n+2)}$$

$$= \dfrac{n^2 + 2n - n^2 - 2n - 1}{(n+1)(n+2)}$$

$$= \dfrac{-1}{(n+1)(n+2)}.$$

(v) $2b - \dfrac{b-1}{b-4} = \dfrac{2b(b-4) - (b-1)}{b-4}$

$$= \dfrac{2b^2 - 9b + 1}{b-4}$$

(vi) $\dfrac{2x-1}{x+2} - \dfrac{x+1}{2x} = \dfrac{2x(2x-1) - (x+1)(x+2)}{2x(x+2)}$

$$= \dfrac{3x^2 - 5x - 2}{2x(x+2)}$$

$$= \dfrac{(3x+1)(x-2)}{2x(x+2)}$$

10

(i) (a) x^2y^2 (b) $\dfrac{b}{4a}$ (c) -5 (d) c^3

(e) $\dfrac{(p+q)}{p(q-p)}$ (f) $\dfrac{-m}{l}$ (g) $\dfrac{y}{z(x+1)^2}$

(ii) (a) $\tfrac{2}{3}$ (b) $\dfrac{3(2x+y)}{2x}$ (c) $\dfrac{2c}{b(a+1)}$ (d) $\dfrac{c}{a^2}$

(e) $\dfrac{4(p+1)}{2p+1}$

(iii) (a) $-\dfrac{(k+15)}{24}$ (b) $\dfrac{2b-a}{b(a-b)}$ (c) $\dfrac{a^2+b^2}{ab(a+b)}$

(d) $\dfrac{2(1-x)}{(3x+1)(x-2)}$ (e) $\dfrac{n^2-n-3}{(n+1)(n-2)}$

Section 6.5 Solutions

1

(i) $a = 1$, $b = 4$, $c = 2$, so

$$x = \dfrac{-4 \pm \sqrt{16 - 4(1)(2)}}{2} = \dfrac{-4 \pm \sqrt{8}}{2}.$$

Thus $x = -0.59$ or $x = -3.41$.

(ii) $a = 5$, $b = 6$, $c = -3$, so

$$x = \dfrac{-6 \pm \sqrt{36 - 4(5)(-3)}}{2(5)} = \dfrac{-6 \pm \sqrt{96}}{10}.$$

Thus $x = 0.38$ or $x = -1.58$.

(iii) $a = 5$, $b = -9$, $c = 3$

$$x = \dfrac{-(-9) \pm \sqrt{81 - 4(5)(3)}}{2(5)} = \dfrac{9 \pm \sqrt{21}}{10}$$

Thus $x = 0.44$ or $x = 1.36$.

Countdown to Mathematics

(iv) $a = 10, b = -6, c = -15$
$$x = \frac{-(-6) \pm \sqrt{36 - (4)(10)(-15)}}{2(10)}$$
$$= \frac{6 \pm \sqrt{636}}{20}$$
Thus $x = 1·56$ or $x = -0·96$.

(v) $a = 3, b = 5, c = -7$
$$x = \frac{-5 \pm \sqrt{25 - 4(3)(-7)}}{2(3)} = \frac{-5 \pm \sqrt{109}}{6}$$
Thus $x = 0·91$ or $x = -2·57$.

2

(i) $a = 1, b = -1·2, c = 0·3$. Hence
$b^2 - 4ac = (1·2)^2 - 4(1)(0·3) = 0·24$,
which is greater than zero, so the equation has two solutions.

(ii) $a = 2, b = -2, c = \frac{1}{2}$. Hence
$b^2 - 4ac = 4 - 4 = 0$,
so the equation has one solution.

(iii) $a = 1, b = -3·5, c = 7·4$. Hence
$b^2 - 4ac = (-3·5)^2 - 4(1)(7·4) = -17·35$,
which is less than zero, so the equation has no solutions.

(iv) $a = -6·25, b = -2·5, c = 1$. Hence
$b^2 - 4ac = (-2·5)^2 - 4(-6·25)(1) = 31·25$,
which is greater than zero, so the equation has two solutions.

3

(i) $x^2 - 3x = -2x + 6$ (subtract $4x^2$ from both sides)
$x^2 - x = 6$ (add $2x$ to both sides)
$x^2 - x - 6 = 0$ (subtract 6 from both sides)
Hence $(x - 3)(x + 2) = 0$ and $x = 3$ or $x = -2$.
Alternatively you could just subtract $(4x^2 - 2x + 6)$ from both sides straight away, but make sure that you get the signs right.

(ii) $2x^2 + 5x + 4 = 7$ (add $5x$ to both sides)
$2x^2 + 5x - 3 = 0$ (subtract 7 from both sides)
Hence $(2x - 1)(x + 3) = 0$ and $x = \frac{1}{2}$ or $x = -3$.

(iii) Take all the terms to the right hand side.
$-6x + 2 = 6x^2 - 7x - 3$ (subtract x^2 from both sides)
$2 = 6x^2 - x - 3$ (add $6x$ to both sides)
$0 = 6x^2 - x - 5$ (subtract 2 from both sides)
Hence $(x - 1)(6x + 5) = 0$ and $x = 1$ or $x = -\frac{5}{6}$.

4

(i) Provided $x \neq -2$, cross multiply to get
$1 = 3(x + 2)$, or $1 = 3x + 6$.
Hence $-5 = 3x$, and $x = -\frac{5}{3}$.

(ii) Provided $x \neq \frac{4}{5}$ $((5x - 4) \neq 0)$ and $x \neq 0$, cross multiply to get $x = 5x - 4$.
Hence $4x = 4$, and $x = 1$.

(iii) Provided $b \neq -1$ and $b \neq -3$, cross multiply to get $3(b + 3) = 5(1 + b)$, or $3b + 9 = 5 + 5b$.
Hence $4 = 2b$, and $b = 2$.

(iv) Provided $d \neq 0$ and $d \neq -\frac{5}{2}$, cross multiply to get $2(2d + 5) = 3d$, or $4d + 10 = 3d$.
Hence $d = -10$.

5

(i) Provided $x \neq 0$, cross multiply to get
$x(x + 1) = 2$, or $x^2 + x - 2 = 0$.
$x^2 + x - 2 = 0$ factorises into $(x + 2)(x - 1)$, so $x = -2$ or $x = 1$.

(ii) Provided $a \neq 0$ and $a \neq \frac{5}{2}$, cross multiply to get $(a + 2)(2a - 5) = a^2$, which is equivalent to $2a^2 - a - 10 = a^2$ or $a^2 - a - 10 = 0$.
Using the formula
$$a = \frac{1 \pm \sqrt{41}}{2}$$
so $a = 3·70$ or $a = -2·70$.

(iii) Provided $y \neq -\frac{5}{3}$ and $y \neq -2$, cross multiply to get $(4y + 3)(y + 2) = (2y + 5)(3y + 5)$.
$4y^2 + 11y + 6 = 6y^2 + 25y + 25$, or $2y^2 + 14y + 19 = 0$.
Using the formula
$$y = \frac{-14 \pm \sqrt{44}}{4}$$
so $y = -1·84$ or $y = -5·16$.

(iv) Provided $r \neq -2$ and $r \neq -9$, cross multiply to get $(5r + 4)(r + 9) = (4r + 11)(2r + 4)$.
Hence $5r^2 + 49r + 36 = 8r^2 + 38r + 44$, or $3r^2 - 11r + 8 = 0$.
$3r^2 - 11r + 8 = 0$ factorises into $(3r - 8)(r - 1)$, so $r = \frac{8}{3}$ or $r = 1$.

6

(i) First express the right hand side as a single fraction.
$$\frac{2}{3} + \frac{1}{x} = \frac{2x + 3}{3x}$$
The equation then becomes
$$\frac{x + 1}{3x - 2} = \frac{2x + 3}{3x}.$$
Provided $x \neq \frac{2}{3}$ and $x \neq 0$, cross multiply to get
$3x(x + 1) = (2x + 3)(3x - 2)$.
Hence $3x^2 + 3x = 6x^2 + 5x - 6$, or
$3x^2 + 2x - 6 = 0$.
Using the formula
$$x = \frac{-2 \pm \sqrt{76}}{6}$$
so $x = 1·12$ or $x = -1·79$.

(ii) First express the right hand side as a single fraction.

$$\frac{1}{2x + 7} + \frac{1}{3} = \frac{3 + 2x + 7}{3(2x + 7)} = \frac{2x + 10}{3(2x + 7)}$$

The equation then becomes

$$\frac{3}{x + 5} = \frac{2x + 10}{3(2x + 7)}.$$

Provided $x \neq -5$ and $x \neq -\frac{7}{2}$, cross multiply to get

$$3(3)(2x + 7) = (2x + 10)(x + 5).$$

Hence $18x + 63 = 2x^2 + 20x + 50$, or $2x^2 + 2x - 13 = 0$.

Using the formula

$$x = \frac{-2 \pm \sqrt{108}}{4}$$

so $x = 2 \cdot 10$ or $x = -3 \cdot 10$.

7

(i) Cross multiply to get $b = ax$.

Hence $x = \dfrac{b}{a}$.

(ii) Cross multiply to get $45t(s + t) = 45v(t - s)$.

Hence $t(s + t) = v(t - s)$ (divide both sides by 45)

so $v = \dfrac{t(s + t)}{t - s}$. (divide both sides by $(t - s)$)

(iii) Cross multiply to get
$$(b + c)(c - 2a) = (c + a)(b - 2c).$$

Hence $bc + c^2 - 2ac - 2ab = bc + ab - 2c^2 - 2ac$. Take all the terms involving b to the left hand side, and all the other terms to the other side to get $-3ab = -3c^2$.

So $b = \dfrac{-3c^2}{-3a} = \dfrac{c^2}{a}$. (divide both sides by $-3a$)

(iv) Cross multiply to get $mf - nd = df(d - f)$.

Hence $mf = df(d - f) + nd$ (leave the term involving m on the left hand side)

so $m = \dfrac{df(d - f) + nd}{f}$. (divide both sides by f)

8

(i) First express the right hand side as a single fraction

$$x - \frac{4}{x} = \frac{x^2 - 4}{x}.$$

Thus

$$\frac{1}{y} = \frac{x^2 - 4}{x}.$$

Cross multiply to get $x = y(x^2 - 4)$.

Hence $y = \dfrac{x}{x^2 - 4}$. (divide both sides by $x^2 - 4$)

(ii) First express the left hand side as a single fraction.

$$\frac{m}{c} - \frac{a}{y} = \frac{my - ac}{cy}$$

Thus

$$\frac{my - ac}{cy} = y(m - a).$$

Cross multiply to get $my - ac = cy^2(m - a)$, or $my - ac = cmy^2 - acy^2$.

Hence

$$my = ac + cmy^2 - acy^2$$

$$= c(a + my^2 - ay^2)$$

and

$$c = \frac{my}{a + my^2 - ay^2}.$$

(iii) First express the left hand side as a single fraction

$$\frac{1}{m + n} + \frac{1}{m + p} = \frac{m + p + m + n}{(m + n)(m + p)}$$

$$= \frac{2m + n + p}{(m + n)(m + p)}.$$

Thus

$$\frac{2m + n + p}{(m + n)(m + p)} = \frac{2}{(m - n)}.$$

Cross multiply to get $(2m + n + p)(m - n) = 2(m + n)(m + p)$, or $2m^2 - mn + mp - n^2 - np = 2m^2 + 2mn + 2mp + 2np$.

Hence

$$-3mn - mp = n^2 + 3np.$$

So

$$-m(3n + p) = n^2 + 3np$$

or $$m = \frac{-(n^2 + 3np)}{3n + p}.$$

Alternatively

$$m = \frac{-n(n + 3p)}{3n + p}.$$

(iv) First express the right hand side as a single fraction

$$\frac{1}{u} + \frac{1}{v} = \frac{v + u}{uv}.$$

Thus

$$\frac{1}{f} = \frac{v + u}{uv}.$$

Cross multiply to get $uv = f(v + u)$ or $uv = fv + fu$.

Hence $uv - fu = fv$ (take fu to the left hand side)

$u(v - f) = fv$ (factorise)

$$u = \frac{fv}{v - f}.$$ (divide both sides by $(v - f)$)

Countdown to Mathematics

9

(i) (a) $r = 5\cdot24$ or $r = -3\cdot24$
(b) $f = -0\cdot56$ or $f = -8\cdot94$
(c) $x = 2\cdot17$ or $x = -1\cdot57$
(d) since $b^2 - 4ac = -11$, the equation has no solutions
(e) $y = -0\cdot23$ or $y = 8\cdot73$.

(ii) (a) $x = 2\cdot15$ or $x = 8\cdot85$
(b) only one solution, $x = \frac{2}{7}$, is valid. $x = -5$ gives a zero denominator in the original equation.
(c) $y = 0\cdot73$ or $y = -0\cdot23$
(d) $m = \dfrac{-17}{7}$
(e) The equation $x^2 + x + 4 = 0$ has no solutions.

(iii) (a) $y = \dfrac{x}{x(p + q)^2 - 1}$
(b) $x = \dfrac{4y}{y - 1}$
(c) $a = \dfrac{my(1 - cy)}{c(1 - y^2)}$
(d) $m = \dfrac{ac(1 - y^2)}{y(1 - cy)}$

MODULE ⑦

7.1 Straight Lines

7.2 Quadratics

7.3 Other Curves

7.4 Solving Equations

7.5 Algebraic Methods of Solving
    Linear Simultaneous Equations

7.1 Straight Lines

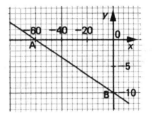
This section builds upon the work of Module 3, so we assume that you can plot a straight line, find its gradient and intercept, and relate these characteristics to the equation. These ideas are now revised and extended through a series of examples and exercises.

See Module 3, Sections 3.3 and 3.4.
Many of the exercises take the form of investigations, and you will find that if you work carefully through these you can develop the ideas for yourself.

7.1(i) PLOTTING STRAIGHT LINES

You should already be able to plot a straight line of the form

$$y = ax + b.$$

However, if the equation is *not* given in this form then it is probably a good idea to rearrange it so that y is the subject of the equation.

EXAMPLE

Plot the graph of $4y - 3x = 7$.

SOLUTION

First make y the subject of the equation.

$$4y = 3x + 7,$$

(Add 3x to both sides.)

so

$$y = \frac{3x + 7}{4} \text{ or } y = \frac{3x}{4} + \frac{7}{4}.$$

(Divide both sides by 4.)

A suitable table of values is:

x	-3	-2	-1	0	1	2	3
$y = 0.75x + 1.75$	-0.5	0.25	1	1.75	2.5	3.25	4

The equation is written in decimal form so that a calculator can be used.

Since we were not told a range of values for x, the range of values in the table above was an arbitrary choice. However, it is best to include important points such as those where the graph crosses the axes, and to restrict the table to small numbers.

Try and choose some negative numbers and some positive numbers.

CHECK YOUR ANSWERS

1

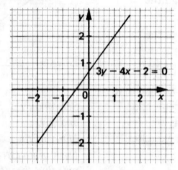

Section 7.1(i)

2 The gradient of AB is $-\frac{1}{6}$; the y intercept is -10. Hence the equation of AB is

$$y = -\frac{1}{6}x - 10 \text{ or } 6y + x + 60 = 0.$$

Section 7.1(ii)

3 (i) $y = mx + b - ma$

Section 7.1(iii)

(ii) The equation of PQ is given by

$$\frac{5-1}{4-2} = \frac{y-1}{x-2}$$

or $y = 2x - 3$.

One of the hardest parts of plotting a graph onto a given space is choosing the most appropriate scales for the axes. This involves looking closely at the range of both co-ordinates. We want to plot the graph of $4y - 3x = 7$, so that it fits onto the diagram in the margin.

See Module 3, Section 3.1(iv).

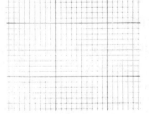

Consequently, since x ranges from -3 to $+3$, a suitable scale for the horizontal axis is 1 large square: 4 units. Similarly, since y ranges from -0.5 to 4, a suitable scale for the y-axis is also 1 large square: 4 units.

At first you may find it difficult to determine where the axes should cross and you may well need to use trial and error. However, with practice you will find that you can intuitively sense the layout. The graph of $y = 0.75x + 1.75$ is illustrated below.

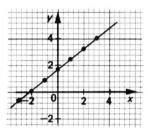

It is important to remember that every graph should be clear, easy to read and should fill the available space sensibly. If your graph is cramped into a corner then you should realise for yourself that you could have used more appropriate scales.

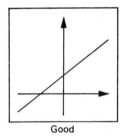

Good

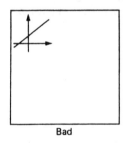

Bad

In fact it is not necessary to draw up a detailed table of values when plotting a straight line. You could just plot two points and join them with a straight line, but it is wiser to plot three points, in case you make a mistake. The advantage of plotting only a few points is that easy values of x, such as 0, 1 or -1, can be selected and the corresponding value of y worked out in your head.

Label the axes to indicate the scales used. The accuracy of your graph depends upon how accurately you plot the points.

Notice that this quick method only works for straight lines. To plot a curve it is important to plot as many points as possible.

EXAMPLE

Plot the graph of $4y = 3x - 7$.

SOLUTION

Choose three easy values of x: $x = 1$, $x = 0$ and $x = -1$.

When $x = 1$, $y = \dfrac{3 - 7}{4}$, so $y = -1$.

When $x = 0$, $y = \dfrac{-7}{4}$, so $y = -1.75$.

When $x = -1$, $y = \dfrac{-3 - 7}{4}$, so $y = -2.5$.

$4y = 3x - 7$ is the same as

$$y = \frac{3x}{4} - \frac{7}{4} \text{ or}$$

$$y = \frac{3x - 7}{4}.$$

The graph is illustrated below.

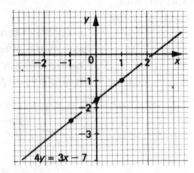

TRY SOME YOURSELF

1   Plot each of the following graphs:
(i) $y = 2x + 1$ (ii) $3y = 2x + 1$ (iii) $2y - x + 3 = 0$.

If you want, you could plot all three graphs on the same axes.

An equation which corresponds to a straight line graph is said to be a *linear equation*. This exercise shows that any equation of the form

$$ay + bx + c = 0$$

is a linear equation.

a, b and c may be positive, negative, or zero.

7.1(ii) GRADIENTS AND INTERCEPTS

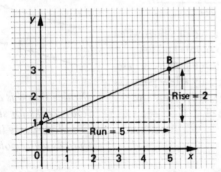

You probably remember that the gradient of the line AB is given by

$$\text{gradient} = \frac{\text{Vertical rise from A to B}}{\text{Horizontal run from A to B}}$$

$$= \frac{2}{5} = 0 \cdot 4.$$

See Module 3, Section 3.3(i).

This works for positive and negative gradients, as the next example illustrates.

EXAMPLE

Find the gradient of AB in the diagram opposite.

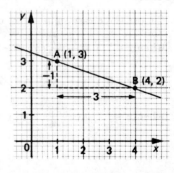

SOLUTION

In fact the graph falls from A to B so that the vertical rise is negative.

The vertical rise from A to B is $2 - 3 = -1$.

The horizontal run from A to B is $4 - 1 = 3$.

Hence the gradient $= \dfrac{\text{Rise}}{\text{Run}} = \dfrac{-1}{3} = -0\cdot33.$

Notice that the graph slopes down towards the right, so the gradient is negative.

For both rise and run we've taken the distance from A to B. We could have taken the distances from B to A. This gives the same gradient, since
$\dfrac{3-2}{1-4} = -\dfrac{1}{3}.$
Notice however that both the rise and the run must start from the same point.

TRY SOME YOURSELF

2(i)   Plot each of the following points on suitable axes:
     A $(3, 1)$ B $(3, 4)$ C $(0, 4)$ D $(-4, 0)$.
(ii)   Calculate the gradients of each of the following lines:
     (a) BC   (b) BD   (c) AC.

TRY SOME YOURSELF

3   Plot the points L $(2, 1)$, M $(4, 5)$ and N $(7, 11)$.
(i)   Find the gradient of LM.
(ii)   Find the gradient of MN.
(iii) What do parts (i) and (ii) suggest about the three points L, M and N?

Exercise 3 shows that the gradient of a straight line is constant. Thus the gradient of a straight line can be calculated by considering *any* two points which lie on the line.

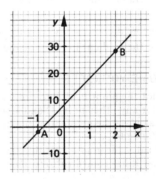

Equation of a straight line

The graph of $y = 10x + 8$ is illustrated in the margin.

The gradient of the line can be calculated by considering the points $(-1, -2)$ and $(2, 28)$.

Thus the gradient $= \dfrac{28 - (-2)}{2 - (-1)} = \dfrac{30}{3} = 10.$

*Notice that it is essential to take the **scales** of the axes into consideration.*

The y-intercept is the point where the graph cuts the y-axis, the value of y corresponding to $x = 0$. From the graph, the y-intercept of $y = 10x + 8$, is $y = 8$.

This illustrates that the equation of a straight line can always be expressed in the form

    $y = (\text{gradient} \times x) + y\text{-intercept}.$

See Module 3, Section 3.3(ii).

Countdown to Mathematics

TRY SOME YOURSELF

4   Write down the equation of each of the following graphs:

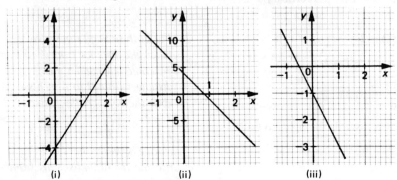

(i)   (ii)   (iii)

TRY SOME YOURSELF

5(i) Write down the gradient and y-intercept of each of the following
      linear equations:

   (a) $y = \frac{2}{3}x + 6$ (b) $2y = 3x - 6$ (c) $y = ax + b$

   (d) $ax + by + c = 0$ (e) $lx - \frac{y}{p} = 1$.

(ii) Write down the linear equations whose graphs have the following
      characteristics:
      (a) gradient 0, y-intercept c
      (b) gradient m, y-intercept 0
      (c) gradient m, y-intercept c.

   The next exercise invites you to investigate a more general expression
   for the gradient in terms of the co-ordinates.

TRY SOME YOURSELF

6(i)   Plot the point P with co-ordinates (2, 3) on some graph paper.
(ii)   Plot any other point Q and label the co-ordinates (a, b).
(iii) Calculate the gradient of the line PQ. Leave your answer in terms
       of a and b.
(iv)   What is the gradient of the line RQ where Q has co-ordinates (a, b)
       and R has co-ordinates (c, d)?

   This exercise shows that the gradient of a line joining the points
   P (a_1, b_1) and Q (a_2, b_2) is given by

$$\text{gradient} = \frac{b_2 - b_1}{a_2 - a_1}.$$

   This means that the gradient can be calculated without plotting
   the points.

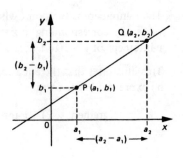

7.1(iii) ALTERNATIVE WAYS OF DERIVING THE EQUATION

We've shown that it's easy to write down the equation of a line when given the gradient and the intercept. But it is also possible to derive the equation without being given the gradient and/or without knowing the y-intercept. We now investigate these alternative approaches.

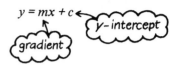

TRY SOME YOURSELF

7(i) Plot the point P with co-ordinates $(2, 3)$. Through P draw straight lines with the following gradients:
(a) $\frac{3}{2}$ (b) $-\frac{3}{4}$ (c) 0.

(ii) Mark any point Q on the line which you drew for Part (i) (a) and label the co-ordinates of Q, (x, y).
(a) What is the gradient of PQ in terms of x and y?
(b) Part (i) (a) of this exercise states that the gradient of PQ is $\frac{3}{2}$. Use this information to derive an equation involving x and y.
(c) Check that this equation is the equation of the line PQ.

(iii) Use this same method to derive the equation of the straight line passing through the point P $(2, 3)$
(a) with gradient $-\frac{3}{4}$
(b) with gradient 0.

For example, in Part (a) you will need to measure a rise of 3 units from P and a run of 2 units.

More generally, this gives the equation of the straight line passing through the point P, (a, b) with gradient m.

Choose any point Q lying on the line passing through P and label the co-ordinates of Q (x, y).

The gradient of PQ $= \dfrac{y - b}{x - a}$.

But the gradient of PQ is m. Hence $\dfrac{y - b}{x - a} = m$.

Thus $y - b = m(x - a)$

$$\boxed{\text{or } y = mx + b - ma.}$$

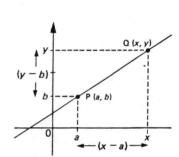

This shows that the y-intercept is $(b - ma)$.

This shows that it is not necessary to know the y-intercept. The equation can be derived given the gradient, and the co-ordinates of *any* point lying on the line. The next exercise investigates what happens when you are given the co-ordinates of two points lying on the line.

TRY SOME YOURSELF

8 Consider the points A $(2, 1)$ and B $(5, 7)$. There is no need to plot these points.
(i) Write down the gradient of AB.
(ii) Now suppose that the point Q, with co-ordinates (x, y) lies on the line joining A and B.
(a) Write down the gradient of AQ. Leave your answer in terms of x and y.
(b) Since the points A, B and Q lie on a straight line the gradients of AB and AQ are the same. Use this information to derive an equation involving x and y.

(c) Check that this equation is the equation of the line AB.

(d) Determine whether the point R with co-ordinates (19, 35) lies on the same line.

There is no need to plot the line, just substitute the co-ordinates into both sides of the equation.

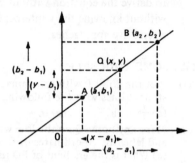

This exercise shows that the equation can be derived from the co-ordinate of two points lying on the line.

If the two points are A (a_1, b_1) and B (a_2, b_2), then the gradient of AB is

$$\frac{b_2 - b_1}{a_2 - a_1}.$$

The gradient can be calculated from the co-ordinates of the two points.

Choose any point Q lying on the line through AB and label the co-ordinates of Q (x, y). The gradient of AQ is

$$\frac{y - b_1}{x - a_1}.$$

Since AQB is a straight line the gradient is constant.

Hence

$$\frac{b_2 - b_1}{a_2 - a_1} = \frac{y - b_1}{x - a_1}.$$

This is probably the easiest form to remember.

This can be rearranged to give

$$y = \left(\frac{b_2 - b_1}{a_2 - a_1}\right)x + b_1 - \left(\frac{b_2 - b_1}{a_2 - a_1}\right)a_1.$$

Compare this with the result on page 137.

TRY SOME YOURSELF

9(i) Find the equation of the line joining A (3, 1) and B (5, 3).

(ii) Find the equation of the line joining A (3, 1) and C (7, −2).

After you have worked through this section you should be able to

a Plot the graph of any linear equation

b Determine the gradient of the straight line joining any two points

c Write down the gradient and y-intercept of the graph of a linear equation

d Derive the equation of the straight line passing through a given point with given gradient

e Derive the equation of the line passing through two given points

Finally, here are some exercises if you want more practice.

TRY SOME MORE YOURSELF

10(i) Plot each of the following straight lines:

(a) $y = \frac{1}{2}x - 3$ (b) $3y + 2x = 7$ (c) $6y - 7x + 3 = 0$.

(ii)   Find the equations of each of the following straight lines:
(a) the line passing through the point P $(1, 0)$ with gradient 2
(b) the line passing through the point Q $(-2, 1)$ with gradient 3
(c) the line passing through the point R $(2, -1)$ with gradient -4.

(iii) Find the equations of the straight lines passing through each of the following pairs of points:
(a) A $(1, 2)$ B $(5, 7)$ (b) A $(0, 3)$ B $(7, 1)$
(c) A $(-1, 0)$ B $(4, 2)$.

7.2 Quadratics

TRY THESE QUESTIONS FIRST

1 (i) Complete the table of values below.

x	-2.5	-2	-1.5	-1	-0.5	0	0.5	1	1.5	2	2.5
$y = 1.5x^2$											

(ii) Use the table to plot the graph of $y = 1.5x^2$.

2 (i) Write down a key sequence to evaluate $3 - 2x^2 + 5x$.

(ii) Use the key sequence to complete the table of values below and so plot the graph of $y = 3 - 2x^2 + 5x$.

x	-1	-0.5	0	0.5	1	1.5	2	2.5	3	3.5
$y = 3 - 2x^2 + 5x$										

3 Use the graph opposite to solve $2x^2 - 2x - 1 = 0$.

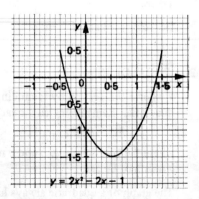

CHECK YOUR ANSWERS

1 (i)

x	-2·5	-2	-1·5	-1	-0·5	0	0·5	1	1·5	2	2·5
$y = 1·5x^2$	9·4	6	3·4	1·5	0·4	0	0·4	1·5	3·4	6	9·4

Section 7.2(i)

(ii)

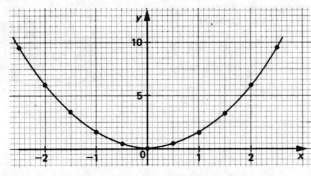

2 (i) We don't give a key sequence here as there are several   *Section 7.2(ii)*
possibilities. Check that your key sequence works for
$x = 1$ by evaluating $3 - 2(1)^2 + 5(1)$. You should
get 6.

(ii)

x	-1	-0·5	0	0·5	1	1·5	2	2·5	3	3·5
$y = 3 - 2x^2 + 5x$	-4	0	3	5	6	6	5	3	0	-4

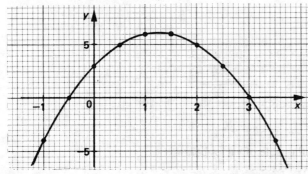

3 The solutions are given by the values of x where the graph cuts the   *Section 7.2(iii)*
x-axis.

Hence $x \simeq 1·4$ and $x \simeq -0·4$.

7.2(i) PARABOLAS

We begin this section by reminding you how to plot the graph of a
quadratic. Remember that a quadratic relationship has the form   *See Module 3, Section 3.4(i).*

$$y = ax^2 + bx + c$$

where the coefficients a, b and c may be positive or negative and
a must not be zero.

*Otherwise $y = bx + c$ is just a
linear equation.*

The graph of a quadratic always has the same basic shape, a
parabola.

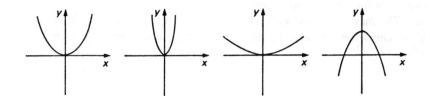

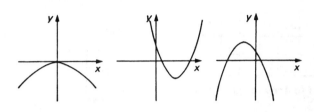

The reflector of a torch and the receiver of a radio telescope are both parabolas.

The shape may be elongated or flattened, turned upside down or moved up and down and left or right: it is still a parabola.

The following exercises are intended to refresh your memory as to how to plot some common quadratics.

TRY SOME YOURSELF

1(i)   Complete the table of values below.

x	$-2 \cdot 5$	-2	$-1 \cdot 5$	-1	$-0 \cdot 5$	0	$0 \cdot 5$	1	$1 \cdot 5$	2	$2 \cdot 5$
$y = x^2$											

(ii)   Use the table to plot the graph of $y = x^2$. Use the following scales for the axes

        x axis: 1 cm:1 unit
        y axis: 1 cm:1 unit.

Make sure that your graph is a smooth curve with no bumps or corners.

You may want to plot some extra points to get a more accurate curve.

The next exercise shows that the scales used for the axes can significantly affect the shape of the graph.

TRY SOME YOURSELF

2   Draw the graph of $y = x^2$ using each of the following scales:
   (i) x-axis 1 cm:1 unit; y-axis 1 cm:2 units
   (ii) x-axis 1 cm:1 unit; y-axis 2 cm:1 unit
   (iii) x-axis 2 cm:1 unit; y-axis 1 cm:2 units.

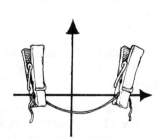

The solution to this exercise indicates that the graphs look very different although they all correspond to the same equation. To avoid unnecessary confusion, you should always

      (i)   clearly indicate the scales on both axes

and   (ii)   label the graph itself.

Countdown to Mathematics

In the exercises which follow you may find that our solutions differ in appearance from yours. This may be because we have used different scales. You can still check the accuracy of your graph by comparing co-ordinates.

Of course if you find that your graph is not smooth you should recheck anyway,

TRY SOME YOURSELF

3(i) Complete the table of values below and so draw the graphs of:
(a) $y = 2x^2$ (b) $y = 2x^2 + 1$.

You should be able to draw both graphs on the same axes.

x	$-2{\cdot}5$	-2	$-1{\cdot}5$	-1	$-0{\cdot}5$	0	$0{\cdot}5$	1	$1{\cdot}5$	2	$2{\cdot}5$
$y = 2x^2$											
$y = 2x^2 + 1$											

(ii) Complete a similar table of values and so draw the graphs of:
(a) $y = 0{\cdot}5x^2$ (b) $y = 0{\cdot}5x^2 + 1$.

(iii) Complete a similar table of values and so draw the graphs of:
(a) $y = -2x^2$ (b) $y = -2x^2 + 1$.

This exercise shows that there is no quick method for plotting a quadratic. Your graph will be more accurate if you plot lots of points. It's always a good idea to plot several points around the bottom of the parabola (or top if it's upside down) to get a better shape. Of course the accuracy also depends upon the scales that you choose, so if you need a particularly accurate graph use large scales.

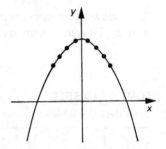

7.2(ii) PLOTTING MORE COMPLICATED QUADRATICS

In Section 7.2(i) we suggested that you use a calculator to evaluate the squares of decimal numbers. For more complicated equations a calculator is invaluable for performing quick calculations. However it is easy to make mistakes when using a calculator, so we now discuss how you might investigate and test possible key sequences to evaluate quadratics.

Once you are sure that the key sequence works you can use it with confidence.

EXAMPLE

Construct a key sequence to evaluate $2x^2 + x + 1$.

SOLUTION

It's best to check the key sequence for an easy value of x, such as $x = 1$. It should be possible to evaluate the expression almost as it is written using the key sequence

press the x^2 key

You should get
$2(1) + 1 + 1 = 4$.

$\boxed{1}$ represents the current value of x.

Notice that we have calculated

$$(x^2 \times 2) + x + 1$$

to avoid any difficulties.

You may find that you can evaluate the expression *exactly* as it is written, although this doesn't work for all calculators. Write down a key sequence now which works for your calculator.

Check with the maker's handbook if you get into difficulties.

When the expression has to be evaluated for several values of x you may find it helpful to use the memory. This should give a key sequence such as

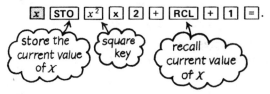

Check with the maker's handbook how to store and recall using your calculator.

Check this key sequence on your calculator for $x = 1$.

This key sequence can now be used to construct a table of values for $y = 2x^2 + x + 1$, and hence to plot the graph.

Again, you should get 4 for the answer. If not, check with the maker's handbook and write down a sequence which works for your calculator.

x	-3	$-2\cdot5$	-2	$-1\cdot5$	-1	$-0\cdot5$	0	$0\cdot5$	1	$1\cdot5$	2	$2\cdot5$	3
$y = 2x^2 + x + 1$	16	11	7	4	2	1	1	2	4	7	11	16	22

The graph is illustrated below.

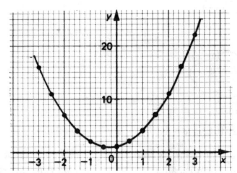

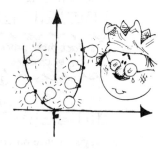

TRY SOME YOURSELF

4(i) (a) Write down a key sequence to evaluate $2x^2 - x + 1$.
     (b) Check your key sequence by substituting $x = 1$.
     (c) Use your key sequence to complete the table of values below.

Make sure the key sequence works for your calculator.

x	$-2\cdot5$	-2	$-1\cdot5$	-1	$-0\cdot5$	0	$0\cdot5$	1	$1\cdot5$	2	$2\cdot5$
$y = 2x^2 - x + 1$											

     (d) Use the table to plot the graph of $y = 2x^2 - x + 1$.

(ii) (a) Write down a key sequence to evaluate $0 \cdot 3x^2 + x - 0 \cdot 2$.
(b) Check your key sequence by substituting $x = 1$.
(c) Use your key sequence to complete the table of values below.

x		$-3 \cdot 5$	-3	$-2 \cdot 5$	-2	$-1 \cdot 5$	-1	$-0 \cdot 5$	0	$0 \cdot 5$	1	$1 \cdot 5$
$y = 0 \cdot 3x^2 + x - 0 \cdot 2$												

(d) Use your table to plot the graph of $y = 0 \cdot 3x^2 + x - 0 \cdot 2$.

Now try writing down a key sequence to evaluate $2x^2 - 3x - 9$.

Again, check it for $x = 1$;
$2(1) - 3 - 9 = -10$.

You may find that you can still evaluate the expression as it is written, but you may need to use brackets, viz

$$(2 \times x^2) - (3 \times x) - 9.$$

We now introduce an alternative way of writing down the expression which avoids such difficulties. This involves some rather unusual algebraic manipulation.

$2x^2 - 3x - 9$ can be written as $(2x^2 - 3x) - 9$.

Notice that the brackets make no difference here.

x can now be taken out of the brackets as a common factor to give

$$x(2x - 3) - 9.$$

Finally this can be written as

$$(2x - 3)x - 9.$$

This expression has now been re-written to avoid using the symbol x^2.

The advantage of this arrangement is that it can be calculated directly from left to right. A possible key sequence is

$$\boxed{(}\;\boxed{2}\;\boxed{\times}\;\boxed{x}\;\boxed{-}\;\boxed{3}\;\boxed{)}\;\boxed{\times}\;\boxed{x}\;\boxed{-}\;\boxed{9}\;\boxed{=}\;.$$

in fact these brackets can be omitted

and replaced with an equals sign

$$\boxed{2}\;\boxed{\times}\;\boxed{x}\;\boxed{-}\;\boxed{3}\;\boxed{=}\;\boxed{\times}\;\boxed{x}\;\boxed{-}\;\boxed{9}\;\boxed{=}\;.$$

Try this key sequence on your calculator substituting $x = 1$.

You should get -10.

Notice that this last key sequence avoids the use of brackets *and* the $\boxed{x^2}$ key. Rearranging an expression in this form is called *nesting*. If you compare the two expressions

This key sequence should work for all calculators.

$$2x^2 \;-\; 3x \;-\; 9$$
$$(2x \;-\; 3)x \;-\; 9$$

you will find that the coefficients correspond. However, before the expression can be nested it must be in the form

$$ax^2 + bx + c$$

This provides a way of checking that you have nested the expression correctly.

with the x^2 term first, followed by the x term, followed by the constant. If it is not in this form then the first step is to rewrite it so that it is.

EXAMPLE

Plot the graph of $y = 3x - 2x^2 + 1$.

SOLUTION

$$3x - 2x^2 + 1 = -2x^2 + 3x + 1$$
$$= (-2x^2 + 3x) + 1$$
$$= x(-2x + 3) + 1$$
$$= (-2x + 3)x + 1$$

First rewrite the expression so that the x^2 term is first.

Check that the coefficients agree with the coefficients in $-2x^2 + 3x + 1$.

A suitable key sequence is

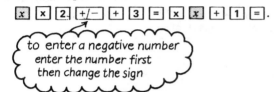

to enter a negative number enter the number first then change the sign

Again it is probably better practice to calculate $x \times (-2)$ rather than $(-2) \times x$.

Check the key sequence by substituting $x = 1$. You should always check key sequences by substituting an easy value of x, one that you can substitute mentally if possible.

$3(1) - 2(1) + 1 = 2$

You may prefer to use a different key sequence. This doesn't matter as long as you check that it works first.

For more complicated values of x you may wish to use the memory. Store the value of x first, then the sequence should be almost the same. For example, a possible key sequence is

store the current value of x

recall x from the memory

Try putting $x = 0.013421$ and compare the two sequences for yourself.

Having checked the key sequence we can proceed to construct a table of values.

x	-3	-2·5	-2	-1·5	-1	-0·5	0	0·5	1	1·5	2	2·5	3
$y = 3x - 2x^2 + 1$ $(-2x + 3)x + 1$	-26	-19	-13	-8	-4	-1	1	2	2	1	-1	-4	-8

The graph is illustrated in the margin.

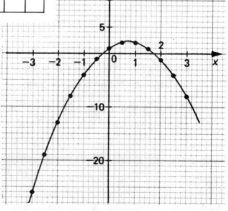

TRY SOME YOURSELF

5(i) Write down a key sequence to evaluate each of the following expressions:

(a) $2x^2 - 3x + 1$ (b) $5x^2 + 6x - 3$ (c) $2 - x^2 - 3x$.

(ii) Check each of the key sequences you obtained in Part (i) by substituting $x = 1$.

(iii) Evaluate each of the expressions in Part (i) for $x = -0.12$.

(iv) (a) Use Part (i) (a) to construct a table of values for $y = 2x^2 - 3x + 1$ for x ranging from -2 to 3. Use the table to plot the graph of $y = 2x^2 - 3x + 1$.

(b) Use Part (i) (b) to construct a table of values for $y = 5x^2 + 6x - 3$ for x ranging from -3 to 2. Use the table to plot the graph of $y = 5x^2 + 6x - 3$.

(c) Use Part (i) (c) to construct a table of values for $y = 2 - x^2 - 3x$ for x ranging from -5 to 2. Use the table to plot the graph of $y = 2 - x^2 - 3x$.

There is no point in making the table too accurate since you will only be able to plot the points approximately. It's probably best to round off to one decimal place.

7.2(iii) SOLVING QUADRATIC EQUATIONS

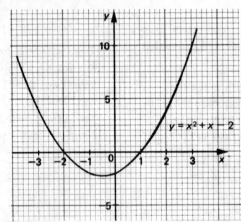

It's quite straightforward to read off a value of y which corresponds to a given value of x. For example, when

$$x = 1.6, \ y \simeq 2.$$

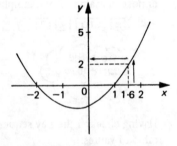

Start at $x = 1.6$ on the x-axis. Move vertically up to the graph then horizontally across to the y-axis.

A similar process is used to find the value of x corresponding to a given value of y: move horizontally across to the graph then vertically down to the x-axis.

Notice however that when $y = 5$ there are two corresponding values of x, $x \simeq -3.2$ and $x \simeq 2.2$.

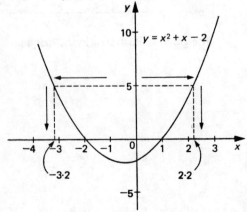

TRY SOME YOURSELF

6(i) Use the graph of $y = x^2 + x - 2$ above to find:
  (a) the value of y corresponding to $x = -2\cdot5$
  (b) the values of x corresponding to $y = 3$
  (c) the values of x corresponding to $y = -5$.
(ii) (a) Use the graph of $y = x^2 + x - 2$ to find the values of x
    corresponding to $y = 0$.
  (b) These values of x are solutions to $x^2 + x - 2 = 0$. Use an
    algebraic method to verify this.

See Module 6, Section 6.2.

This exercise shows that a quadratic equation can be solved by
drawing the corresponding graph and reading off the x-co-ordinates
of the points where the graph cuts the x-axis.

In Module 6 we showed algebraically that a quadratic equation of
the form $ax^2 + bx + c = 0$ has two, one or zero solutions, depending
on whether $b^2 - 4ac$ is positive, zero or negative. The next
exercise gives a graphical interpretation to this result.

See Module 6, Section 6.5(i).

TRY SOME YOURSELF

7(i) (a) Plot the graph of $y = x^2 - 2x - 3$.
  (b) Hence solve $x^2 - 2x - 3 = 0$.
(ii) (a) Plot the graph of $y = x^2 - 2x + 1$.
  (b) Hence solve $x^2 - 2x + 1 = 0$.
(iii) (a) Plot the graph of $y = x^2 - 2x + 2$.
  (b) Hence solve $x^2 - 2x + 2 = 0$.

*In each case construct a table for
x ranging from $x = -2$ to $x = 4$.*

*Check the sign of $b^2 - 4ac$ and
compare the number of solutions
on your graph with the algebraic
result.*

This exercise illustrates that a quadratic equation has

  (i) two roots if the graph cuts the x-axis twice
  (ii) one root if the graph just touches the x-axis
  (iii) no roots if the graph does not cut the x-axis at all.

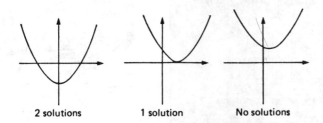

2 solutions   1 solution   No solutions

After you have worked through this section you should be able to

a Write down a suitable key sequence to evaluate an expression of the form $ax^2 + bx + c$
b Nest an expression such as $ax^2 + bx + c$ into the form $(ax + b)x + c$
c Plot the graph of a quadratic of the form $y = ax^2 + bx + c$
d Solve a quadratic equation of the form $ax^2 + bx + c = 0$ by plotting the graph of $y = ax^2 + bx + c$

Finally here are some exercises if you want more practice.

TRY SOME MORE YOURSELF

8(i) Plot each of the following graphs:
    (a) $y = 3x^2 - 4x + 1$ (x ranging from -2 to 3)
    (b) $y = 4x^2 - 2x - 2$ (x ranging from -2 to 2)
    (c) $y = 2 - 3x - x^2$ (x ranging from -4 to 2)
    (d) $y = 4x^2 - 20x + 25$ (x ranging from 0 to 5)
    (e) $y = 0\cdot3x^2 + 0\cdot2x + 1\cdot1$ (x ranging from -3 to 2)

(ii) Use the graphs which you drew in Part (i) to solve each of the following equations:
    (a) $3x^2 - 4x + 1 = 0$ (b) $4x^2 - 2x - 2 = 0$
    (c) $2 - 3x - x^2 = 0$ (d) $4x^2 - 20x + 25 = 0$
    (e) $0\cdot3x^2 + 0\cdot2x + 1\cdot1 = 0.$

7.3 Other Curves

TRY THESE QUESTIONS FIRST

1 Sketch the possible shapes of a cubic graph.

2 Write down a key sequence to evaluate $3x^2 - 2x + 1 + x^3$.

3 (i) Complete the table of values below and so plot the graph of $y = 3x^2 - 2x + 1 + x^3$.

x	-4	-3	-2	$-1\cdot5$	-1	$-0\cdot5$	0	$0\cdot5$	1	$1\cdot5$	2
y											

    (ii) Use your graph to find the solution to $3x^2 - 2x + 1 + x^3 = 0$.

4 Plot the graph of $y = \dfrac{4}{x + 3}$ (for x ranging from -6 to 0).

7.3(i) CUBICS

A *cubic* equation has the form
$$ax^3 + bx^2 + cx + d = 0$$
where a, b, c and d stand for any numbers and a must not be zero.

It is called a cubic because the highest power of x is x^3.

If $a = 0$ then the equation is a quadratic (if $b \neq 0!$).

We begin this section by investigating the shape of the graph of a cubic. The simplest example is

$$y = x^3.$$

You should be able to find the cube of a number using your calculator. For example, try finding 2^3. You could do this by evaluating $2 \times 2 \times 2$, but your calculator may have a key which automatically calculates the power of a number. This is often labelled $\boxed{y^x}$ or $\boxed{x^y}$. Investigate this key by finding

$$2^3, 2^4, 2^5, 2^6.$$

Check with the maker's handbook.

As a check work out 2^3, 2^4 etc on paper.

$$(-2)^3 = (-2) \times (-2) \times (-2)$$
$$= -8.$$

Now, try finding $(-2)^3$.

Your calculator may not be able to cope with the power of a negative number, in which case it will display an error message. If this happens you will need to apply some mathematical reasoning. Notice that

$$(-2)^3 = (-2) \times (-2) \times (-2) = -8 = -(2^3)$$

and

$$(-2)^5 = (-2) \times (-2) \times (-2) \times (-2) \times (-2) = -32 = -(2)^5.$$

Similarly

$$(-2)^2 = (-2) \times (-2) = 4 = 2^2$$
$$(-2)^4 = (-2) \times (-2) \times (-2) \times (-2) = 16 = 2^4$$

and

$$(-2)^6 = (-2) \times (-2) \times (-2) \times (-2) \times (-2) \times (-2) = 64 = 2^6.$$

This suggests that if the power is odd,

$$(-a)^m = -(a^m)$$

Here m stands for an odd number,

and if the power is even,

$$(-a)^n = a^n.$$

and n stands for an even number.

This means that you should be able to use your calculator to evaluate powers of both positive and negative numbers.

TRY SOME YOURSELF

1 Use your calculator to find each of the following:
(i) (a) 3^4 (b) $0 \cdot 1^3$ (c) $1 \cdot 314^5$
(ii) (a) $(-3)^4$ (b) $(-3)^3$ (c) $(-5)^5$ (d) $(-1 \cdot 314)^5$.

The basic characteristics of a cubic graph are revealed in the exercises on page 151.

Countdown to Mathematics

CHECK YOUR ANSWERS

1 A cubic graph has one of the two basic shapes illustrated below. *Section 7.3(i)*

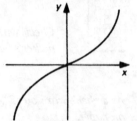 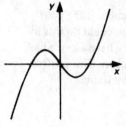

2 Nest the expression to get $((x + 3)x - 2)x + 1$. *Section 7.3(ii)*

A suitable key sequence is therefore

$\boxed{x}$ $\boxed{\text{STO}}$ $\boxed{+}$ $\boxed{3}$ $\boxed{=}$ $\boxed{x}$ $\boxed{\text{RCL}}$ $\boxed{-}$ $\boxed{2}$ $\boxed{=}$ $\boxed{x}$ $\boxed{\text{RCL}}$ $\boxed{+}$ $\boxed{1}$ $\boxed{=}$.

You may have written down another key sequence. This doesn't matter as long as you check it. For example, when $x = 1$,

$$3x^2 - 2x + 1 + x^3 = 3 - 2 + 1 + 1 = 3.$$

3 (i) *Section 7.3(iii)*

x	−4	−3	−2	−1·5	−1	−0·5	0	0·5	1	1·5	2
y	−7	7	9	7·4	5	2·6	1	0·9	3	8·1	17

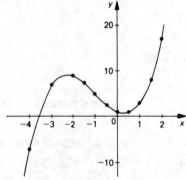

(ii) From the graph the solution is $x \simeq -3·5$.

4 Notice that $x = -3$ is excluded from the graph. This is indicated with a dotted line. *Section 7.3(iv)*

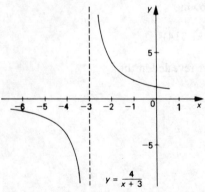

$$y = \frac{4}{x + 3}$$

TRY SOME YOURSELF

2(i)   Use your calculator to complete the table of values below.

x	−3	−2	−1·5	−1	−0·5	0	0·5	1	1·5	2	3
$y = x^3$											

(ii)   Use the table to plot the graph of $y = x^3$.

Your graph should be a smooth curve. Make sure there are no bumps or corners.

Write down a suitable key sequence to evaluate $x^3 + x$. Check it by substituting $x = 1$.

TRY SOME YOURSELF

3(i)   (a) Complete the table of values below.

x	−3	−2	−1·5	−1	−0·5	0	0·5	1	1·5	2	3
$y = x^3 + x$											

(b) Use the table to plot the graph of $y = x^3 + x$.

(ii)   Complete the table of values below.

x	−3	−2	−1·5	−1	−0·5	0	0·5	1	1·5	2	3
$y = x^3 - x$											

(b) Use the table to plot the graph of $y = x^3 - x$.

Again, check your key sequence for $x = 1$.

These exercises suggest that a cubic graph may have one of two basic shapes.

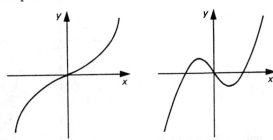

Notice that in both cases the graph crosses to the opposite quadrant. Again, the shapes may be elongated or flattened, turned upside down and moved up or down and left or right.

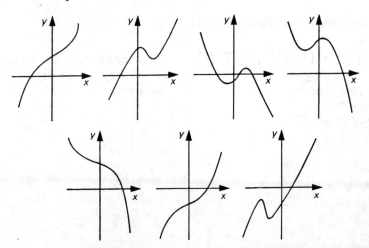

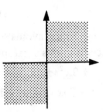

7.3(ii) KEY SEQUENCES FOR MORE COMPLICATED CUBICS

In Section 7.2(ii) we discussed how to evaluate more complicated quadratics using a calculator. The same principle applies to cubic expressions. Once again, it is essential to check your key sequences by substituting easy values, and since some calculators cannot handle powers of negative numbers, you may need to check your sequences for both positive *and* negative numbers.

Try writing down a key sequence for

$$2x^3 + 3x^2 + 4x + 1.$$

Watch out—you may need to use brackets.

Check your key sequence by substituting $x = 1$ and $x = -1$.

$$2(1)^3 + 3(1)^2 + 4(1) + 1 = 10$$
$$2(-1)^3 + 3(-1)^2 + 4(-1) + 1 = -2$$

Don't worry if you aren't successful. It can be difficult to evaluate such expressions and we haven't given an answer because calculators vary so much. To avoid such difficulties it's best to nest the expression.

See Section 7.2(ii).

$2x^3 + 3x^2 + 4x + 1$ can be rewritten as

$$(2x^3 + 3x^2 + 4x) + 1.$$

x can now be taken out of the brackets as a common factor to give

$$x(2x^2 + 3x + 4) + 1$$

or

$$(2x^2 + 3x + 4)x + 1.$$

The process can now be repeated.

$$\begin{aligned}(2x^2 + 3x + 4)x + 1 &= ((2x^2 + 3x) + 4)x + 1 \\ &= (x(2x + 3) + 4)x + 1 \\ &= ((2x + 3)x + 4)x + 1\end{aligned}$$

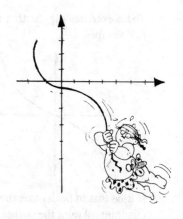

This rearrangement avoids terms involving x^2 and x^3. Notice again that the coefficients correspond.

$$2x^3 + 3x^2 + 4x + 1$$
$$= ((2x + 3)x + 4)x + 1$$

This expression can now be calculated directly from left to right and a possible key sequence is

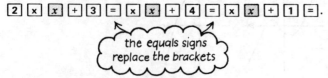

the equals signs replace the brackets

Check the key sequence on your calculator by substituting $x = 1$ and $x = -1$.

Alternatively, using the memory a suitable sequence is

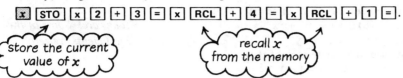

$\boxed{x}$ $\boxed{\text{STO}}$ $\boxed{x}$ $\boxed{2}$ $\boxed{+}$ $\boxed{3}$ $\boxed{=}$ $\boxed{x}$ $\boxed{\text{RCL}}$ $\boxed{+}$ $\boxed{4}$ $\boxed{=}$ $\boxed{x}$ $\boxed{\text{RCL}}$ $\boxed{+}$ $\boxed{1}$ $\boxed{=}$.

store the current value of x

recall x from the memory

TRY SOME YOURSELF

4(i) Work through this key sequence on your calculator substituting:
(a) $x = 1$ (b) $x = -1$.

(ii) Use the key sequence to evaluate $2x^3 + 3x^2 + 4x + 1$ when:
(a) $x = 2$ (b) $x = -0.5$ (c) $x = -0.1321$.

If the key sequence doesn't work check with the maker's handbook; you may need to use brackets.

When an expression is rearranged in this way, notice that one set of brackets nests inside the other; that's why the process is called nesting. Any cubic expression can be nested provided it is first written in the form

$$ax^3 + bx^2 + cx + d.$$

$((2x + 3)x + 4) + 1$

Notice that the powers of x are written in descending order from left to right.

EXAMPLE

(i) Rewrite $2x + x^3 - 3x^2 + 1$ in nested form.

(ii) Evaluate $2x + x^3 - 3x^2 + 1$ when $x = 0.523$.

SOLUTION

(i) $2x + x^3 - 3x^2 + 1 = x^3 - 3x^2 + 2x + 1$
$$= (x^2 - 3x + 2)x + 1$$
$$= ((x - 3)x + 2)x + 1$$

Rewrite the powers in descending order.

Check that the coefficients correspond.

$$x^3 - 3x^2 + 2x + 1$$

$$((x - 3)x + 2)x + 1$$

(ii) A suitable key sequence is

$\boxed{x}$ $\boxed{-}$ $\boxed{3}$ $\boxed{=}$ $\boxed{x}$ $\boxed{x}$ $\boxed{+}$ $\boxed{2}$ $\boxed{=}$ $\boxed{x}$ $\boxed{x}$ $\boxed{+}$ $\boxed{1}$ $\boxed{=}$.

Check the key sequence for $x = 1$.

When $x = 0.523$, $2x + x^3 - 3x^2 + 1 = 1.368$ (to three decimal places).

The expression can be nested even if some of the coefficients are zero.

EXAMPLE

Rewrite $3 - 2x - 4x^3$ in nested form.

SOLUTION

$$3 - 2x - 4x^3 = -4x^3 - 2x + 3$$
$$= (-4x^2 - 2)x + 3$$
$$= ((-4x)x - 2)x + 3$$

In this case it's probably as easy to evaluate $(-4x^2 - 2)x + 3$. Try this for yourself; substitute $x = 1$.

Countdown to Mathematics

TRY SOME YOURSELF

5(i)   Rewrite each of the following expressions in nested form:
    (a) $2x^3 + 3x^2 - 2x - 3$ (b) $2 + x + 2x^2 + 3x^3$
    (c) $2 - x + x^3$ (d) $1 - x^2 - 2x^3$.

(ii)   Write down a key sequence to evaluate each of these
    expressions. Check your key sequences for $x = 1$.

(iii)   Use these key sequences to evaluate:
    (a) $2x^3 + 3x^2 - 2x - 3$ when $x = 0 \cdot 5$
    (b) $2 + x + 2x^2 + 3x^3$ when $x = -0 \cdot 5$
    (c) $2 - x + x^3$ when $x = 4$
    (d) $1 - x^2 - 2x^3$ when $x = -5 \cdot 71$.

*Take care! Some of the
coefficients are zero.*

7.3(iii) PLOTTING GRAPHS OF MORE COMPLICATED CUBICS

Having discussed how to write down key sequences, it should now
be easy to construct a table of values, and so plot the graph of a
cubic.

EXAMPLE

Plot the graph of $y = 2x^3 + 3x^2 + 4x + 1$.

We investigated a key sequence for this expression on page 152.
This gives the following table of values:

x		-2	$-1 \cdot 5$	-1	$-0 \cdot 5$	0	$0 \cdot 5$	1	$1 \cdot 5$
$y = 2x^3 + 3x^2 + 4x + 1$		-11	-5	-2	$-0 \cdot 5$	1	4	10	$20 \cdot 5$

The graph is illustrated below.

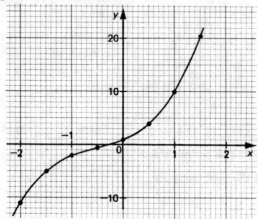

TRY SOME YOURSELF

6(i)   (a) Complete the table of values below for $y = 1 - x^2 - 2x^3$.

x	-2	$-1 \cdot 5$	-1	$-0 \cdot 5$	0	$0 \cdot 5$	1	$1 \cdot 5$	2
y									

    (b) Use the table to plot the graph of $y = 1 - x^2 - 2x^3$.

*Use your solution to
Exercise 5 (i) (d).*

*Plot some more points if you're
not sure about the shape of the
graph.*

(ii) (a) Complete the table of values below for $y = 4x^3 + 8x^2 + x - 3$.

Check your key sequence first, before completing the table.

x	-2·5	-2	-1·5	-1	-0·5	0	0·5	1	1·5
y									

(b) Use the table to plot the graph of $y = 4x^3 + 8x^2 + x - 3$.

Reading values

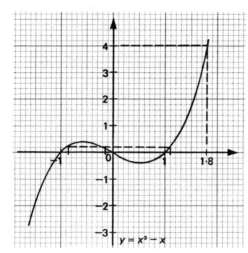

This graph illustrates that some values of y have only one corresponding value of x, whereas other values of y have three corresponding values of x. For example when $y = 4$, $x \simeq 1·8$, but, when $y = 0·2$ there are *three* corresponding values of x; $x \simeq 1·1$, $x \simeq -0·15$ and $x \simeq -0·85$.

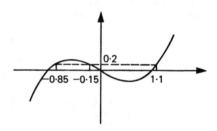

Notice too, that $y = 0·4$ and $y = -0·4$ both have two corresponding values of x.

TRY SOME YOURSELF

7(i) Use your graph of $y = x^3 + x$ (Exercise 3 (i) (b)) to find:
(a) the value of y corresponding to $x = -1·6$
(b) the value of x corresponding to $y = 8$
(c) the values of y which have only one corresponding value of x.
(ii) (a) Use the graph of $y = x^3 - x$ above to find the values of x corresponding to $y = 0$.
(b) Check that these answers are the solutions to $x^3 - x = 0$.

Check your solutions by substituting into the equation.

(iii) Use your graph of $y = 1 - x^2 - 2x^3$ (Exercise 6 (i)) to find the solutions to $1 - x^2 - 2x^3 = 0$.
(iv) Use your graph of $y = 4x^3 + 8x^2 + x - 3$ (Exercise 6 (ii)) to find the solutions to $4x^3 + 8x^2 + x - 3 = 0$.

Thus, a cubic equation may have one solution (for example $x^3 + x = 0$), or it may have three solutions (for example $x^3 - x = 0$).

A cubic equation may also have two solutions. Consider $x^3 - x = 0·4$ and $x^3 - x = -0·4$.

Countdown to Mathematics

Although algebraic methods do exist for the solution of a cubic equation they are very cumbersome. Consequently graphical methods are particularly useful for solving such equations. In fact, provided you can draw the graph, this graphical method can be used to solve any equation.

Remember that the solutions will only be approximations. The level of accuracy depends upon how accurately you draw the graph.

7.3(iv) HYPERBOLAS

In Module 3 we discussed graphs of the form $y = 1/x$. However, at that stage we considered only positive values of x. We now extend the discussion by including negative values.

See Module 3, Section 3.4(iii).

TRY SOME YOURSELF

8(i) Complete the table of values below.

x	-2	-1	$-\frac{1}{2}$	$-\frac{1}{3}$	$-\frac{1}{4}$	$\frac{1}{4}$	$\frac{1}{3}$	$\frac{1}{2}$	1	2
$y = \dfrac{1}{x}$										

(ii) What happens when $x = 0$?

(iii) Use the table to plot the graph of $y = 1/x$.

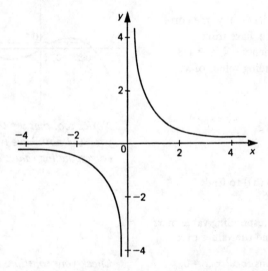

The graph of $y = 1/x$ is a *hyperbola*. Notice that as x gets bigger $1/x$ becomes smaller and smaller, and as x gets closer to zero $1/x$ becomes bigger and bigger. There is a gap in the graph when $x = 0$ because $1/0$ is undefined.

When x is positive 1/x is positive and when x is negative 1/x is negative. The graph therefore falls into two parts, in opposite quadrants.

TRY SOME YOURSELF

9(i) Complete the table of values below.

x		-1	0	1	$1 \cdot 5$	$2 \cdot 5$	3	4	5
$y = \dfrac{1}{(x-2)}$									

(ii) (a) Which value of x satisfies $x - 2 = 0$?

(b) What does this imply for $\dfrac{1}{x-2}$?

(iii) Use parts (i) and (ii) to draw the graph of $y = \dfrac{1}{(x-2)}$.

This exercise suggests that a hyperbola always excludes one value of x. This value of x is obtained by putting the denominator equal to zero.

EXAMPLE

Which value of x should be excluded from

$$y = \frac{1}{2x-1}?$$

SOLUTION

The 'gap' occurs when the denominator is zero.

When $2x - 1 = 0$, $x = \frac{1}{2}$.

Thus $x = \frac{1}{2}$ should be excluded from $y = \dfrac{1}{2x-1}$. This is usually written as

$$y = \frac{1}{2x-1}, \ x \neq \tfrac{1}{2}.$$

TRY SOME YOURSELF

10(i) Which values of x should be excluded from each of the following?

(a) $y = \dfrac{1}{2x}$ (b) $y = \dfrac{2x-1}{2x}$ (c) $y = \dfrac{1}{(x-3)}$.

(ii) Plot each of the following graphs:

(a) $y = \dfrac{1}{2x}$ (x ranging from -4 to 4)

(b) $y = \dfrac{2x-1}{2x}$ (x ranging from -4 to 4)

(c) $y = \dfrac{1}{(x-3)}$ (x ranging from 0 to 6).

All these graphs are hyperbolas. Notice that the graph always falls into two parts.

Since each of the equations has the form

$$\frac{cx + d}{ax + b}$$

one value of x must always be excluded from the graph. The basic shape may be elongated or flattened, turned upside down or moved up or down and left and right.

$ax + b$ is a linear expression, so $ax + b = 0$ has one solution.

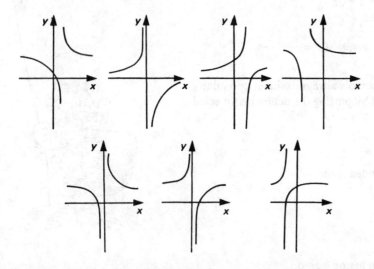

After you have worked through this section you should be able to

a   Nest an expression such as $ax^3 + bx^2 + cx + d$ into the form $((ax + b)x + c)x + d$
b   Write down a key sequence to evaluate an expression of the form $ax^3 + bx^2 + cx + d$
c   Plot the graph of a cubic of the form $y = ax^3 + bx^2 + cx + d$
d   Solve a cubic equation of the form $ax^3 + bx^2 + cx + d = 0$ by plotting the graph of $y = ax^3 + bx^2 + cx + d$
e   Plot the graph of a hyperbola of the form $y = \dfrac{cx + d}{ax + b}$

Finally here are some exercises if you want more practice.

TRY SOME MORE YOURSELF

11(i)   Plot each of the following graphs:
(a) $y = 2x^3 - 3x^2 - x - 1$ (x ranging from -2 to 3)
(b) $y = 2x^3 + 3x^2 - 2x - 3$ (x ranging from -3 to 2)
(c) $y = 2 - x - x^3$ (x ranging from -2 to 2).

(ii)   Use the graphs which you drew in Part (i) to solve each of the following equations:
(a) $2x^3 - 3x^2 - x - 1 = 0$ (b) $2x^3 + 3x^2 - 2x - 3 = 0$
(c) $2 - x - x^3 = 0$.

(iii)   Plot each of the following graphs:
(a) $y = -\dfrac{1}{x}$ (x ranging from -4 to 4)

(b) $y = -\dfrac{2}{x + 1}$ (x ranging from -4 to 2)   (c) $y = \dfrac{2x + 1}{2x - 1}$ (x ranging from -4 to 4).

7.4 Solving Equations

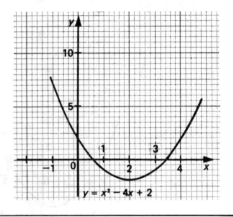
7.4(i) SOLVING SEVERAL EQUATIONS FROM THE SAME GRAPH

In Sections 7.2(iii) and 7.3(iii) we indicated that an equation can be solved by drawing the corresponding graph and reading off the x-co-ordinates of the points where the graph cuts the x-axis.

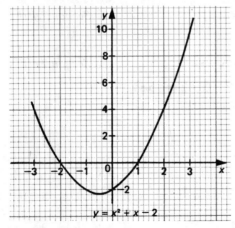

For example, from this graph the solutions to
$$x^2 + x - 2 = 0$$
are $x = -2$ and $x = 1$.

The process of solving an equation from a graph can be extended, and in fact the same graph can be used to solve a whole family of equations.

159

Consider the equation

$$x^2 + x - 3 = 0.$$

Notice that the left hand side of this equation is almost the same as $x^2 + x - 2$. With some manipulation the equation can be rearranged to give

$$x^2 + x - 2 = 1.$$

Add 1 to both sides of $x^2 + x - 3 = 0$, to get $x^2 + x - 3(+1) = 1$.

The solutions to $x^2 + x - 2 = 1$ can now be read directly from the graph of $y = x^2 + x - 2$.

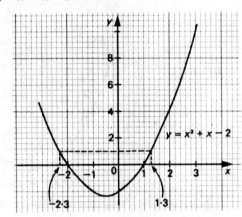

When $y = 1$, $x \simeq -2 \cdot 3$ and $x \simeq 1 \cdot 3$.

Thus, the solutions to $x^2 + x - 3 = 0$ are $x \simeq -2 \cdot 3$ and $x \simeq 1 \cdot 3$.

*Check by substituting $x = 1 \cdot 3$ and $x = -2 \cdot 3$ into $x^2 + x - 3 = 0$. Remember that these are **approximate** solutions so there will be some error.*

CHECK YOUR ANSWERS

1 $x^2 - 4x - 2 = 0$ is equivalent to $x^2 - 4x + 2 = 4$.

From the graph, when $y = 4$, $x \simeq -0 \cdot 5$ or $x \simeq 4 \cdot 5$.

Section 7.4(i)

2 $x^2 - 3x - 1 = 0$ is equivalent to $x^2 - 4x + 2 = 3 - x$.

Draw the line $y = 3 - x$ on the graph of $y = x^2 - 4x + 2$ and read off the x-co-ordinates of the points of intersection to get $x \simeq -0 \cdot 3$ or $x \simeq 3 \cdot 3$.

Section 7.4(ii)

3

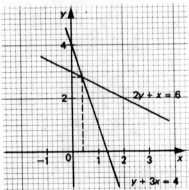

From the graph the solutions are $x \simeq 0 \cdot 4$ and $y \simeq 2 \cdot 8$.

Section 7.4(iii)

The same process can be used to solve the following equations:

$$x^2 + x - 6 = 0$$
$$x^2 + x - 4 = 0$$
$$x^2 + x = 0,$$

since

$x^2 + x - 6 = 0$ is equivalent to $x^2 + x - 2 = 4$ *(add 4 to both sides)*

$x^2 + x - 4 = 0$ is equivalent to $x^2 + x - 2 = 2$ *(add 2 to both sides)*

$x^2 + x = 0$ is equivalent to $x^2 + x - 2 = -2.$ *(subtract 2 from both sides)*

TRY SOME YOURSELF

1   Use the graph of $y = x^2 + x - 2$ to solve each of the following equations:
(i) $x^2 + x - 6 = 0$ (ii) $x^2 + x - 4 = 0$ (iii) $x^2 + x = 0.$

Check your solutions by substituting into the original equation.

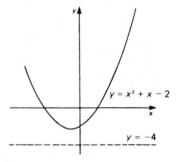

The equation $x^2 + x + 2 = 0$ is equivalent to $x^2 + x - 2 = -4$.

However, when $y = -4$ there are no corresponding values of x.
This means that there are no solutions to $x^2 + x + 2 = 0$.

Check this for yourself algebraically.

In fact the graph just touches the line $y = -2 \cdot 25$. This means that
the equation

$$x^2 + x - 2 = -2 \cdot 25$$

has one solution. From the graph, the solution is $x = -0 \cdot 5$.

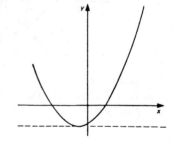

TRY SOME YOURSELF

2(i)   Use an algebraic method to show that $x^2 + x - 2 = -2\frac{1}{4}$ has only one root.

See Module 6, Section 6.5(i).

(ii)   (a) Plot the graph of $y = x^2 - 5x + 2$.
     (b) Use your graph to solve $x^2 - 5x - 6 = 0$.
     (c) For which value of a does the line $y = a$ touch the graph of
        $y = x^2 - 5x + 2$ only once?
     (d) Find the solution to $x^2 - 5x + 2 = a$ for the value of a
        obtained in Part (c).

Check your solution algebraically.

This method depends on recognising the similarity between the equation you wish to solve and the equation of the graph. You must then rearrange the equation so that values can be read directly from the graph. At this stage it is easy to make mistakes in the algebraic manipulation, so you should always check your working.

Remember that in order to preserve the balance, whatever you do to one side of the equation you must do to the other.

7.4(ii) EXTENDING THE PROCESS

The graph of $y = x^2 + x - 2$ can be used to solve a wide range of equations.

Consider

$$x^2 - x - 2 = 0.$$

Adding $2x$ to both sides gives

$$x^2 + x - 2 = 2x.$$

The left hand side is similar but it contains the term $(-x)$ rather than $(+x)$.

This suggests that the solutions to $x^2 - x - 2 = 0$ are given by the x-co-ordinates of the points where the graph of $y = x^2 + x - 2$ cuts the line $y = 2x$.

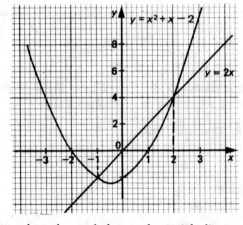

The points where the parabola cuts the straight line are called the *points of intersection*. The x-co-ordinates of these points are $x = 2$ and $x = -1$.

Check algebraically that $x = 2$ and $x = -1$ satisfy
$$x^2 + x - 2 = 2x$$
and
$$x^2 - x - 2 = 0.$$

EXAMPLE

Use the graph of $y = x^2 + x - 2$ to solve $x^2 + 3x - 4 = 0$.

SOLUTION

$x^2 + 3x - 4 = 0$ is equivalent to $x^2 + x - 2 = -2x + 2$.

Thus the solutions to $x^2 + 3x - 4 = 0$ are given by the
x-co-ordinates of the points of intersection of the graph of
$y = x^2 + x - 2$ and the graph of $y = -2x + 2$.

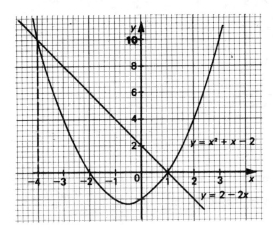

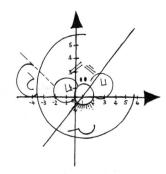

From the graph, the solutions are $x = -4$ and $x = 1$.

*Check by substituting $x = -4$ and
$x = 1$ into $x^2 + 3x - 4 = 0$.*

TRY SOME YOURSELF

3(i) Plot the graph of $y = x^2 + 2x - 2$ (x ranging from -4 to $+3$).
(ii) From your graph, write down the solutions to $x^2 + 2x - 2 = 0$.
(iii) Rearrange the equation $x^2 + x - 2 = 0$ into the form
      $x^2 + 2x - 2 = mx$.
(iv) Hence use the graph of $y = x^2 + 2x - 2$ to solve $x^2 + x - 2 = 0$.
(v)   Use the graph of $y = x^2 + 2x - 2$ to solve:
      (a) $x^2 + 3x - 2 = 0$ (b) $x^2 + x - 3 = 0$.

*Find the value of m.
Check your solutions by
substituting into the equation.*

We've illustrated this graphical technique with quadratic equations
so that you can check the solutions algebraically, but the same
process can be applied to the solution of cubics and more complicated equations. Remember though that these solutions can only
be approximations dependent upon the accuracy of the scales used
to draw the graphs.

7.4(iii) GRAPHICAL METHODS OF SOLVING SIMULTANEOUS EQUATIONS

Two equations are called *simultaneous equations* if they are to be
solved simultaneously. This means that a solution to one equation
must also satisfy the other equation. For example

$$\begin{cases} y = x + 3 \\ y = 2x + 2 \end{cases}$$

are simultaneous equations. The solution must satisfy both
equations at the same time. This means finding values of x and y
so that both equations are true. One way of solving the equations
is to draw their graphs.

*Simultaneous equations are often
bracketed together like this.*

*Because both equations are linear,
these equations are called
simultaneous **linear** equations.*

Both $y = x + 3$ and $y = 2x + 2$ are equations of straight lines.

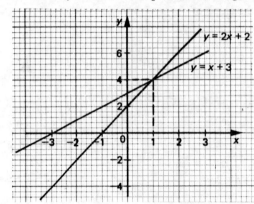

Any point on the line $y = x + 3$ satisfies this equation $y = x + 3$.

For example, (0, 3) lies on $y = x + 3$ and (0, 2) lies on $y = 2x + 2$.

Similarly any point on the line $y = 2x + 2$ satisfies the equation $y = 2x + 2$.

Notice that there is one point which lies on both lines, namely the point of intersection (1, 4).

Thus, when $x = 1, x + 3 = 4$

and when $x = 1, 2x + 2 = 4$.

Hence $x = 1, y = 4$ is a solution to both $y = x + 3$ and $y = 2x + 2$. In other words $x = 1, y = 4$ is the solution to the simultaneous equations

$$\begin{cases} y = x + 3 \\ y = 2x + 2. \end{cases}$$

$x = 1$ and $y = 4$ satisfy both equations simultaneously.

Indeed, the solution to any pair of linear simultaneous equations, is given by the co-ordinates of the point of intersection. Notice that the solution comprises an x-value *and* a y-value, so *both* co-ordinates are needed.

EXAMPLE

Solve the simultaneous equations
$$\begin{cases} 3y = 2x + 6 \\ 2y = 6 - 3x. \end{cases}$$

SOLUTION

$3y = 2x + 6$ and $2y = 6 - 3x$ are linear equations, so their graphs are straight lines.

Since they are straight lines, we only need to plot three points for each graph.

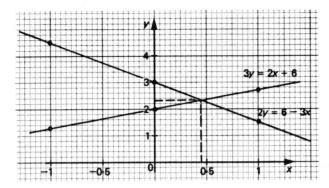

The solution to

$$\begin{cases} 3y = 2x + 6 \\ 2y = 6 - 3x \end{cases}$$

is given by the co-ordinates of the point of intersection.

From the graph this is the point $(0{\cdot}45, 2{\cdot}3)$. Hence the solution is $x \simeq 0{\cdot}45, y \simeq 2{\cdot}3$.

Check the solutions by substituting. Remember that they are approximations, so there will be some error.

TRY SOME YOURSELF

4(i) (a) Plot the graphs of $y = 3x + 4$ and $y = x - 2$ on the same diagram (x ranging from -4 to 2).
      (b) Use your graphs to solve the simultaneous equations
$$\begin{cases} y = 3x + 4 \\ y = x - 2. \end{cases}$$

(ii) Use a graphical method to solve the simultaneous equations
$$\begin{cases} y + 4x = 3 \\ 2y - 2x = 1. \end{cases}$$

(iii) Use a graphical method to solve the simultaneous equations
$$\begin{cases} 3y - 2x + 1 = 0 \\ 2y + x + 3 = 0. \end{cases}$$

Check your solutions by substituting back into the equations.

Take care, you will need to ensure that the point of inter-section lies on your diagram.

Two straight lines cannot intersect at more than one point. Consequently two simultaneous linear equations have at most one solution.

If two lines do not intersect at all, then the corresponding simultaneous equations do not have a solution. For example
$$\begin{cases} y = x + 2 \\ y = x + 3 \end{cases}$$

correspond to two parallel lines. Since the lines are parallel they never meet.

See Module 5, Section 5.2(iv).

Hence the simultaneous equations

$$\begin{cases} y = x + 2 \\ y = x + 3 \end{cases}$$

have no solution.

Simultaneous equations do not necessarily have to be linear.

$$\begin{cases} y = x^2 - 4 \\ y = 2 - x \end{cases}$$

are two simultaneous equations. Since $y = x^2 - 4$ is a quadratic, it seems likely that there will be two solutions. The graphs of $y = x^2 - 4$ and $y = 2 - x$ are illustrated below.

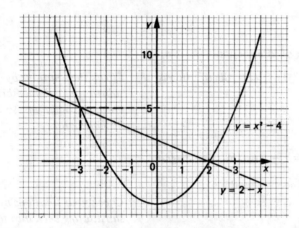

There are two points of intersection, $(-3, 5)$ and $(2, 0)$.

Thus $x = -3, y = 5$ and $x = 2, y = 0$ are solutions to the simultaneous equations

$$\begin{cases} y = x^2 - 4 \\ y = 2 - x. \end{cases}$$

You can check this algebraically.

Since $y = x^2 - 4$ and $y = 2 - x$,

$$y = x^2 - 4 = 2 - x$$

or

$$x^2 + x - 6 = 0.$$

The values of x satisfy a quadratic equation.

This equation factorises into

$$(x - 2)(x + 3) = 0$$

which has solutions $x = 2$ and $x = -3$.

Now, when $x = 2, y = 0$
and when $x = -3, y = 5$.

Notice that the algebraic method gives exact solutions.

TRY SOME YOURSELF

5(i) (a) Plot the line $2y = 3x + 1$ on the graph of $y = x^2 - 4$ above.
      (b) Hence solve the simultaneous equations

$$\begin{cases} y = x^2 - 4 \\ 2y = 3x + 1. \end{cases}$$

Check your answers by substituting.

Make sure that both points of intersection lie on your diagram.

(ii) (a) Plot the graphs of $y = x^2$ and $y = x + 2$ on the same diagram.
      (b) Hence solve the simultaneous equations

$$\begin{cases} y = x^2 \\ y = x + 2. \end{cases}$$

Check your solutions by substituting.

(iii) Use a graphical method to solve the simultaneous equations

$$\begin{cases} y = x^2 - x - 2 \\ y = 3 + x. \end{cases}$$

Again, there may be situations where the two graphs do not intersect at all.

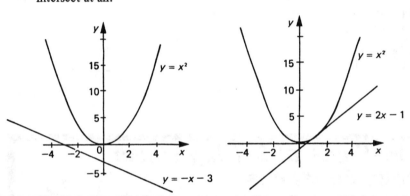

The simultaneous equations

$$\begin{cases} y = x^2 \\ y = -x - 3 \end{cases}$$

have no solution since their graphs do not intersect.

Consider the quadratic equation in x,

$$x^2 = -x - 3,$$

or $x^2 + x + 3 = 0$.

Check algebraically that this equation has no solutions.

The simultaneous equations

$$\begin{cases} y = x^2 \\ y = 2x - 1 \end{cases}$$

have one solution since the line $y = 2x - 1$ just touches the graph of $y = x^2$.

Consider the equation

$$x^2 = 2x - 1$$

or $x^2 - 2x + 1 = 0$.

This factorises into

$$(x - 1)^2 = 0.$$

> **After you have worked through this section you should be able to**
>
> a Use the graph of one equation to solve a series of related equations, by drawing suitable straight lines and finding the x-co-ordinates of the points of intersection
> b Solve two simultaneous equations by drawing their graphs and finding the co-ordinates of the points of intersection
> c Appreciate that two simultaneous equations have no solution if their graphs do not intersect at all

Finally here are some exercises if you want more practice.

TRY SOME MORE YOURSELF

6(i) Plot the graph of $y = x^2 - 5x + 2$ and so solve:
(a) $x^2 - 5x + 4 = 0$ (b) $x^2 - 3x + 2 = 0$ (c) $x^2 - 3x + 4 = 0$.

(ii) Use a graphical method to solve each of the following pairs of simultaneous equations:

(a) $\begin{cases} y = x + 1 \\ y = 2x - 4 \end{cases}$ (b) $\begin{cases} 2y = 3x + 4 \\ y = 9 - 2x \end{cases}$

(c) $\begin{cases} 2y - 3x = 2 \\ 4y - 6x = 8 \end{cases}$ (d) $\begin{cases} y = x^2 + 2x - 2 \\ y = x + 1. \end{cases}$

7.5 Algebraic Methods of Solving Linear Simultaneous Equations

> *TRY THESE QUESTIONS FIRST*
>
> 1 Use an algebraic method to solve the simultaneous equations
> $\begin{cases} x + 2y = 7 & \boxed{1} \\ x - 4y = 13 & \boxed{2}. \end{cases}$
>
> 2 Use an algebraic method to solve the simultaneous equations
> $\begin{cases} 2a - 6b = 4 & \boxed{1} \\ 5a + 4b = 7 & \boxed{2}. \end{cases}$
>
> 3 Solve the simultaneous equations
> $\begin{cases} 2x - 3y = 1 & \boxed{1} \\ 6x - 9y = 3 & \boxed{2}. \end{cases}$

7.5(i) SUBSTITUTION

In the last section we discussed how to solve two simultaneous equations by drawing the graphs and finding the co-ordinates of the point(s) of intersection. If the graphs do not intersect at all, then the two equations have no solution. Thus, this graphical approach provides a visual explanation of the principles involved in solving simultaneous equations.

The equations do not necessarily have to be linear.

However, one of the difficulties in using graphical methods to solve simultaneous equations is ensuring that the point of intersection actually lies on your diagram. Also, a graphical solution is often not sufficiently accurate, since it depends completely upon the accuracy of the scales used for the axes.

This often involves adjusting the range of values of x.

In this section we investigate *algebraic methods* of solving *simultaneous linear equations*. These methods are probably more efficient and are certainly more accurate than using the graphs, since they are based upon the manipulation of the equations themselves. We begin an investigation of the *method of substitution* by considering the equations

$$\begin{cases} y - 3x = 1 & \boxed{1} \\ y + 2x = 11 & \boxed{2}. \end{cases}$$

The equations are numbered for easy reference later on.

This algebraic method relies on the fact that the values of x and y which satisfy equation $\boxed{1}$ are exactly the same values which satisfy equation $\boxed{2}$.

The two equations can be rearranged so that y is isolated on the left hand side.

$$\begin{cases} y = 1 + 3x & \boxed{3} \\ y = 11 - 2x & \boxed{4}. \end{cases}$$

Again, the equations are labelled for easy reference.

Since the values of y in equations $\boxed{3}$ and $\boxed{4}$ must be the same we can substitute $y = 11 - 2x$ into equation $\boxed{3}$ to get

$$11 - 2x = 1 + 3x$$

or $10 - 5x = 0.$

The solution to this equation is $x = 2$.

The value of x can now be substituted back into equation $\boxed{1}$ to give the corresponding value of y

$$y - (3 \times 2) = 1$$

so

$$y = 7.$$

We could substitute into any of equations $\boxed{1}$, $\boxed{2}$, $\boxed{3}$ or $\boxed{4}$, although as a general rule it is best to substitute into one of the original equations.

The solution $x = 2, y = 7$ can now be checked by substituting into equation $\boxed{2}$.

$$y + 2x = 7 + 2(2) = 11.$$

Hence the solution is $x = 2, y = 7$.

You should always check the solution by substituting into the other original equation.

This example was straightforward since it was easy to rearrange each
equation into the form

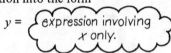

$$y = \text{expression involving } x \text{ only.}$$

The next example involves a little more manipulation.

EXAMPLE

Solve the simultaneous equations

$$\begin{cases} 2y - 3x = 4 & \boxed{1} \\ y + 2x = 9 & \boxed{2}. \end{cases}$$

SOLUTION

The first step is to isolate one of the variables. Again we will choose
to isolate y. The equations then become

*This is an arbitrary choice. We
could choose to isolate x.*

$$2y = 4 + 3x \qquad \boxed{3}$$
$$y = 9 - 2x \qquad \boxed{4}.$$

Notice that in this case, the left hand side of equation $\boxed{3}$ is $2y$
whereas the left hand side of equation $\boxed{4}$ is y. In order to
substitute as before, the left hand side of both equations must
be the same. We can remedy this by multiplying equation $\boxed{4}$ by
2 giving equation $\boxed{5}$. Now consider equations $\boxed{3}$ and $\boxed{5}$

$y = 9 - 2x$, so
$2y = 2(9 - 2x)$, or
$2y = 18 - 4x$.

$$2y = 4 + 3x \qquad \boxed{3}$$
$$2y = 18 - 4x \qquad \boxed{5}.$$

We can now substitute $2y = 18 - 4x$ into equation $\boxed{3}$ to get

$$18 - 4x = 4 + 3x$$

or $\quad 14 - 7x = 0.$

The solution to this equation is $x = 2$.

Substituting $x = 2$ into equation $\boxed{2}$ gives

$$y + 2(2) = 9$$

so $\quad y = 5.$

*This time it's easier to
substitute into equation $\boxed{2}$.*

We now check the solution by substituting into equation $\boxed{1}$.

$$2y - 3x = 2(5) - 3(2) = 4.$$

Hence the solution is $x = 2$, $y = 5$.

The method of substitution can be summarised as follows.

---

1 Isolate one of the variables on one side of the equation

2 Ensure that the coefficient of the isolated variable is exactly the same in both equations. This may involve multiplying one or both equations.

3 Obtain an equation by equating the 'non isolated' sides of both equations

4 Solve this equation to find the value of one variable

5 Substitute back into one of the original equations to find the required value of the other variable

6 Check your solution by substituting into the other original equation

It doesn't matter which variable you isolate as long as it's the same in both equations.

EXAMPLE

Solve the simultaneous equations

$$\begin{cases} 2x - 3y = 5 & \boxed{1} \\ 3x + 2y = 14 & \boxed{2} \end{cases}$$

SOLUTION

Isolate y.   *Step 1*

$$3y = 2x - 5 \qquad \boxed{3}$$
$$2y = 14 - 3x \qquad \boxed{4}.$$

Multiply equation $\boxed{3}$ by 2 and multiply equation $\boxed{4}$ by 3 to give   *Step 2:*
Make the term involving y the same in both equations.

$$6y = 4x - 10 \qquad \boxed{5}$$
$$6y = 42 - 9x \qquad \boxed{6}.$$

Substitute $6y = 42 - 9x$ into equation $\boxed{5}$.   *Step 3*

$$42 - 9x = 4x - 10$$

so $\quad 52 = 13x.$

The solution to this equation is $x = 4$.   *Step 4*

Substitute $x = 4$ into equation $\boxed{1}$.   *Step 5*

$$8 - 3y = 5$$

so $\quad y = 1.$

Check by substituting into equation $\boxed{2}$ *Step 6*

$$3x + 2y = 3(4) + 2(1) = 14.$$

Hence the solution is $x = 4$, $y = 1$.

TRY SOME YOURSELF

1   Use the same method to solve each of the following pairs of
simultaneous equations:

(i) $\begin{cases} y - 2x = 4 & \boxed{1} \\ y + x = 7 & \boxed{2} \end{cases}$ (ii) $\begin{cases} 3y - 4x = 1 & \boxed{1} \\ 2y + x = 8 & \boxed{2} \end{cases}$

(iii) $\begin{cases} 2a - 3b = 2 & \boxed{1} \\ 4a + 6b = 4 & \boxed{2} \end{cases}$ (iv) $\begin{cases} 6w + 3t = 1 & \boxed{1} \\ 4w - 5t = 5 & \boxed{2} \end{cases}$.

7.5(ii) ELIMINATION

We now introduce an alternative method for solving linear
simultaneous equations. It is very similar to the method of
substitution and we include it here so that you have a choice.
We describe this alternative approach by working through the
same examples again.

*Since the approaches are
similar you should use the
method which suits you best.*

EXAMPLE

Solve the simultaneous equations

$$\begin{cases} y - 3x = 1 & \boxed{1} \\ y + 2x = 11 & \boxed{2} \end{cases}.$$

SOLUTION

We can *eliminate* the term involving y by subtracting equation $\boxed{1}$
from equation $\boxed{2}$. This gives

$$2x - (-3x) = 11 - 1$$

or $5x = 10$.

The solution to this equation is $x = 2$.

The method is now exactly the same as before. Substituting $x = 2$
into equation $\boxed{1}$ gives

$$y - 3(2) = 1$$

so $y = 7$.

We now check the solution by substituting into equation $\boxed{2}$.

$$y + 2x = 7 + 2(2) = 11.$$

Hence the solution is $x = 2, y = 7$.

In order to eliminate one of the variables the coefficient of that
variable must be the same in both equations. Again this may involve
multiplying one or both equations.

*This involves subtracting the left
hand side of equation $\boxed{1}$ from
the left hand side of equation $\boxed{2}$,
so $y - y = 0$. To preserve the
balance we must also subtract
the right hand side of equation $\boxed{1}$
from the right hand side of
equation $\boxed{2}$.*

EXAMPLE

Solve the simultaneous equations

$$\begin{cases} 2y - 3x = 4 & \boxed{1} \\ y + 2x = 9 & \boxed{2} \end{cases}.$$

SOLUTION

We choose to eliminate y.

However, in equation $\boxed{1}$ the coefficient of y is 2 and in equation $\boxed{2}$ the coefficient of y is 1. In order to eliminate y, the coefficients must be the same. This suggests that we need to multiply equation $\boxed{2}$ by 2. This gives

$$2y - 3x = 4 \qquad \boxed{1}$$
$$2y + 4x = 18 \qquad \boxed{3}.$$

Again, we could have chosen to eliminate x, but it is probably easier to eliminate y.

Now we can subtract equation $\boxed{3}$ from equation $\boxed{1}$ to get

$$-3x - 4x = 4 - 18$$

so $\quad -7x = -14.$

The solution to this equation is $x = 2$.

Substituting $x = 2$ into equation $\boxed{2}$ gives

$$y + 2(2) = 9$$

so $\quad y = 5.$

The coefficient of y is now the same in both equations so y can be eliminated by subtracting one equation from the other. See what happens if you subtract equation $\boxed{1}$ from $\boxed{3}$.

We now check the solution by substituting into equation $\boxed{1}$

$$2y - 3x = 2(5) - 3(2) = 4.$$

Hence the solution is $x = 2$, $y = 5$.

If the coefficients of a variable involve the same number in both equations but the *signs* are different, then that variable can be eliminated by *adding* the equations.

EXAMPLE

Solve the simultaneous equations

$$\begin{cases} 2x - 3y = 5 & \boxed{1} \\ 3x + 2y = 14 & \boxed{2}. \end{cases}$$

SOLUTION

We choose to eliminate the term involving y.

Multiply equation $\boxed{1}$ by 2 and multiply equation $\boxed{2}$ by 3 to get

$$\begin{cases} 4x - 6y = 10 & \boxed{3} \\ 9x + 6y = 42 & \boxed{4}. \end{cases}$$

The number 6 is the same in both cases but the signs are different.

Notice that equation $\boxed{3}$ contains the term $-6y$. If the equations are added, $6y + (-6y) = 0$, so y will be eliminated.

Add equation $\boxed{3}$ to equation $\boxed{4}$.

$$4x + 9x = 10 + 42$$

so $\quad 13x = 52.$

The solution to this equation is $x = 4$.

Substituting $x = 4$ into equation $\boxed{1}$,

$$2(4) - 3y = 5$$

so $\quad y = 1$.

The solution $x = 4$, $y = 1$ can now be checked by substituting into equation $\boxed{2}$.

The method of elimination can be summarised as follows:

1 Decide which variable you want to eliminate

2 Ensure that the coefficient of the term involving this variable is the same in both equations. This may involve multiplication of one or both equations
   The coefficients may have different signs.

3 Eliminate the variable by addition or subtraction of one equation to/from the other
   Subtract if the signs are the same. Add if the signs are different.

4 Solve the resulting equation to find the value of one variable

5 Substitute back into one of the original equations to find the required value of the other variable

6 Check your solution by substituting into the other original equation

TRY SOME YOURSELF

2 Use this method to solve each of the following pairs of simultaneous equations:

(i) $\begin{cases} x + 3y = 3 & \boxed{1} \\ x - y = 7 & \boxed{2} \end{cases}$

(ii) $\begin{cases} 2a - 3b = 2 & \boxed{1} \\ 3a + 6b = 24 & \boxed{2} \end{cases}$

(iii) $\begin{cases} 4x + 2y = 5 & \boxed{1} \\ 3x - 4y = 1 & \boxed{2} \end{cases}$

(iv) $\begin{cases} 5t + 4w = 40 & \boxed{1} \\ 9t - 7w = 1 & \boxed{2} \end{cases}$.

Thus, algebraic methods provide a systematic and reliable way of solving simultaneous linear equations. The solutions can be given in terms of fractions, which means that they are exact. The process can be extended to non-linear equations although the algebra becomes more complicated.

Nevertheless, the graphical approach is also worthwhile because it enables you to visualise what is happening. It also provides an explanation for situations where there are no solutions.

7.5(iii) NO SOLUTION?

In Section 7.4(iii) we gave a graphical interpretation of the situation where the simultaneous equations have no solution. We now consider an algebraic explanation. We will attempt to solve the following equations by elimination.

$$\begin{cases} y = x + 2 & \boxed{1} \\ y = x + 3 & \boxed{2} \end{cases}$$

We choose to eliminate y. Since the coefficient of y is the same in both equations we can immediately subtract equation $\boxed{2}$ from equation $\boxed{1}$. Hence

$$\begin{aligned} y - y &= x + 2 - (x + 3) \\ &= (x - x) + (2 - 3). \end{aligned}$$

Thus

$$0 = -1.$$

This, of course, is nonsense. By eliminating one variable we have also eliminated the other variable.

When the algebra leads to an impossible situation such as this, it means that the simultaneous equations have no solution.

So, algebraic methods allow you to deduce that the equations have no solution, but, although the algebra produces the result, it does not explain *why*. The graphical approach provides this explanation.

There is another situation which lends itself to similar analysis.

In Section 7.4(iii) we showed that these equations correspond to parallel lines, so there is no point of intersection.

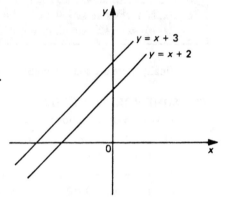

EXAMPLE

Solve the simultaneous equations

$$\begin{cases} x + y = 2 & \boxed{1} \\ 2x + 2y = 4 & \boxed{2}. \end{cases}$$

SOLUTION

We choose to eliminate x. To ensure that the coefficients are the same we must multiply equation $\boxed{1}$ by 2. This gives

$$\begin{aligned} 2x + 2y &= 4 & \boxed{3} \\ 2x + 2y &= 4 & \boxed{4}. \end{aligned}$$

But equation $\boxed{3}$ is exactly the same as equation $\boxed{4}$, so if we subtract one from the other *everything* is eliminated.

Again, the algebra produces the result but it does not offer any explanation.

This is provided by the graphs.

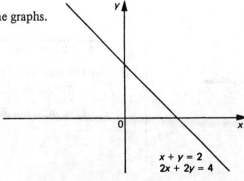

This diagram shows that

$$x + y = 2 \text{ and } 2x + 2y = 4$$

have exactly the same graph. The lines coincide exactly. Thus *any* point on the line gives a solution.

For example $x = 1$, $y = 1$ is a solution; so is $x = 2$, $y = 0$, and $x = 3$, $y = -1$ and so on.

In fact there are an infinite number of solutions.

Thus, if the equations represent the same straight line then there is no single solution.

If the graphs coincide then there is a whole family of solutions.

After you have worked through this section you should be able to

a Solve two simultaneous linear equations using the method of substitution
b Solve two simultaneous equations using the method of elimination
c Explain why two simultaneous linear equations have no solution
d Explain why two simultaneous linear equations have an infinite number of solutions

---

Finally, here are some exercises if you want more practice.

TRY SOME MORE YOURSELF

3 Solve each of the following pairs of simultaneous equations:

(i) $\begin{cases} 2x + 7y = 10 \\ 3x + 5y = 4 \end{cases}$ (ii) $\begin{cases} 3x + 3y - 12 = 0 \\ 3x - 3y - 6 = 0 \end{cases}$

(iii) $\begin{cases} 3a + 7b - 15 = 0 \\ 4a + b - 20 = 0 \end{cases}$ (iv) $\begin{cases} 6x + 4y = 2 \\ 9x - 5y = 16 \end{cases}$

(v) $\begin{cases} 2t - 4w = 8 \\ t - 2w = 3 \end{cases}$ (vi) $\begin{cases} 3b - c + 1 = 0 \\ 9b - 3c + 3 = 0. \end{cases}$

Section 7.1 Solutions

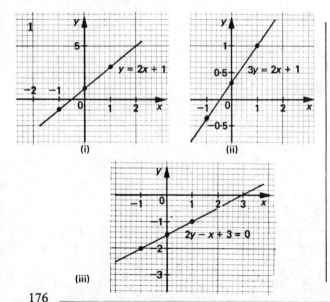

1

(i)

(ii)

(iii)

2
(i)

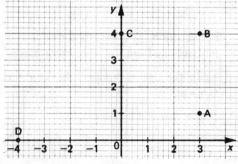

(ii) (a) The gradient of BC (or CB)
$$= \frac{\text{Rise from C to B}}{\text{Run from C to B}} = \frac{0}{3} = 0.$$
Thus BC is horizontal.

(b) The gradient of BD (or DB)

$= \dfrac{\text{Rise from D to B}}{\text{Run from D to B}} = \dfrac{4}{7}.$

(c) The gradient of AC (or CA)

$= \dfrac{\text{Rise from C to A}}{\text{Run from C to A}} = -\dfrac{3}{3} = -1.$

3

(i) The gradient of LM

$= \dfrac{\text{Rise from L to M}}{\text{Run from L to M}} = \dfrac{4}{2} = 2.$

(ii) The gradient of MN

$= \dfrac{\text{Rise from M to N}}{\text{Run from M to N}} = \dfrac{6}{3} = 2.$

(iii) LM and MN have the same gradient. This shows that the points L, M and N lie on the same line. This is illustrated by the diagram below.

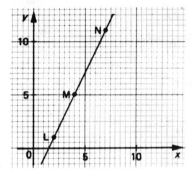

4

(i) From the graph the gradient is
$\dfrac{(-4) - 2}{0 - 2} = \dfrac{-6}{-2} = 3$, and the y-intercept is
$y = -4$.
Hence the equation is $y = 3x - 4$.

(ii) From the graph the gradient is
$\dfrac{4 - (-1)}{0 - 1} = \dfrac{5}{-1} = -5$, and the y-intercept is
$y = 4$.
Hence the equation is $y = -5x + 4$.

(iii) From the graph the gradient is
$\dfrac{1 - (-3)}{-1 - 1} = \dfrac{4}{-2} = -2$, and the y-intercept is
$y = -1$.
Hence the equation is $y = -2x - 1$.

5

(i) (a) The gradient is $\frac{2}{3}$ and the y-intercept is 6.

(b) Rearrange the equation first to get
$y = \frac{3}{2}x - 3$.
Hence the gradient is $\frac{3}{2}$ and the y-intercept is -3.

(c) The gradient is a and the y-intercept is b.

(d) Rearrange the equation first.
$ax + by + c = 0$
so
$by = -ax - c$
and
$y = -\dfrac{a}{b}x - \dfrac{c}{b}.$
Hence the gradient is $-\dfrac{a}{b}$ and the y-intercept is $-\dfrac{c}{b}.$

(e) Rearrange the equation first.
$lx - \dfrac{y}{p} = 1$
so
$\dfrac{y}{p} = lx - 1$
and
$y = plx - p.$
Hence the gradient is pl and the y-intercept is $-p$.

(ii) (a) $y = 0(x) + c$, or $y = c$.
(b) $y = mx + 0$, or $y = mx$.
(c) $y = mx + c$.

6

(i)
(ii)

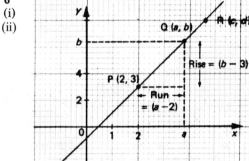

(iii) The gradient of PQ
$= \dfrac{\text{Rise from P to Q}}{\text{Run from P to Q}} = \dfrac{b - 3}{a - 2}.$

(iv) The gradient of the line joining Q and R is obtained in the same way. It is given by the difference between the y-co-ordinates divided by the difference between the x-co-ordinates. Hence,
the gradient of QR $= \dfrac{b - d}{a - c}$ or $\dfrac{d - b}{c - a}.$

7

(i)

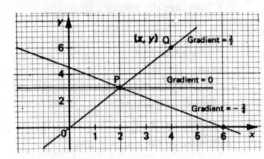

(ii) (a) The gradient of PQ $= \dfrac{y-3}{x-2}$.

(b) Since the gradients are equal, $\dfrac{y-3}{x-2} = \dfrac{3}{2}$.

Hence $y - 3 = \frac{3}{2}(x - 2)$

and $y = \frac{3}{2}(x - 2) + 3$

or $y = \frac{3}{2}x$.

(c) The diagram above shows that the line PQ passes through $(0, 0)$ with gradient $\frac{3}{2}$.

(iii) (a) The equation is given by

$\dfrac{y-3}{y-2} = -\dfrac{3}{4}$.

Hence $(y - 3) = -\frac{3}{4}(x - 2)$

so $y = -\frac{3}{4}x + \frac{9}{2}$.

As a check, the diagram above shows that the line with gradient $-\frac{3}{4}$ has y-intercept $\hat{=} 4\frac{1}{2}$.

(b) The equation is given by

$\dfrac{y-3}{x-2} = 0$.

Hence $y - 3 = 0$, or $y = 3$.

As a check, the diagram above confirms that $y = 3$ passes through $(2, 3)$ with gradient 0.

8

(i) AB has gradient $\dfrac{7-1}{5-2} = \dfrac{6}{3} = 2$.

(ii) (a) AQ has gradient $\dfrac{y-1}{x-2}$.

(b) Since the gradients are equal

$\dfrac{y-1}{x-2} = 2$.

Hence $y - 1 = 2(x - 2)$ or $y = 2x - 3$.

(c) A is the point $(2, 1)$. Substituting into the right hand side of the equation, $2(2) - 3 = 1$ (= left hand side). Thus A lies on $y = 2x - 3$. Similarly, $2(5) - 3 = 7$, so B $(5, 7)$ lies on the line.

(d) When $x = 19$, $2(19) - 3 = 35$. Hence $(19, 35)$ lies on the line $y = 2x - 3$.

9

(i) The gradient of AB $= \dfrac{3-1}{5-3} = 1$.

Hence the equation of the line AB is given by

$1 = \dfrac{y-1}{x-3}$ or $y = x - 2$.

(ii) The gradient of AC $= \dfrac{-2-1}{7-3} = -\dfrac{3}{4}$.

Hence the equation of the line AC is given by

$\dfrac{-3}{4} = \dfrac{y-1}{x-3}$.

So $-3(x - 3) = 4(y - 1)$

$-3x + 9 = 4y - 4$

and $4y = -3x + 13$.

10

(i)

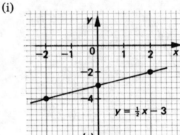

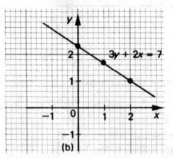

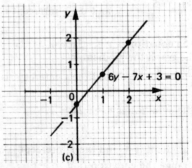

(ii) (a) $y = 2x - 2$ (b) $y = 3x + 7$
(c) $y = 7 - 4x$

(iii) (a) $4y = 5x + 3$ (b) $7y = 21 - 2x$
(c) $5y = 2x + 2$.

Section 7.2 Solutions

1

(i)

x	$-2 \cdot 5$	-2	$-1 \cdot 5$	-1	$-0 \cdot 5$	0	$0 \cdot 5$	1	$1 \cdot 5$	2	$2 \cdot 5$
$y = x^2$	$6 \cdot 3$	4	$2 \cdot 3$	1	$0 \cdot 3$	0	$0 \cdot 3$	1	$2 \cdot 3$	4	$6 \cdot 3$

Notice that, where necessary, we have rounded
off the values of y to one decimal place. It is
not worth giving more accurate results since the
points can only be plotted approximately.

(ii)

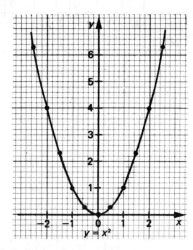

2

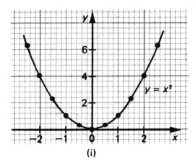

(i)

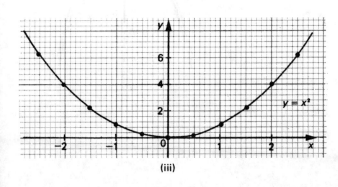

(iii)

(ii)

3

(i)

x	−2·5	−2	−1·5	−1	−0·5	0	0·5	1	1·5	2	2·5
$y = 2x^2$	12·5	8	4·5	2	0·5	0	0·5	2	4·5	8	12·5
$y = 2x^2 + 1$	13·5	9	5·5	3	1·5	1	1·5	3	5·5	9	13·5

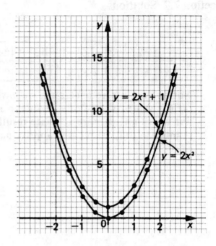

(ii)

x	−2·5	−2	−1·5	−1	−0·5	0	0·5	1	1·5	2	2·5
$y = 0·5x^2$	3·1	2	1·1	0·5	0·1	0	0·1	0·5	1·1	2	3·1
$y = 0·5x^2 + 1$	4·1	3	2·1	1·5	1·1	1	1·1	1·5	2·1	3	4·1

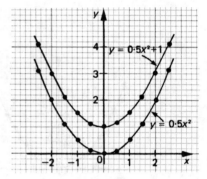

(iii)

x	−2·5	−2	−1·5	−1	−0·5	0	0·5	1	1·5	2	2·5
$y = -2x^2$	−12·5	−8	−4·5	−2	−0·5	0	−0·5	−2	−4·5	−8	−12·5
$y = -2x^2 + 1$	−11·5	−7	−3·5	−1	0·5	1	0·5	−1	−3·5	−7	−11·5

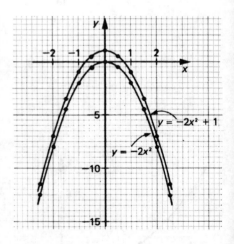

4

(i) (a) We don't give a key sequence here because calculators vary so much. However Part (b) should indicate whether your sequence works for your calculator.

(b) $2(1) - 1 + 1 = 2$

(c)

x	−2·5	−2	−1·5	−1	−0·5	0	0·5	1	1·5	2	2·5
$y = 2x^2 - x + 1$	16	11	7	4	2	1	1	2	4	7	11

(d)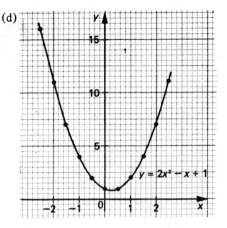

(ii) (a) Again we don't give a key sequence. Check your sequence from Part (b).

(b) $0·3(1) + 1 - 0·2 = 1·1$

(c)

x	−3·5	−3	−2·5	−2	−1·5	−1	−0·5	0	0·5	1	1·5
$y = 0·3x^2 + x - 0·2$	0	−0·5	−0·8	−1	−1	−0·9	−0·6	−0·2	0·4	1·1	2

(d)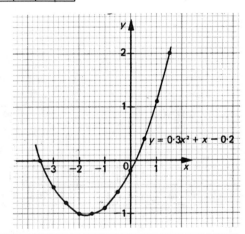

5

(i) (a) $2x^2 - 3x + 1 = (2x - 3)x + 1$

Hence a suitable key sequence is

$\boxed{x}\;\boxed{\times}\;\boxed{2}\;\boxed{-}\;\boxed{3}\;\boxed{=}\;\boxed{\times}\;\boxed{x}\;\boxed{+}\;\boxed{1}\;\boxed{=}$.

(b) $5x^2 + 6x - 3 = (5x + 6)x - 3$

Hence a suitable key sequence is

$\boxed{x}\;\boxed{\times}\;\boxed{5}\;\boxed{+}\;\boxed{6}\;\boxed{=}\;\boxed{\times}\;\boxed{x}\;\boxed{-}\;\boxed{3}\;\boxed{=}$.

(c) $2 - x^2 - 3x = -x^2 - 3x + 2 = (-x - 3)x + 2$

Hence a suitable key sequence is

$\boxed{x}\;\boxed{+/-}\;\boxed{-}\;\boxed{3}\;\boxed{=}\;\boxed{\times}\;\boxed{x}\;\boxed{+}\;\boxed{2}\;\boxed{=}$.

Your key sequences may differ slightly from ours. This doesn't matter as long as your answers agree in Part (ii).

(ii) (a) $2(1) - 3(1) + 1 = 0$

(b) $5(1) + 6(1) - 3 = 8$

(c) $2 - 1 - 3(1) = -2$.

(iii) When $x = -0·12$

(a) $2x^2 - 3x + 1 = 1·39$ (to two decimal places)

(b) $5x^2 + 6x - 3 = -3·65$ (to two decimal places)

(c) $2 - x^2 - 3x = 2·35$ (to two decimal places).

Countdown to Mathematics

(iv) (a)

x		-2	-1.5	-1	-0.5	0	0.5	1	1.5	2	2.5	3
$y = 2x^2 - 3x + 1$		15	10	6	3	1	0	0	1	3	6	10

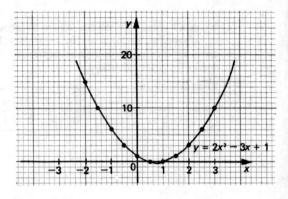

(b)

x		-3	-2.5	-2	-1.5	-1	-0.5	0	0.5	1	1.5	2
$y = 5x^2 + 6x - 3$		24	13.3	5	-0.8	-4	-4.8	-3	1.3	8	17.3	29

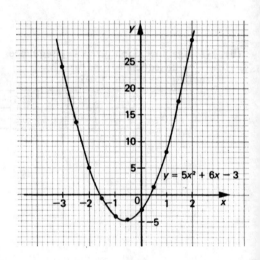

(c)

x		-5	-4	-3	-2.5	-2	-1.5	-1	-0.5	0	1	2
$y = 2 - x^2 - 3x$		-8	-2	2	3.3	4	4.3	4	3.3	2	-2	-8

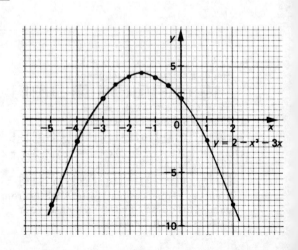

6

(i) (a) When $x = -2.5$, $y \simeq 1.7$.

(b) When $y = 3$, $x \simeq 1.8$ and $x \simeq -2.8$.

(c) When $y = -5$ there are no corresponding values of x since the graph of $y = x^2 + x - 2$ lies completely above $y = -5$.

(ii) (a) When $y = 0$, $x = -2$ and $x = 1$.

(b) $x^2 + x - 2 = 0$ factorises into $(x + 2)(x - 1) = 0$, hence the solutions are $x = -2$ and $x = 1$.

7

(i) (a)

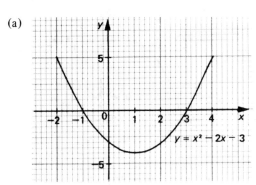

(b) From the graph the solutions are $x = -1$ and $x = 3$.

(ii) (a)

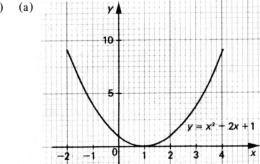

(b) From the graph the solution is $x = 1$.

(iii) (a)

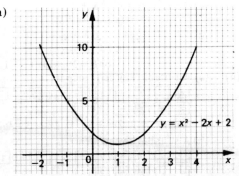

(b) The graph shows that there are no solutions to $x^2 - 2x + 2 = 0$.

8

(i) (a)

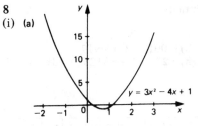

(b)

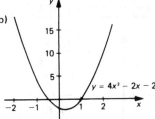

(c)

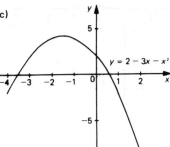

(d)

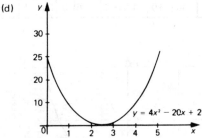

(e)

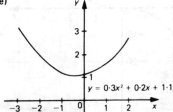

(ii) (a) $x \simeq 0.3$ and $x = 1$ (b) $x = -0.5$ and $x = 1$

(c) $x \simeq -3.5$ and $x \simeq 0.5$ (d) $x = 2.5$

(e) The equation has no solutions.

Section 7.3 Solutions

1

(i)   (a) 81   (b) 0·001   (c) 3·917

(ii)   (a) 81   (b) −27   (c) −3125   (d) −3·917

2

(i)

x	−3	−2	−1·5	−1	−0·5	0	0·5	1	1·5	2	3
$y = x^3$	−27	−8	−3·4	−1	−0·1	0	0·1	1	3·4	8	27

(ii)

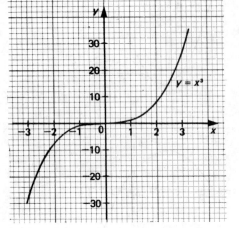

3

(i)   (a)

x	−3	−2	−1·5	−1	−0·5	0	0·5	1	1·5	2	3
$y = x^3 + x$	−30	−10	−4·9	−2	−0·6	0	0·6	2	4·9	10	30

(b)

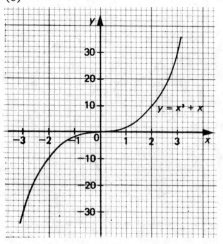

(ii)   (a)

x	−3	−2	−1·5	−1	−0·5	0	0·5	1	1·5	2	3
$y = x^3 - x$	−24	−6	−1·9	0	0·4	0	−0·4	0	1·9	6	24

(b)

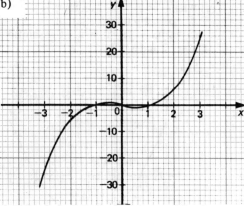

This exercise shows that the graph of $y = x^3 + x$ looks very similar to that of $y = x^3$, whereas the graph of $y = x^3 - x$ is quite different.

4

(i)   (a) You should get $2(1)^3 + 3(1)^2 + 4(1) + 1 = 10$.

      (b) You should get
$2(-1)^3 + 3(-1)^2 + 4(-1) + 1 = -2$.

(ii)   (a) When $x = 2$, $2x^3 + 3x^2 + 4x + 1 = 37$.

      (b) When $x = -0\cdot5$, $2x^3 + 3x^2 + 4x + 1 = -0\cdot5$.

      (c) When $x = -0\cdot1321$, $2x^3 + 3x^2 + 4x + 1$
$= 0\cdot5193$ (to four decimal places).

5

(i)   (a) $2x^3 + 3x^2 - 2x - 3 = ((2x + 3)x - 2)x - 3$.

      (b) $2 + x + 2x^2 + 3x^3 = 3x^3 + 2x^2 + x + 2$
$= ((3x + 2)x + 1)x + 2$

      (c) $2 - x + x^3 = x^3 - x + 2$
$= (x^2 - 1)x + 2$

      (d) $1 - x^2 - 2x^3 = -2x^3 - x^2 + 1$
$= (-2x^2 - x)x + 1$,
or $((-2x - 1)x)x + 1$.

(ii)   (a) A suitable key sequence is

      $\boxed{x}\ \boxed{\times}\ \boxed{2}\ \boxed{+}\ \boxed{3}\ \boxed{=}\ \boxed{\times}\ \boxed{x}\ \boxed{-}\ \boxed{2}$
$\boxed{=}\ \boxed{\times}\ \boxed{x}\ \boxed{-}\ \boxed{3}\ \boxed{=}$.

      When $x = 1$, $2x^3 + 3x^2 - 2x - 3 = 0$.

      (b) A suitable key sequence is

      $\boxed{x}\ \boxed{\times}\ \boxed{3}\ \boxed{+}\ \boxed{2}\ \boxed{=}\ \boxed{\times}\ \boxed{x}\ \boxed{+}\ \boxed{1}$
$\boxed{=}\ \boxed{\times}\ \boxed{x}\ \boxed{+}\ \boxed{2}\ \boxed{=}$.

      When $x = 1$, $2 + x + 2x^2 + 3x^3 = 8$.

(c) A suitable key sequence is

$\boxed{x}\ \boxed{x^2}\ \boxed{-}\ \boxed{1}\ \boxed{=}\ \boxed{x}\ \boxed{x}\ \boxed{+}\ \boxed{2}\ \boxed{=}$.

When $x = 1$, $2 - x + x^3 = 2$

(d) It is probably easiest to evaluate
$(-2x - 1)x^2 + 1$, in which case a suitable
key sequence is

$\boxed{x}\ \boxed{x}\ \boxed{2}\ \boxed{+/-}\ \boxed{-}\ \boxed{1}$
$\boxed{=}\ \boxed{x}\ \boxed{x}\ \boxed{x}\ \boxed{x}\ \boxed{+}\ \boxed{1}\ \boxed{=}$.

When $x = 1$, $1 - x^2 - 2x^3 = -2$.

(iii) (a) -3 (b) $1\cdot63$ (c) 62 (d) $340\cdot7$

6

(i) (a)

x	-2	$-1\cdot5$	-1	$-0\cdot5$	0	$0\cdot5$	1	$1\cdot5$	2
y	13	$5\cdot5$	2	1	1	$0\cdot5$	-2	-8	-19

(b)

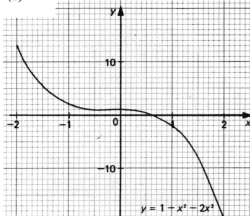

$y = 1 - x^2 - 2x^3$

(ii) (a)

x	$-2\cdot5$	-2	$-1\cdot5$	-1	$-0\cdot5$	0	$0\cdot5$	1	$1\cdot5$
y	-18	-5	0	0	-2	-3	0	10	30

(b)

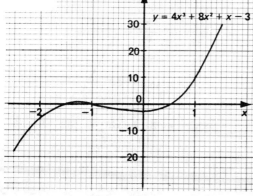

$y = 4x^3 + 8x^2 + x - 3$

7

(i) (a) When $x = -1\cdot6$, $y \simeq -6$.
(b) When $y = 8$, $x \simeq 1\cdot8$.
(c) All values of y have only one corresponding value of x.

(ii) (a) When $y = 0$, $x = -1$, $x = 0$ or $x = 1$.
(b) When $x = -1$, $x^3 - x = (-1)^3 - (-1) = 0$.
When $x = 0$, $x^3 - x = (0)^3 - 0 = 0$.
When $x = 1$, $x^3 - x = (1)^3 - 1 = 0$.

(iii) There is only one solution, $x \simeq 0\cdot6$.

(iv) There are three solutions, $x = -1\cdot5$, $x = -1$ and $x = 0\cdot5$.

8

(i)

x	-2	-1	$-\frac{1}{2}$	$-\frac{1}{3}$	$-\frac{1}{4}$	$\frac{1}{4}$	$\frac{1}{3}$	$\frac{1}{2}$	1	2
$y = \dfrac{1}{x}$	$-\frac{1}{2}$	-1	-2	-3	-4	4	3	2	1	$\frac{1}{2}$

(ii) When $x = 0$, $\frac{1}{0}$ is undefined. This suggests that $x = 0$ should be excluded from the graph.

(iii)

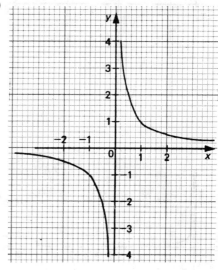

9

(i)

x	−1	0	1	1·5	2·5	3	4	5
$y = \dfrac{1}{x-2}$	−0·3	−0·5	−1	−2	2	1	0·5	0·3

(ii) (a) $x = 2$

(b) When $x = 2$, $x - 2 = 0$ and $\dfrac{1}{x-2}$ is undefined.

This suggests that $x = 2$ must be excluded from the graph.

(iii)

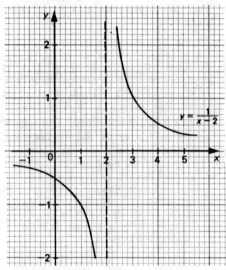

10

(i) (a) $x = 0$ (b) $x = 0$ (c) $x = 3$

(ii)

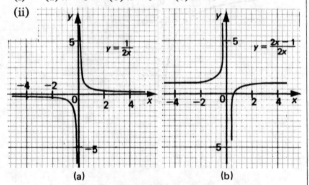

(a)   (b)

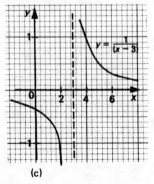

(c)

11

(i)

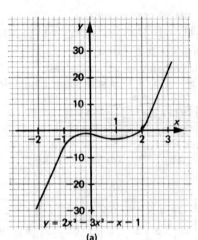

$y = 2x^3 - 3x^2 - x - 1$

(a)

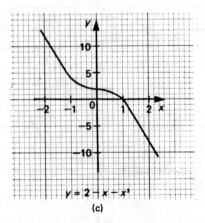

$y = 2x^3 + 3x^2 - 2x - 3$

(b)

$y = 2 - x - x^3$

(c)

(ii) (a) $x \doteq 1 \cdot 8$
    (b) $x = -1 \cdot 5$, $x = -1$ and $x = 1$. This cubic has three solutions (though the closeness of them means that this is not readily apparent from the graph).
    (c) $x = 1$

(iii)

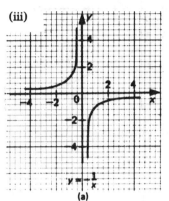

(a)

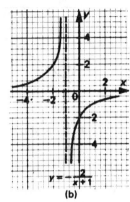

(b)

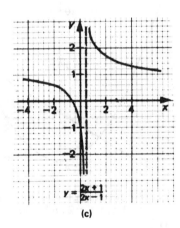

(c)

Section 7.4 Solutions

1
(i) $x^2 + x - 6 = 0$ is equivalent to $x^2 + x - 2 = 4$.
From the graph, when $y = 4$, $x = 2$ and $x = -3$.
(ii) $x^2 + x - 4 = 0$ is equivalent to $x^2 + x - 2 = 2$.
From the graph, when $y = 2$, $x \doteq 1 \cdot 5$ and $x \doteq -2 \cdot 5$.
(iii) $x^2 + x = 0$ is equivalent to $x^2 + x - 2 = -2$.
From the graph, when $y = -2$, $x = -1$ and $x = 0$.

2
(i) $x^2 + x - 2 = -2\frac{1}{4}$ is equivalent to $x^2 + x + \frac{1}{4} = 0$, or $4x^2 + 4x + 1 = 0$.
This factorises into $(2x + 1)^2 = 0$.
This indicates that there is just one solution, $x = -\frac{1}{2}$.

(ii) (a)

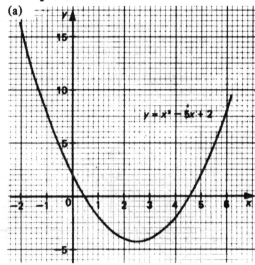

    (b) $x^2 - 5x - 6 = 0$ is equivalent to $x^2 - 5x + 2 = 8$.
From the graph the solutions are $x = -1$ and $x = 6$.
    (c) $a \doteq -4 \cdot 3$
    (d) From the graph the solution to $x^2 - 5x + 2 = -4 \cdot 3$ is $x \doteq 2 \cdot 5$. (In fact $x = 2 \cdot 5$ is the solution to $x^2 - 5x + 2 = -4 \cdot 25$.)

3
(i)

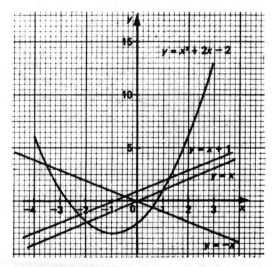

(ii) The solutions are $x \doteq -2 \cdot 7$ and $x \doteq 0 \cdot 7$.
(iii) $x^2 + x - 2 = 0$ is equivalent to $x^2 + 2x - 2 = x$.

(iv) The line $y = x$ is shown on the diagram above. The x-co-ordinates of the points of intersection are $x = -2$ and $x = 1$.
Hence the solutions to $x^2 + x - 2 = 0$ are $x = -2$ and $x = 1$.

(v) (a) $x^2 + 3x - 2 = 0$ is equivalent to $x^2 + 2x - 2 = -x$.
From the graph the solutions are $x \doteqdot -3 \cdot 6$ and $x \doteqdot 0 \cdot 6$.

(b) $x^2 + x - 3 = 0$ is equivalent to $x^2 + 2x - 2 = x + 1$.
From the graph the solutions are $x \doteqdot -2 \cdot 3$ and $x \doteqdot 1 \cdot 2$.

4

(i) (a)

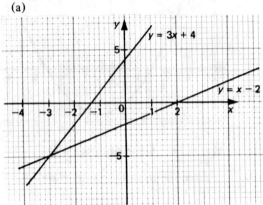

(b) From the graph the solution is $x = -3$, $y = -5$.

(ii)

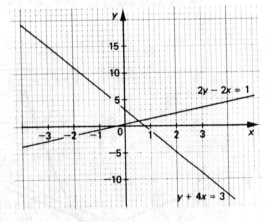

From the graph the solution is $x \doteqdot 0 \cdot 5$, $y \doteqdot 1$.

(iii)

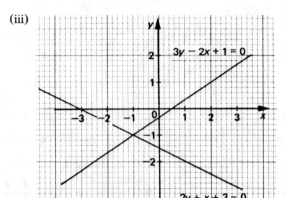

From the graph the solution is $x = -1$, $y = -1$.

5

(i)

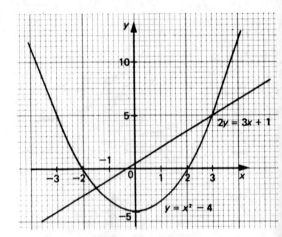

(b) From the graph the solutions are $x = -1 \cdot 5$, $y \doteqdot -2$ and $x = 3$, $y = 5$.

(ii) (a)

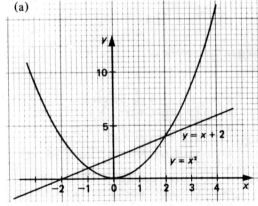

(b) From the graph the solutions are $x = -1$, $y = 1$ and $x = 2$, $y = 4$.

(iii)

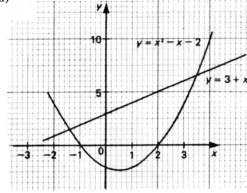

From the graph the solutions are
$x \simeq -1\cdot4$, $y \simeq 1\cdot5$ and $x \simeq 3\cdot4$, $y \simeq 6\cdot5$.

6
(i)

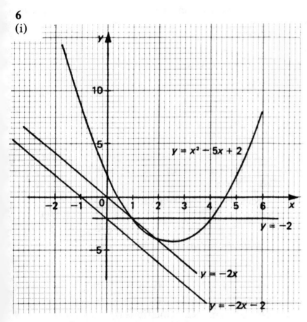

(a) $x^2 - 5x + 4 = 0$ is equivalent to
$x^2 - 5x + 2 = -2$.
From the graph the solutions are $x = 4$ and
$x = 1$.
(b) $x^2 - 3x + 2 = 0$ is equivalent to
$x^2 - 5x + 2 = -2x$.
From the graph the solutions are $x = 1$ and
$x = 2$.
(c) $x^2 - 3x + 4 = 0$ is equivalent to
$x^2 - 5x + 2 = -2 - 2x$.
These two graphs do not intersect, so
$x^2 - 3x + 4 = 0$ has no solutions.
(ii) (a) $x = 5$, $y = 6$ (b) $x = 2$, $y = 5$
(c) The graphs are parallel lines so there is no
solution.
(d) $x \simeq 1\cdot3$, $y \simeq 2\cdot3$ and $x \simeq -2\cdot3$, $y \simeq -1\cdot3$.

Section 7.5 Solutions

1
(i)   Isolate y (*Step 1*)
$y = 4 + 2x$ $\boxed{3}$
$y = 7 - x$ $\boxed{4}$.
Substitute $y = 7 - x$ into equation $\boxed{3}$ (*Step 3*)
$7 - x = 4 + 2x$
so $x = 1$.   (*Step 4*)
Substitute $x = 1$ into equation $\boxed{1}$ (*Step 5*)
$y = 4 + 2(1) = 6$.
Check by substitution into
equation $\boxed{2}$ (*Step 6*)
$y + x = 6 + 1 = 7$.
Hence the solution is $x = 1$, $y = 6$.

(ii)   We choose to isolate x although you could have
equally chosen to isolate y.
$4x = 3y - 1$ $\boxed{3}$
$x = 8 - 2y$ $\boxed{4}$
Multiply equation $\boxed{4}$ by 4   (*Step 2*)
$4x = 32 - 8y$ $\boxed{5}$.
Substitute $4x = 32 - 8y$ into
equation $\boxed{3}$ (*Step 3*)
$32 - 8y = 3y - 1$
so $y = 3$.   (*Step 4*)
Substitute $y = 3$ into equation $\boxed{2}$ (*Step 5*)
$2(3) + x = 8$
so $x = 2$.
Check by substituting into
equation $\boxed{1}$ (*Step 6*)
$3y - 4x = 3(3) - 4(2) = 1$.
Hence the solution is $x = 2$, $y = 3$.

(iii) We choose to isolate b.   (*Step 1*)
$3b = 2a - 2$ $\boxed{3}$
$6b = 4 - 4a$ $\boxed{4}$
Multiply equation $\boxed{3}$ by 2   (*Step 2*)
$6b = 4a - 4$ $\boxed{5}$.
Substitute $6b = 4a - 4$ into
equation $\boxed{4}$ (*Step 3*)
$4a - 4 = 4 - 4a$
so $a = 1$.   (*Step 4*)
Substitute $a = 1$ into equation $\boxed{1}$ (*Step 5*)
$2(1) - 3b = 2$
so $b = 0$.
Check by substituting into
equation $\boxed{2}$ (*Step 6*)
$4a + 6b = 4(1) + 0 = 4$.
Hence the solution is $a = 1$, $b = 0$.

(iv) We choose to isolate w.   (*Step 1*)

$$6w = 1 - 3t \quad \boxed{3}$$
$$4w = 5 + 5t \quad \boxed{4}$$

Multiply equation $\boxed{3}$ by 2 and
equation $\boxed{4}$ by 3   (*Step 2*)

$$12w = 2 - 6t \quad \boxed{5}$$
$$12w = 15 + 15t \quad \boxed{6}$$

Substitute $12w = 15 + 15t$ into
equation $\boxed{5}$ (*Step 3*)

$$15 + 15t = 2 - 6t$$
so $t = \frac{-13}{21}$.   (*Step 4*)

Substitute $t = \frac{-13}{21}$ in equation $\boxed{1}$ (*Step 5*)

$$6w + 3\left(\frac{-13}{21}\right) = 1$$
so $6w = 1 + \frac{39}{21} = \frac{60}{21}$
and $w = \frac{10}{21}$.

Check by substituting into
equation $\boxed{2}$ (*Step 6*)

$$4w - 5t = 4\left(\tfrac{10}{21}\right) - 5\left(\tfrac{-13}{21}\right) = \tfrac{105}{21} = 5.$$

Hence the solution is $w = \frac{10}{21}$, $t = -\frac{13}{21}$.

2

(i) We choose to eliminate x.   (*Step 1*)
Subtract equation $\boxed{2}$ from
equation $\boxed{1}$ (*Step 3*)

$$3y - (-y) = 3 - 7, \text{ or } 4y = -4$$
so $y = -1$.   (*Step 4*)

Substitute $y = -1$ into equation $\boxed{1}$ (*Step 5*)

$$x + 3(-1) = 3$$
so $x = 6$.

Check by substituting into
equation $\boxed{2}$ (*Step 6*)

$$x - y = 6 - (-1) = 7.$$

Hence the solution is $x = 6$, $y = -1$.

(ii) We choose to eliminate b.   (*Step 1*)
Multiply equation $\boxed{1}$ by 2   (*Step 2*)

$$4a - 6b = 4 \quad \boxed{3}$$
$$3a + 6b = 24 \quad \boxed{2}.$$

Eliminate b by adding equations
$\boxed{3}$ and $\boxed{2}$.   (*Step 3*)

$$4a + 3a = 4 + 24$$
so $7a = 28$
and $a = 4$.   (*Step 4*)

Substitute $a = 4$ into equation $\boxed{1}$ (*Step 5*)

$$2(4) - 3b = 2$$
so $b = 2$.

Check by substituting into
equation $\boxed{2}$ (*Step 6*)

$$3a + 6b = 3(4) + 6(2) = 24.$$

Hence the solution is $a = 4$, $b = 2$.

(iii) We choose to eliminate y.   (*Step 1*)
Multiply equation $\boxed{1}$ by 2   (*Step 2*)

$$8x + 4y = 10 \quad \boxed{3}$$
$$3x - 4y = 1 \quad \boxed{2}.$$

Eliminate y by adding equations $\boxed{3}$
and $\boxed{2}$.   (*Step 3*)

$$8x + 3x = 10 + 1$$
so $11x = 11$
and $x = 1$.   (*Step 4*)

Substitute $x = 1$ into equation $\boxed{1}$.   (*Step 5*)

$$4(1) + 2y = 5$$
so $y = \frac{1}{2}$.

Check by substituting into
equation $\boxed{2}$ (*Step 6*)

$$3x - 4y = 3(1) - 4\left(\tfrac{1}{2}\right) = 1.$$

Hence the solution is $x = 1$, $y = \frac{1}{2}$.

(iv) We choose to eliminate t.   (*Step 1*)
Multiply equation $\boxed{1}$ by 9 and
multiply equation $\boxed{2}$ by 5.   (*Step 2*)

$$45t + 36w = 360 \quad \boxed{3}$$
$$45t - 35w = 5 \quad \boxed{4}.$$

Subtract equation $\boxed{4}$ from
equation $\boxed{3}$.   (*Step 3*)

$$36w + 35w = 360 - 5$$
so $71w = 355$
and $w = \frac{355}{71} = 5$.   (*Step 4*)

Substitute $w = 5$ into equation $\boxed{1}$.   (*Step 5*)

$$5t + 4(5) = 40$$
so $t = 4$.

Check by substituting into
equation $\boxed{2}$ (*Step 6*)

$$9t - 7w = 9(4) - 7(5) = 36 - 35 = 1.$$

Hence the solution is $w = 5$, $t = 4$.

3

(i) $x = -2$, $y = 2$ (ii) $x = 3$, $y = 1$
(iii) $a = 5$, $b = 0$ (iv) $x = \frac{37}{33}$, $y = \frac{-13}{11}$
(v)   No solution. The equations correspond to
      parallel lines which do not intersect.
(vi) $3b - c + 1 = 0$ and $9b - 3c + 3 = 0$ have
      exactly the same graph. There is no *single*
      solution. Any point on the line $3b - c + 1 = 0$
      provides a solution.

MODULE 8

8.1 Sines and Cosines

8.2 The Trigonometric Ratios and Right Angled Triangles

8.3 Finding the Angle

8.4 Right Angled Triangles

8.5 Investigations

8.1 Sines and Cosines

TRY THESE QUESTIONS FIRST

1 Convert $41° \, 15'$ to radians.

2 Use this diagram to write down $\cos \theta$.

3 Draw a rough sketch to show the graph of $y = \sin \theta$ for θ ranging from $0°$ to $90°$. (There is no need to use graph paper, just indicate the general shape of the graph.)

4 (i) Without using a calculator write down the value of $\sin \dfrac{3\pi}{2}$.

   (ii) Draw a rough sketch to show the graph of $y = \cos \theta$ for θ ranging from $0°$ to $360°$. (Just indicate the general shape.)

5 Without using a calculator write down the value of $\cos (-450°)$.

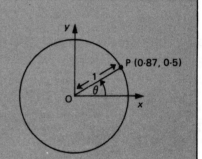

8.1(i) ANGLES

In Module 5 we introduced the concept of an angle as a rotation from a fixed line OA in an anticlockwise direction. Each point, P, on the circumference of the circle gives rise to a unique angle θ. Conversely, each angle θ defines a unique point on the circumference. Angles can be measured in degrees (°) or radians. Usually, when an angle is measured in radians no unit of measurement is given. Thus $1·7°$ means the angle is measured in degrees whereas $1·7$ means the angle is measured in radians. You will find that it is essential to be able to handle angles in both systems of measurement, so we now briefly remind you of how to convert from one unit to the other.

See Module 5, Section 5.1(iv).

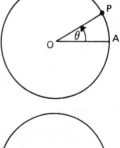

A complete revolution corresponds to $360°$ or 2π,

so $360° = 2\pi$

or $1° = \dfrac{2\pi}{360}$

and $y° = y \times \dfrac{2\pi}{360}$ radians.

This gives a formula to convert from degrees to radians.

Remember that although an angle measured in degrees may be given as a decimal or in degrees and minutes, in order to convert to radians the angle *must* be in decimal form.

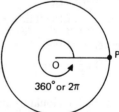

To convert from radians to degrees use the formula

$$x \; radians = x \times \frac{360°}{2\pi}$$

CHECK YOUR ANSWERS

1 $41° \ 15' = 41·25° = 0·72$ radians (correct to two decimal places). *Section 8.1(i)*

2 $\cos \theta = 0·87$ *Section 8.1(ii)*

3 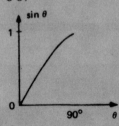 *Section 8.1(iii)*

4 (i) $\sin \dfrac{3\pi}{2} = -1$ *Section 8.1(iv)*

(ii)

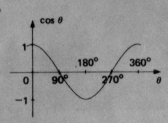

5 $\cos (-450°) = 0$ *Section 8.1(v)*

EXAMPLE

Convert $87° \ 20'$ to radians.

SOLUTION

$$87° \ 20' = 87·33°$$
$$= 87·33 \times \frac{2\pi}{360} = 1·52 \text{ (correct to two decimal places)}.$$

Using the $\boxed{\pi}$ *key on a calculator.*

TRY SOME YOURSELF

1(i) Convert each of the following angles to radians:
 (a) $20°$ (b) $78·3°$ (c) $-41° \ 21'$.

(ii) Convert each of the following angles to degrees:

 (a) $\dfrac{\pi}{4}$ (b) $\dfrac{\pi}{8}$ (c) $\dfrac{2\pi}{3}$ (d) -1.

Where necessary give your answers correct to two decimal places.

Your calculator should be able to handle angles measured in both degrees and radians. When it is operating in the degree mode it assumes that all angles are measured in degrees; similarly, when it is operating in the radian mode it assumes that all angles are measured in radians. You should be able to change from either mode to the other.

Check with the maker's handbook on how to change the mode on your calculator and which is the normal operating mode.

When you first switch your calculator on it will automatically assume one mode. This is called the *normal operating mode*.

Changing the mode does not necessarily convert the angle from degrees to radians, it just changes the way the calculator '*thinks*' of the angle.

Try the following investigation.

Switch your calculator on and enter 1.

Depending upon the normal operating mode your calculator may treat this as $1°$ or 1 radian.

Using the formula above
$1° \simeq 0·017$ rad
1 radian $\simeq 57·30°$.

Now press the change of mode key. Several things can happen.

(i) The number currently on display is also changed. This means that the change of mode key also converts the angle from degrees to radians and vice versa.

   (a) If your calculator now displays $\boxed{0·017}$ then this means that the normal operating mode is degrees and, having changed the mode, it is now operating in radians and treats 0·017 as 0·017 radians.

   (b) If your calculator now displays $\boxed{57·3}$ then this means that the normal operating mode is radians and, having changed the mode, it is now operating in degrees and treats 57·3 as 57·3°.

(ii) The number currently on display is left unaltered. This means that the change of mode key does not convert the angle measurement, it just changes the way the calculator treats the angle.

If this happens you will need to check with the maker's handbook whether it is possible to convert angle measurement directly.

If your calculator is able to convert directly from degrees to radians and vice versa, try working through Exercise 1 again, using this key. You can check your answers with those you obtained using the formula. This is a good opportunity to get used to entering angles in the appropriate mode. For example, to enter $\frac{\pi}{4}$ you must first ensure that your calculator is operating in the radian mode.

Use the $\boxed{\pi}$ key to enter angles such as $\frac{\pi}{4}$.

8.1(ii) COSINES

In order to define what is meant by the *cosine of an angle* we must go back to the original definition of angle. Suppose that the circle has unit radius ($r = 1$) and that the fixed line OA lies on the x-axis with the centre of the circle at the origin. The point P has co-ordinates (a, b).

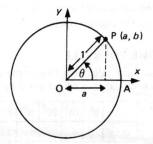

> The cosine of θ is defined to be the x-co-ordinate of the point P.

cos θ is pronounced coz theta.

The cosine of θ is written as cos θ, so cos $\theta = a$.

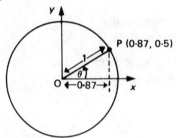

In the figure above, P has co-ordinates (0·87, 0·5), so cos θ = 0·87.

In fact θ = 30°, so cos 30° = 0·87.

You can measure θ using a protractor.

Using your calculator

Your calculator may have a cosine key. Since angles may be measured in degrees or radians it is important to ensure that the calculator is operating in the appropriate mode when entering an angle.

Check with the maker's handbook.

The following investigation should help you to quickly identify the normal operating mode. Try keying

1·5   cos .

Notice that you must enter the angle first, then find its cosine.

Depending on the mode, your calculator will treat 1·5 as 1·5° or 1·5 radians, so it will calculate cos 1·5° or cos 1·5 rad.

1·5° is a small angle, very close to 0°, and 1·5 rad is a much larger angle ($\simeq$ 86°), very close to 90°.

Remember that if no units are indicated then the angle is measured in radians.

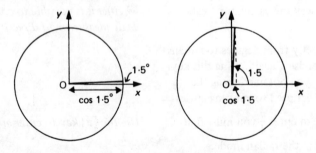

This diagram shows that cos 1·5° is very close to 1 and cos 1·5 is very close to zero. So if your calculator gives 0·9997 as cos 1·5, then the normal operating mode is degrees, and if it gives 0·0707, then the normal operating mode is radians.

Notice that
cos 1·5° = 0·9997
cos 1·5 = 0·0707.

TRY SOME YOURSELF

2   Use your calculator to complete each of the following tables. In each case round off cos θ to two decimal places:

(i)

θ	0°	10°	20°	30°	45°	60°	70°	80°	90°
cos θ									

Make sure that your calculator is in the appropriate mode before you enter the angle.

(ii) In this table θ is measured in radians so no units are indicated.

θ	0	$\frac{\pi}{12}$	$\frac{\pi}{6}$	$\frac{\pi}{4}$	$\frac{\pi}{3}$	$\frac{5\pi}{12}$	$\frac{\pi}{2}$
$\cos\theta$							

Use the $\boxed{\pi}$ *key.*

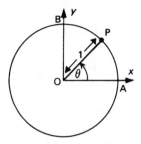

You may have noticed from Part (i) of this exercise that as θ increases from $0°$ to $90°$, the value of $\cos\theta$ decreases from 1 to 0. This can be explained by taking another look at the definition of $\cos\theta$. $\cos\theta$ is defined as the x-co-ordinate of P. As P moves round the circle from A to B, θ increases from $0°$ to $90°$. When P is at A $\cos\theta = 1$. This is just the radius of the circle. When P is at B $\cos\theta = 0$. Thus, as θ increases from $0°$ to $90°$, $\cos\theta$ decreases from 1 to 0.

This shows that the largest value $\cos\theta$ *can take is 1, the radius of the circle.*

Similarly for Part (ii): as θ increases from 0 ($= 0°$) to $\frac{\pi}{2}$ ($90°$) $\cos\theta$ decreases from 1 to 0.

TRY SOME YOURSELF

3 Use your solutions to Exercise 2 to plot the graph of $y = \cos\theta$:
(i) for θ ranging from $0°$ to $90°$
(ii) for θ ranging from 0 to $\frac{\pi}{2}$.

Choose the scales so that you can plot the points easily, giving $\cos\theta$ *to two decimal places.*

8.1(iii) SINES

The sine of an angle is defined similarly to the cosine.

> *The sine of θ is defined to be the y-co-ordinate of the point P.*

The sine of θ is written as $\sin\theta$, so $\sin\theta = b$.

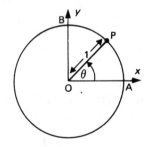

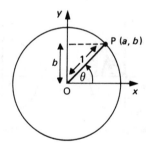

$\sin\theta$ is pronounced 'sign theta'.

Thus, as P moves round the circle from A to B, θ increases from $0°$ to $90°$. When P is at A, $\sin\theta = 0$ and when P is at B, $\sin\theta = 1$. Thus, as θ increases from $0°$ to $90°$, $\sin\theta$ increases from 0 to 1. Once again, the largest value that $\sin\theta$ can take is 1.

Similarly, as θ increases from 0 to $\frac{\pi}{2}$, *$\sin\theta$ increases from 0 to 1.*

Your calculator may have a sine key. Again, you should ensure that your calculator is operating in the appropriate mode *before* entering the angle.

4(i)   Use your calculator to complete the table below.

θ	0°	10°	20°	30°	45°	60°	70°	80°	90°
$\sin\theta$									

(ii)   Use your calculator to complete the table below.

Use the $\boxed{\pi}$ *key.*

θ	0	$\frac{\pi}{12}$	$\frac{\pi}{6}$	$\frac{\pi}{4}$	$\frac{\pi}{3}$	$\frac{5\pi}{12}$	$\frac{\pi}{2}$
$\sin\theta$							

(iii) Use the tables to draw the graph of $y = \sin\theta$:
   (a) for θ ranging from 0° to 90°
   (b) for θ ranging from 0 to $\frac{\pi}{2}$.

8.1(iv) ANGLES UP TO 360° OR 2π

Up until now we have only considered angles between 0° and 90°

(or 0 and $\frac{\pi}{2}$). But the definitions of $\sin\theta$ and $\cos\theta$ hold for *any*

angles.

The x-co-ordinate of the point P gives the value of $\cos\theta$. When
$\theta = 90°$ the point P is on the y-axis and the x-co-ordinate is zero.
As θ increases beyond 90°, P moves round the circle into the
second quadrant and the x-co-ordinate is negative. When $\theta = 180°$
the x-co-ordinate is -1.

cos 90° = 0

cos 180° = −1

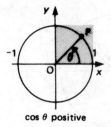

cos θ positive

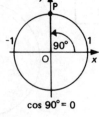

cos 90° = 0

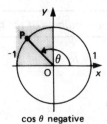

cos θ negative

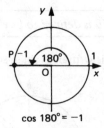

cos 180° = −1

As θ increases still further, P moves round into the third quadrant
and the x-co-ordinate increases from -1 to 0. Finally, as θ increases
from 270° to 360°, the x-co-ordinate of P increases from 0 to 1.

cos 270° = 0
cos 360° = 1

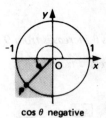

cos θ negative

cos 270° = 0

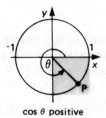

cos θ positive

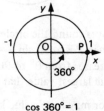

cos 360° = 1

This gives the following points on the graph of cos θ.

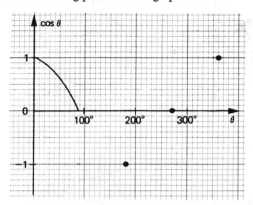

You may be able to guess the shape of the graph from these points but you will get a more accurate picture by plotting more points.

TRY SOME YOURSELF

5(i)   Complete the following table.

θ	120°	150°	210°	240°	300°	330°
cos θ						

(ii)   Add these points to the graph above and join them up as smoothly as you can.

The sketch in the margin should remind you of the shape of $y = \cos θ$, for θ ranging from 0° to 360°. Of course, the same pattern emerges if θ is measured in radians.

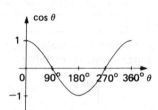

TRY SOME YOURSELF

6(i)   Complete the table below.

θ	$\frac{2\pi}{3}$	$\frac{3\pi}{4}$	$\frac{5\pi}{6}$	π	$\frac{7\pi}{6}$	$\frac{5\pi}{4}$	$\frac{4\pi}{3}$	$\frac{3\pi}{2}$	$\frac{5\pi}{3}$	$\frac{7\pi}{4}$	$\frac{11\pi}{6}$	2π
cos θ												

Round your answers to one decimal place.

(ii)   Use this table and your solution to Exercise 3(ii) to draw the graph of $y = \cos θ$, for θ ranging from 0 to 2π.

You may find that it helps to mark off the horizontal axis in fractions of π.

The values of sin θ for larger values of θ can be deduced in the same way. The following diagrams indicate what happens to sin θ as θ increases from 0° to 360°.

Countdown to Mathematics

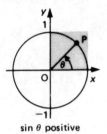

sin θ positive

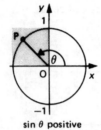

sin 90° = 1

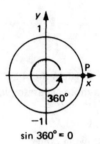

sin θ positive

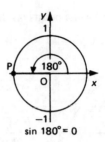

sin 180° = 0

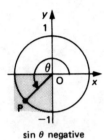

sin θ negative

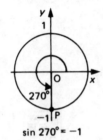

sin 270° = −1

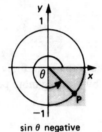

sin θ negative

sin 360° = 0

TRY SOME YOURSELF

7(i)   Complete the table below.

θ	120°	150°	210°	240°	300°	330°
sin θ						

(ii)   Use this table to complete the following graph of $y = \sin θ$
($θ$ ranging from 0° to 360°).

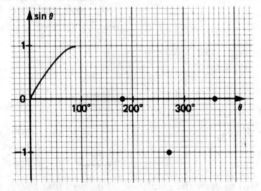

(iii) (a) Complete the table below.

θ	$\frac{2\pi}{3}$	$\frac{3\pi}{4}$	$\frac{5\pi}{6}$	π	$\frac{7\pi}{6}$	$\frac{5\pi}{4}$	$\frac{4\pi}{3}$	$\frac{3\pi}{2}$	$\frac{5\pi}{3}$	$\frac{7\pi}{4}$	$\frac{11\pi}{6}$	2π
sin θ												

(b) Use this table and your solution to Exercise 4(iii) (b) to draw the
graph of $y = \sin θ$ ($θ$ ranging from 0 to 2π).

*Round your answers
to one decimal
place.*

200

8.1(v) EXTENDING THE DEFINITIONS

So far we have only considered angles as fractions of one revolution, ranging from 0° to 360° (or 0 to 2π). However, the definition of angle can be extended to cover larger angles.

For example, $450° = 360° + 90°$,

which corresponds to $1\frac{1}{4}$ revolutions,

and $3\pi = 2\pi + \pi$,

which corresponds to $1\frac{1}{2}$ revolutions.

This provides a definition for *any* angle. Positive angles correspond to anticlockwise rotations and negative angles correspond to clockwise rotations.

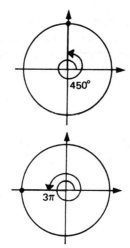

EXAMPLE

Draw a rough sketch of

(i) $\dfrac{9\pi}{4}$ (ii) $-420°$.

SOLUTION

(i) We must first split the angle into a number of complete revolutions plus a fraction of a revolution

$$\frac{9\pi}{4} = 2\tfrac{1}{4}\pi$$

$$= 2\pi + \frac{\pi}{4}.$$

This gives the sketch opposite.

(ii) $-420° = -(360° + 60°)$ which corresponds to the sketch below.

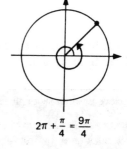

$$2\pi + \frac{\pi}{4} = \frac{9\pi}{4}$$

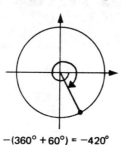

$-(360° + 60°) = -420°$

Notice that the arrow indicates a clockwise direction which shows that the angle is negative.

TRY SOME YOURSELF

8   Draw a rough sketch of each of the following angles:

(i) 5π (ii) $630°$ (iii) $-\dfrac{7\pi}{2}$ (iv) $-780°$.

The graphs of sin θ and cos θ can therefore be extended indefinitely in both directions. Notice that each 360° corresponds to a complete revolution. The definitions of sin θ and cos θ suggest that the values of both sin θ and cos θ repeat every 360°. This repetition, or cycle, is reflected in the graphs, illustrated below.

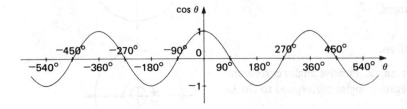

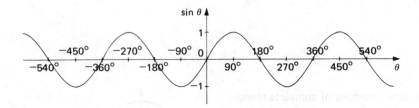

Both sin θ and cos θ lie between −1 and +1. The pattern repeats every 360°.

Notice that both curves have the same basic shape, although one is displaced from the other.

After you have worked through this section you should be able to

a Understand the definitions of cos θ and sin θ based upon the unit circle
b Use your calculator to find the cosine and sine of a given angle (measured in degrees or radians)
c Plot the graph of cos θ and sin θ for θ ranging from 0° to 360° (0 to 2π)
d Provide a rough sketch to illustrate *any* angle

Finally, here are some exercises if you want more practice.

TRY SOME MORE YOURSELF

9(i) Sketch each of the following angles:

(a) $\frac{7\pi}{3}$ (b) 660°   (c) $\frac{11\pi}{4}$ (d) −900°   (e) 480°.

(ii) Use your calculator to find the cosine of each of the angles in Part (i). Your sketch should indicate whether the cosine is positive or negative, thus providing a useful check.

(iii) Use your calculator to find the sine of each of the angles in Part (i).

8.2 The Trigonometric Ratios and Right Angled Triangles

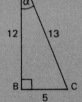

8.2(i) SINES, COSINES AND RIGHT ANGLED TRIANGLES

We already have definitions for $\cos \theta$ and $\sin \theta$. We now derive some equivalent identities in terms of the ratios of the sides of a right angled triangle. These are derived using the properties of similar triangles. In the diagram below OP represents the radius of the unit circle. Thus $OP = 1$.

See Module 5, Section 5.3.

OP = 1 unit; it is quite common in mathematics to omit actual units of measurement (such as cm or in).

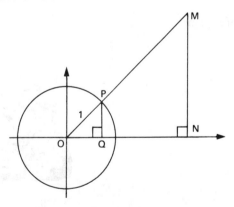

PQ = y-co-ordinate of P
  = sin θ
OQ = x-co-ordinate of P
  = cos θ

Consider $\triangle$OPQ and $\triangle$OMN.

    $\hat{O}$ is common to both triangles.

    $O\hat{Q}P = O\hat{N}M = 90°$

Using the angle sum property $O\hat{P}Q = O\hat{M}N$.

CHECK YOUR ANSWERS

1 (i) $\sin \alpha = \frac{5}{13}$ *Section 8.2(i)*

   (ii) $\cos \alpha = \frac{12}{13}$

2 (i) $\tan \theta = \dfrac{\sin \theta}{\cos \theta}$ *Section 8.2(ii)*

   (ii)

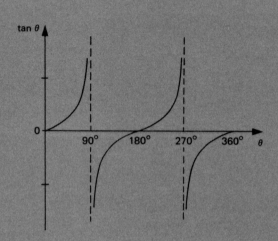

3 (i) $\sin 45° = \dfrac{1}{\sqrt{2}}$ *Section 8.2(iii)*

   (ii) $\tan 30° = \dfrac{1}{\sqrt{3}}$

Hence $\triangle OPQ$ and $\triangle OMN$ are similar.

The ratios of corresponding sides are therefore equal.

So $\dfrac{PQ}{MN} = \dfrac{OP}{OM} = \dfrac{OQ}{ON}.$

Now, $PQ = \sin \theta$ and $OP = 1$, so

   $\dfrac{\sin \theta}{MN} = \dfrac{1}{OM}$

and $\sin \theta = \dfrac{MN}{OM}.$

Similarly,

   $\dfrac{OQ}{ON} = \dfrac{\cos \theta}{ON} = \dfrac{1}{OM}$

so $\cos \theta = \dfrac{ON}{OM}.$

In Module 5 we introduced some terminology for labelling the sides of a right angled triangle.

See Module 5, Section 5.2(iii).

Using this terminology

$$\sin \theta = \frac{\text{side opposite } \theta}{\text{hypotenuse}}$$

and

$$\cos \theta = \frac{\text{side adjacent to } \theta}{\text{hypotenuse}}$$

These are usually remembered as

$$\sin \theta = \frac{\text{opposite}}{\text{hypotenuse}} \text{ and } \cos \theta = \frac{\text{adjacent}}{\text{hypotenuse}}.$$

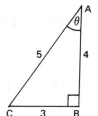

The next example shows how these identities are used to find the sine and cosine of an angle.

EXAMPLE

Use triangle ABC to find $\sin \theta$.

SOLUTION

$$\sin \theta = \frac{\text{opposite}}{\text{hypotenuse}} = \frac{\text{BC}}{\text{AC}} = \frac{3}{5} = 0{\cdot}6$$

As a check, you should always find that the sine and cosine are less than one.

It is important to ensure that the triangle *is* right angled. For example, this identity cannot be used to find $\sin \beta$ in the triangle below because it is not right angled.

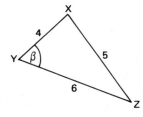

You can verify that $\triangle XYZ$ is not right angled by applying Pythagoras' theorem.
$$4^2 + 5^2 = 41 \text{ but}$$
$$6^2 = 36.$$

TRY SOME YOURSELF

1(i) Find $\sin \theta$ for each of the following triangles:

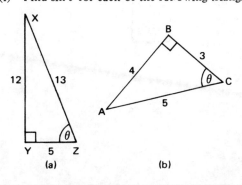

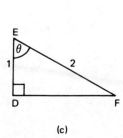

First identify which side is the hypotenuse and which side is the side opposite θ. If the length of a side is not given you can find it using Pythagoras' theorem.

(a) (b) (c)

(ii)   Find cos θ for each of the following triangles:

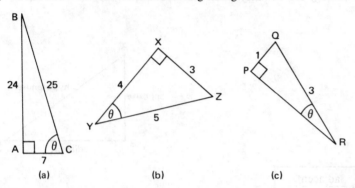

(a)   (b)   (c)

*Identify the hypotenuse, and the
side adjacent to θ.*

You may be wondering why we did not use these identities in the
first place since they seem to be more straightforward. The
problem arises with angles greater than 90° $\left(\frac{\pi}{2}\right)$, since it is impossible
to find a right angled triangle with one angle larger than 90°. (Why
is this?)

The definitions based upon the unit circle define cos θ and sin θ
for *any* angle, no matter how large, and for both positive and
negative angles.

Nevertheless, the identities given by the ratios of sides of a right
angled triangle are very useful.

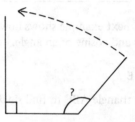

*This is the origin of the interpre-
tation of sin and cos as
trigonometric ratios.*

8.2(ii) TANGENTS

There is one further trigonometric ratio which is derived from the
two ratios we have already considered.

> *The tangent of θ is defined to be the ratio* $\dfrac{\sin \theta}{\cos \theta}$.

The tangent of θ is written as tan θ. Thus $\tan \theta = \dfrac{\sin \theta}{\cos \theta}$.

Your calculator may have a tangent key. As with the sine and
cosine keys, you should ensure your calculator is operating in the
appropriate mode *before* entering the angle.

tan θ is pronounced tan theta.

TRY SOME YOURSELF

2(i)   The table below gives the values of sin θ and cos θ for θ ranging from 0° to 80°. Use the formula tan $\theta = \dfrac{\sin \theta}{\cos \theta}$ to complete the table.

θ	0°	10°	20°	30°	45°	60°	70°	80°
sin θ	0	0·174	0·342	0·500	0·707	0·866	0·940	0·985
cos θ	1	0·985	0·940	0·866	0·707	0·500	0·342	0·174
$y = \tan \theta$								

Compare your answers with those obtained using the tan key on your calculator.

(ii)   Plot the values of $y = \tan \theta$ on some graph paper and join up the points in a smooth curve.

You will probably only be able to plot tan θ correct to one decimal place.

Your graph should indicate that tan θ behaves completely differently to sin θ and cos θ. Tan θ can be larger than 1. Moreover, the values of tan θ seem to get larger and larger as θ increases. The following exercise investigates what happens as θ gets near to 90°.

TRY SOME YOURSELF

3   Use your calculator to find each of the following. Give your answers correct to two decimal places:
(i) tan 85°   (ii) tan 89°   (iii) tan 89·5°   (iv) tan 89·9°.

What happens if you try to find tan 90°? You calculator will either display an error message or a *very* large number. This can be explained by looking at the definition.

$$\tan \theta = \frac{\sin \theta}{\cos \theta}, \text{ so } \tan 90° = \frac{\sin 90°}{\cos 90°} = \frac{1}{0}.$$

But division by zero is not defined, hence the error message.

This suggests that the definition of tan θ must exclude $\theta = 90°$.

This is usually written as

$$\tan \theta = \frac{\sin \theta}{\cos \theta} \quad (\theta \neq 90°).$$

Alternatively

$$\tan \theta = \frac{\sin \theta}{\cos \theta} \quad \left(\theta \neq \frac{\pi}{2}\right)$$

The dotted line on this graph is drawn at $\theta = 90°$. The graph of $y = \tan \theta$ gets larger and larger as θ approaches 90° but it never actually crosses the dotted line.

Since sin θ and cos θ are defined for any angle and tan $\theta = \dfrac{\sin \theta}{\cos \theta}$, the tangent of any angle θ can be found, provided cos $\theta \neq 0$.

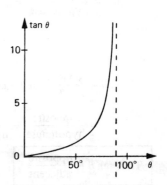

Countdown to Mathematics

TRY SOME YOURSELF

4(i) Use your calculator to complete the table below.

Round your answers to one decimal place.

θ	100°	120°	150°	210°	240°	260°	280°	300°	330°
$y = \tan \theta$									

(ii) Without using a calculator, write down
(a) tan 180°   (b) tan 360°.

(iii) What happens to tan θ when θ = 270°?

(iv) Use your solution to Exercise 2(ii) and the table above to plot the graph of $y = \tan \theta$ for θ ranging from 0° to 360°.

You may want to plot some extra points to get a more accurate graph.

The same picture emerges if θ is measured in radians. The graph of tan θ can be extended indefinitely in both directions.

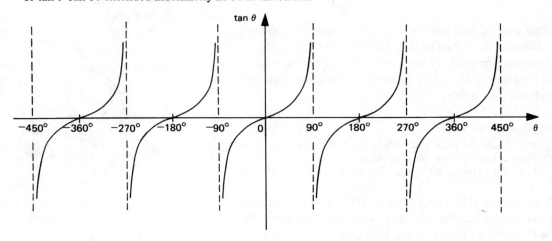

Notice that the graph of tan θ repeats every 180° (π), rather than every 360°.

Right angled triangles

Tan θ can also be expressed in terms of the sides of a right angled triangle. We've already shown that

Provided θ lies between 0° and 90°.

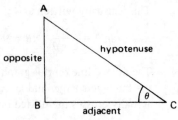

$$\sin \theta = \frac{\text{opposite}}{\text{hypotenuse}} \text{ and } \cos \theta = \frac{\text{adjacent}}{\text{hypotenuse}}.$$

Now

$$\tan \theta = \frac{\sin \theta}{\cos \theta} = \sin \theta \div \cos \theta,$$

$$= \frac{\text{opposite}}{\text{hypotenuse}} \div \frac{\text{adjacent}}{\text{hypotenuse}}.$$

Thus $\tan \theta = \dfrac{\text{opposite}}{\text{adjacent}}$.

$$\sin \theta = \frac{AB}{AC}; \cos \theta = \frac{BC}{AC}$$

$$\tan \theta = \frac{AB}{AC} \div \frac{BC}{AC}$$

$$= \frac{AB}{AC} \times \frac{AC}{BC} = \frac{AB}{BC}$$

Again, when using this identity you must first ensure that the triangle is right-angled.

EXAMPLE

Use triangle XYZ to find tan γ.

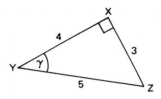

SOLUTION

$$\tan \gamma = \frac{\text{opposite}}{\text{adjacent}} = \frac{XZ}{YX} = \frac{3}{4} = 0 \cdot 75.$$

γ is pronounced gamma.

TRY SOME YOURSELF

5   Find tan θ for each of the following triangles:

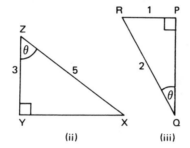

If necessary, use Pythagoras' theorem to find the unknown sides.

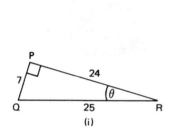

(i)   (ii)   (iii)

8.2(iii) SPECIAL ANGLES

In this section we have considered the three trigonometric ratios in terms of the sides of a right angled triangle. We now look at some common angles and find their sines, cosines and tangents. These angles are commonly used and you will probably find it useful to remember the trigonometric ratios when the angles are given in both degrees and radians.

The angles $\theta = 0°$ $(= 0)$ and $\theta = 90°$ $\left(= \frac{\pi}{2}\right)$ are best illustrated by the unit circle diagram.

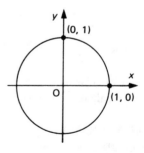

$\cos \theta$ is given by the x-co-ordinate, so $\cos 0° = 1$,

and $\cos 90°$ $\left(= \cos \frac{\pi}{2}\right) = 0$.

$\sin \theta$ is given by the y-co-ordinate, so $\sin 0° = 0$,

and $\sin 90°$ $\left(= \sin \frac{\pi}{2}\right) = 1$.

Since $\tan \theta = \frac{\sin \theta}{\cos \theta}$, $\tan 0° = 0$ and $\tan 90° \left(= \tan \frac{\pi}{2}\right)$ is not defined.

Two other common angles are $30° \left(= \dfrac{\pi}{6} \right)$ and $60° \left(= \dfrac{\pi}{3} \right)$. These angles can be illustrated by $\triangle ABD$.

See Module 5, Section 5.4(i).

$\triangle ABC$ is equilateral of side 2 and AD is the perpendicular bisector of BC.

Notice that BD = DC = 1, since AD bisects BC.

Now, since $\triangle ABD$ is right angled,

$$AB^2 = AD^2 + BD^2,$$

so

$$AD^2 = AB^2 - BD^2$$
$$= 4 - 1 = 3,$$

and $\quad AD = \sqrt{3}.$

We can now write down the trigonometric ratios for $\theta = 60°$ in terms of the sides of $\triangle ABD$.

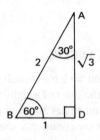

$$\cos 60° = \frac{\text{adjacent}}{\text{hypotenuse}} = \frac{BD}{AB} = \frac{1}{2}$$

$$\sin 60° = \frac{\text{opposite}}{\text{hypotenuse}} = \frac{AD}{AB} = \frac{\sqrt{3}}{2}$$

$$\tan 60° = \frac{\text{opposite}}{\text{adjacent}} = \frac{AD}{BD} = \frac{\sqrt{3}}{1} = \sqrt{3}.$$

Since $60° = \dfrac{\pi}{3}$, this means that

$$\cos \frac{\pi}{3} = \frac{1}{2}; \qquad \sin \frac{\pi}{3} = \frac{\sqrt{3}}{2}; \qquad \tan \frac{\pi}{3} = \sqrt{3}.$$

These particular ratios are usually left in fraction form so that they can be manipulated more easily.

TRY SOME YOURSELF

6   Use $\triangle ABD$ to write down
    (i) cos 30°   (ii) sin 30°   (iii) tan 30°.

$30° = \dfrac{\pi}{6}$ so this exercise also gives $\sin \dfrac{\pi}{6}$, $\cos \dfrac{\pi}{6}$ and $\tan \dfrac{\pi}{6}$.

$45° \left(= \dfrac{\pi}{4} \right)$ is another common angle. It is illustrated by $\triangle XYZ$ below.

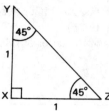

$\triangle XYZ$ is an isosceles right angled triangle with $XY = XZ = 1$.

Since $\triangle XYZ$ is right angled,
$$YZ^2 = XY^2 + XZ^2$$
$$= 1 + 1 = 2$$
and $YZ = \sqrt{2}$.

We can now write down the trigonometric ratios for $\theta = 45°$.

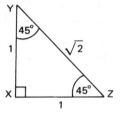

$$\cos 45° = \frac{\text{adjacent}}{\text{hypotenuse}} = \frac{XZ}{YZ} = \frac{1}{\sqrt{2}}$$

$$\sin 45° = \frac{\text{opposite}}{\text{hypotenuse}} = \frac{XY}{YZ} = \frac{1}{\sqrt{2}}$$

$$\tan 45° = \frac{\text{opposite}}{\text{adjacent}} = \frac{XY}{XZ} = \frac{1}{1} = 1.$$

Since $45° = \dfrac{\pi}{4}$, this means that

$$\cos \frac{\pi}{4} = \frac{1}{\sqrt{2}}; \qquad \sin \frac{\pi}{4} = \frac{1}{\sqrt{2}}; \qquad \tan \frac{\pi}{4} = 1.$$

The table below summarises these results for easy reference.

θ (degrees)	θ (radians)	$\sin \theta$	$\cos \theta$	$\tan \theta$
$0°$	0	0	1	0
$30°$	$\dfrac{\pi}{6}$	$\dfrac{1}{2}$	$\dfrac{\sqrt{3}}{2}$	$\dfrac{1}{\sqrt{3}}$
$45°$	$\dfrac{\pi}{4}$	$\dfrac{1}{\sqrt{2}}$	$\dfrac{1}{\sqrt{2}}$	1
$60°$	$\dfrac{\pi}{3}$	$\dfrac{\sqrt{3}}{2}$	$\dfrac{1}{2}$	$\sqrt{3}$
$90°$	$\dfrac{\pi}{2}$	1	0	unde-fined

Check for yourself that in each case

$$\tan \theta = \frac{\sin \theta}{\cos \theta}.$$

After you have worked through this section you should be able to

a   Use your calculator to find the tangent of a given angle (measured in degrees or radians)
b   Plot the graph of tan θ for θ ranging from 0° to 360° (0 to 2π)
c   Write down identities for sin θ, cos θ and tan θ in terms of the ratios of sides of a right angled triangle
d   Derive the values of sin θ, cos θ and tan θ for $\theta = 30° \left(= \frac{\pi}{6} \right)$, $45° \left(= \frac{\pi}{4} \right)$, and $60° \left(= \frac{\pi}{3} \right)$, by considering suitable right angled triangles

Finally here are some exercises if you want more practice.

TRY SOME MORE YOURSELF

7(i)   (a) Complete the table below.

θ	0	$\frac{\pi}{6}$	$\frac{\pi}{4}$	$\frac{\pi}{3}$	$\frac{2\pi}{3}$	$\frac{3\pi}{4}$	$\frac{5\pi}{6}$	π	$\frac{7\pi}{6}$	$\frac{5\pi}{4}$	$\frac{4\pi}{3}$	$\frac{5\pi}{3}$	$\frac{7\pi}{4}$	$\frac{11\pi}{6}$	2π
tan θ															

(b) Use the table to draw the graph of $y = \tan \theta$ for θ ranging from 0 to 2π.

(ii)   Find sin θ, cos θ and tan θ, for each of the right angled triangles below.

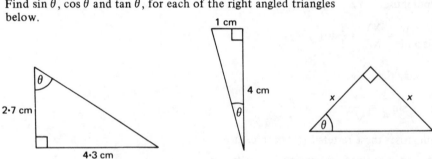

(a)   (b)   (c)

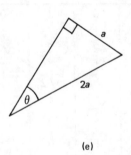

(d)   (e)

(iii)   Without using a calculator, find sin θ, cos θ and tan θ for each of the following triangles:

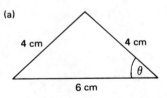

(a)

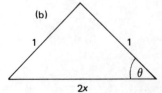

(b)

8.3 Finding the Angle

Finding the Angle

TRY THESE QUESTIONS FIRST

1 Use your calculator to find

   (i) $\sin^{-1} 0 \cdot 3$

   (ii) arctan $0 \cdot 7$.

2 Find the angles corresponding to $\sin^{-1} (-0 \cdot 4)$. Give your answers in degrees, correct to two decimal places.

3 Find the angles corresponding to $\cos^{-1} 0 \cdot 7$. Give your answers in radians, correct to two decimal places.

4 Find the angles corresponding to $\tan^{-1} (-1 \cdot 6)$. Give your answers in degrees, correct to two decimal places.

5 Express $\tan (2\pi - \theta)$ in terms of $\tan \theta$.

8.3(i) USING A CALCULATOR

In Sections 8.1 and 8.2 we discussed how to find the sine, cosine and tangent of a given angle. In this section we consider the reverse process, namely how to find the angle corresponding to a given sine, cosine or tangent.

If, for example, your calculator has a cosine key, then you should also be able to find the angle which corresponds to a given cosine. You might like to think of this as 'undoing the cosine'; the correct mathematical terminology is *finding the inverse cosine* or *cos^{-1}*. The inverse cosine is also known as *arccos*.

cos^{-1} is pronounced coz to the minus one.

We've already shown that $\cos 60° = 0 \cdot 5$. This means that the angle, whose cosine is $0 \cdot 5$, is $60°$.

   Thus $\cos^{-1} 0 \cdot 5 = 60°$

   or arccos $0 \cdot 5 = 60°$.

$cos^{-1} 0 \cdot 5$, or arccos $0 \cdot 5$ is read as 'the angle whose cosine is $0 \cdot 5$'.

Investigate a key sequence on your calculator for $\cos^{-1} 0 \cdot 5$. You should be able to give the answer in degrees ($60°$) or radians

$$\left(\frac{\pi}{3} = 1 \cdot 05 \right).$$

Check with the maker's handbook.

CHECK YOUR ANSWERS

1 (i) A calculator gives $\sin^{-1} 0 \cdot 3 = 17 \cdot 46°$ ($= 0 \cdot 30$ rad) (rounded to 2 decimal places).

Section 8.3(i)

 (ii) $\arctan 0 \cdot 7 = \tan^{-1} 0 \cdot 7 = 34 \cdot 99°$ ($= 0 \cdot 61$ rad) (rounded to two decimal places).

2 The angles lie in the third and fourth quadrants.

Section 8.3(ii)

Using a calculator, $\sin^{-1} (-0 \cdot 4) = -23 \cdot 58°$, so
$$\sin^{-1} (-0 \cdot 4) = 180 + 23 \cdot 58° = 203 \cdot 58°$$
and $\sin^{-1} (-0 \cdot 4) = 360 - 23 \cdot 58° = 336 \cdot 42°$.

3 The angles lie in the first and fourth quadrants, so

Section 8.3(iii)

$$\cos^{-1} 0 \cdot 7 = 0 \cdot 80$$
and $\cos^{-1} 0 \cdot 7 = (2\pi - 0 \cdot 80) = 5 \cdot 49$.

4 The angles lie in the second and fourth quadrants.

Section 8.3(iv)

Using a calculator, $\tan^{-1} (-1 \cdot 6) = -57 \cdot 99°$, so
$$\tan^{-1} (-1 \cdot 6) = 180° - 57 \cdot 99° = 122 \cdot 01°$$
and $\tan^{-1} (-1 \cdot 6) = 360° - 57 \cdot 99° = 302 \cdot 01°$.

5 $\tan (2\pi - \theta) = -\tan \theta$

Section 8.3(v)

It is important to ensure that your calculator is operating in the appropriate mode. If the answer is to be given in radians then it is good practice to ensure that your calculator is in radian mode *before* starting the calculation.

Inverse sine and inverse tangent are defined in the same way. Finding the *inverse sine* or sin^{-1} 'undoes the sine'; finding the *inverse tangent* or tan^{-1} 'undoes the tangent'. For example,

$$\sin^{-1} 0 \cdot 5 = 30° \left(= \frac{\pi}{6} \text{ or } 0 \cdot 52 \right)$$

and

$$\tan^{-1} 1 = 45° \left(= \frac{\pi}{4} \text{ or } 0 \cdot 79 \right).$$

sin^{-1} or arcsin

tan^{-1} or arctan

$sin^{-1} 0 \cdot 5 = 30°$ *is read as the angle whose sine is $0 \cdot 5$ is $30°$.*

Investigate key sequences to find sin^{-1} and tan^{-1}.

TRY SOME YOURSELF

1(i) Find each of the following angles. Give your answers in degrees.
(a) $\cos^{-1} 1$ (b) $\sin^{-1} 1$ (c) $\cos^{-1} 0 \cdot 2$ (d) $\sin^{-1} 0 \cdot 2$
(e) $\cos^{-1} 0 \cdot 6$ (f) $\sin^{-1} 0 \cdot 6$.

(ii) Repeat Part (i), giving your answers in radians.

(iii) What happens if you try to evaluate $\sin^{-1} 2$?

(iv) (a) Find $\tan^{-1} 0 \cdot 2$. Give your answer in radians.
(b) Find $\tan^{-1} 2 \cdot 4$. Give your answer in degrees.
(c) Find $\tan^{-1} 7 \cdot 5$. Give your answers in radians.

Round your answers to two decimal places where necessary.

To give a more complete picture we now look at each trigonometric ratio separately.

8.3(ii) SIN^{-1}

The graph of sin θ is illustrated below.

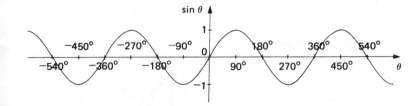

Notice that sin θ always lies between -1 and $+1$.

We're going to concentrate on angles between $0°$ and $360°$. The graph indicates that sin θ is positive when θ lies between $0°$ and $180°$ (0 and π), and sin θ is negative when θ lies between $180°$ and $360°$ (π and 2π). This is also illustrated by the original definition of sin θ.

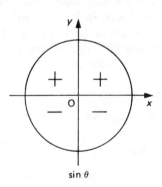

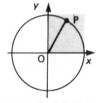 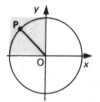 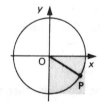

In the first quadrant ($0°$ to $90°$) P lies above the x-axis, so the y-co-ordinate and hence sin θ is positive. Similarly, in the second quadrant ($90°$ to $180°$) sin θ is also positive. In the third and fourth quadrants ($180°$ to $360°$), P lies below the x-axis so the y-co-ordinate and hence sin θ is negative.

Consider first the case where sin θ is positive.

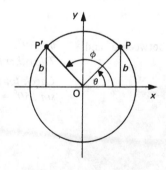

P may lie in the first or second quadrant. In the diagram above P and P' have the same y-co-ordinate, b. So

$$\sin \theta = \sin \phi = b.$$

We now investigate the relationship between θ and ϕ. Consider $\triangle$PNO and $\triangle$P'N'O illustrated in the margin.

$$PN = P'N' = b$$
$$PO = P'O = 1 \text{ (radius of unit circle)}$$
$$P\hat{N}O = P'\hat{N'}O = 90°.$$

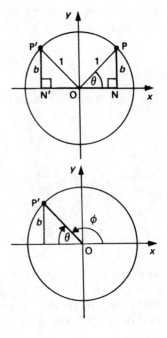

Hence $\triangle$PNO and $\triangle$P'N'O are congruent (right angle, hypotenuse and side). This means that

$$P'\hat{O}N' = P\hat{O}N = \theta.$$

so $\theta + \phi = 180°$

and $\phi = 180° - \theta.$

Since $\sin \phi = \sin \theta = b$, this shows that

$$\sin (180° - \theta) = b = \sin \theta.$$

This result is usually remembered as

$$\boxed{\sin (180° - \theta) = \sin \theta}$$

or if the angles are measured in radians

$$\boxed{\sin (\pi - \theta) = \sin \theta.}$$

So, if the sine of an angle is positive, then there are two corresponding angles, one lying between $0°$ and $90°$ and the other lying between $90°$ and $180°$. A calculator will give you one of these angles (the one lying between $0°$ and $90°$). We will refer to this angle as the *basic angle*. The second angle can be found using the result above.

The angles lie in the first and second quadrants.

θ is the basic angle.
($180° - \theta$) is the second angle.

EXAMPLE

Find $\sin^{-1} 0.5$.

SOLUTION

Using a calculator $\sin^{-1} 0.5 = 30°$. This is the angle between $0°$ and $90°$. The second angle is given by

$$(180° - 30°) = 150°.$$

Hence $\sin^{-1} (0.5) = 30°$ and $\sin^{-1} (0.5) = 150°$.

$\theta = 30°$.
The other angle is ($180° - \theta$).
Check for yourself that
$\sin 150° = 0.5$.

TRY SOME YOURSELF

2(i) Find the two angles which correspond to each of the following. Give your answers in degrees:

(a) $\sin^{-1} 0.866$ (b) $\sin^{-1} \dfrac{1}{\sqrt{2}}$.

(ii) Find $\sin^{-1} 0.2$, giving your answers in radians.

(iii) Find $\sin^{-1} 0$.

In each case the angles should lie in the first or second quadrants.

A similar pattern emerges when $\sin \theta$ is negative. If $\sin \theta$ is negative then the angle lies in the third or fourth quadrant.

Again, we are only interested in angles between $0°$ and $360°$ (0 and 2π).

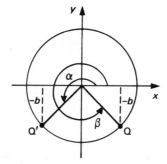

Here, $\sin \alpha = \sin \beta = -b$, so Q and Q' have the same y-co-ordinate, $-b$.

We now show how these angles (α and β) are related to θ where $\sin \theta = b$. The diagram in the margin is an extension of the one used to illustrate the case where $\sin \theta$ is positive.

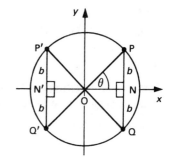

A similar argument to that used above shows that $\triangle$PON, $\triangle$P'ON', $\triangle$Q'ON' and $\triangle$QON are all congruent. This means that

$$P'\hat{O}N' = Q'\hat{O}N = Q\hat{O}N = P\hat{O}N = \theta.$$

Thus

$$\alpha = 180° + \theta$$

and

$$\beta = 360° - \theta.$$

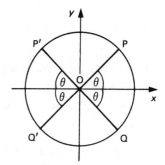

Since $\sin \alpha = \sin \beta = -b$, this shows that

And, if the angles are measured in radians

| $\sin (180° + \theta) = -\sin \theta$ |
| $\sin (360° - \theta) = -\sin \theta.$ |

$$\sin (\pi + \theta) = -\sin \theta$$
$$\sin (2\pi - \theta) = -\sin \theta.$$

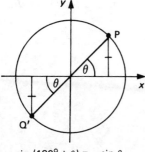

$\sin (180° + \theta) = -\sin \theta$

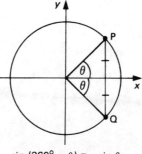

$\sin (360° - \theta) = -\sin \theta$

Thus, if the sine of an angle is negative, there are two corresponding angles. Both these angles can be found from the basic angle, θ, lying between $0°$ and $90°$.

Remember that a negative angle corresponds to a clockwise rotation, so we have also shown that

$$\boxed{\sin(-\theta) = -\sin\theta.}$$

The angles lie in the third and fourth quadrants.

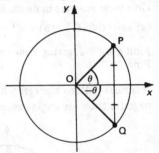

Check for yourself.
Find sin (−30°).

EXAMPLE

Find $\sin^{-1}(-0\cdot5)$. The angles should lie between $0°$ and $360°$.

SOLUTION

If the sine is negative, most calculators will calculate the corresponding angle as a negative angle lying between $-90°$ and $0°$.

Here, $\sin^{-1}(-0\cdot5) = -30°$.

From above

$$\sin(-\theta) = -\sin\theta,$$

so $\sin(-30°) = -\sin 30°.$

This gives the basic angle, $\theta = 30°$ lying between $0°$ and $90°$. We can now find the required angles using the results

$$\sin(180° + \theta) = -\sin\theta$$

and $\sin(360° - \theta) = -\sin\theta.$

$\theta = 30°$, so

$$\sin(180° + 30°) = -0\cdot5$$

and $\sin(360° - 30°) = -0\cdot5.$

Hence $\sin^{-1}(-0\cdot5) = 210°$ and $\sin^{-1}(-0\cdot5) = 330°.$

Try this on your calculator.
Check with the maker's handbook.

The corresponding angles lie in the third and fourth quadrants.

Check that
$\sin 210° = \sin 330° = -0\cdot5$.

TRY SOME YOURSELF

3(i)   Find the two angles corresponding to each of the following. Give your answers in degrees:

(a) $\sin^{-1}(-0\cdot866)$ (b) $\sin^{-1}\left(\dfrac{-1}{\sqrt{2}}\right)$.

(ii)   Find $\sin^{-1}(-0\cdot4)$, giving your answer in radians.
(iii)   Find $\sin^{-1}(-1)$.

Your answers should lie in the third and fourth quadrants.

8.3(iii) COS⁻¹

We now derive similar results for the cosine by examining the original definition of cos θ.

Again, we're going to concentrate on angles between 0° and 360°.

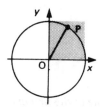 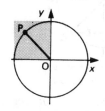 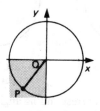 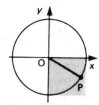

In the first quadrant (0° to 90°) P lies to the right of the y-axis, so the x-co-ordinate and hence cos θ is positive. In the second and third quadrants (90° to 270°) cos θ is negative. Finally, in the fourth quadrant (270° to 360°) cos θ is positive.

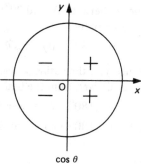

cos θ

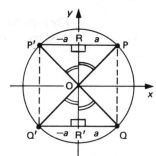

The diagram above illustrates the four possible cases.

P and Q have the same x-co-ordinate, a, so they represent angles with the same cosine. P′ and Q′ also have the same x-co-ordinate, $-a$.

A similar argument to that used for sin θ, shows that ΔPOR, ΔP′OR, ΔQ′OR′ and ΔQOR are congruent.

Try it yourself; they are all right angled triangles.

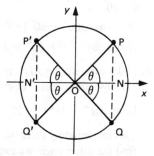

Hence

$$P\hat{O}R = P'\hat{O}R = Q'\hat{O}R = Q\hat{O}R' = (90° - θ)$$

and so

$$P\hat{O}N = P'\hat{O}N' = Q'\hat{O}N' = Q\hat{O}N = θ.$$

Similarly

$$cos (π - θ) = -cos θ$$
$$cos (π + θ) = -cos θ$$
$$cos (2π - θ) = cos θ.$$

This indicates that

> (i) $cos (180° - θ) = -cos θ$
> (ii) $cos (180° + θ) = -cos θ$
> (iii) $cos (360° - θ) = cos θ$
> (iv) $cos (-θ) = cos θ.$

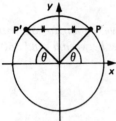 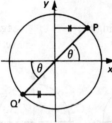 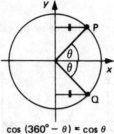

$$\cos (180° - \theta) = -\cos \theta \qquad \cos (180° + \theta) = -\cos \theta \qquad \cos (360° - \theta) = \cos \theta$$
$$\cos (-\theta) = \cos \theta$$

Thus, if the cosine is positive there are two corresponding angles. One lies between $0°$ and $90°$; the other lies between $270°$ and $360°$ and is given by

The angles lie in the first and fourth quadrants.

$$\cos (360° - \theta) = \cos \theta.$$

Similarly, if the cosine is negative, the two corresponding angles can be derived from the basic angle, θ, and are given by

$$\cos (180° - \theta) = -\cos \theta$$

and $\cos (180° + \theta) = -\cos \theta$.

The angles lie in the second and third quadrants.

EXAMPLE

Find

(i) $\cos^{-1} 0 \cdot 5$

(ii) $\cos^{-1} (-0 \cdot 5)$.

SOLUTION

(i) Using a calculator, $\cos^{-1} 0 \cdot 5 = 60°$.

This angle lies between $0°$ and $90°$, so it is the basic angle.

The corresponding angles lie in the first and fourth quadrants.

The second angle is given by

$$\cos (360° - \theta) = \cos \theta.$$

$\theta = 60°$, so

$$\cos (360° - 60°) = 0 \cdot 5.$$

Hence $\cos^{-1} 0 \cdot 5 = 60°$ and $\cos^{-1} 0 \cdot 5 = 300°$.

Check that
$\cos 60° = \cos 300° = 0 \cdot 5$.

(ii) If the cosine is negative, most calculators will calculate the corresponding angle between $90°$ and $180°$.

Try this on your calculator.
Check with the maker's handbook.

Here, $\cos^{-1} (-0 \cdot 5) = 120°$.

This immediately gives one of the corresponding angles. To find the other angle we need to know the basic angle, θ.

The corresponding angles lie in the second and third quadrants.

From above

$$\cos (180° - \theta) = -\cos \theta$$

so $\cos (180° - 120°) = -\cos 60°$.

This gives $\theta = 60°$.

The second angle is obtained from the result

$$\cos(180° + \theta) = -\cos\theta.$$

$\theta = 60°$, so

$$\cos(180° + 60°) = -0.5.$$

Hence $\cos^{-1}(-0.5) = 120°$ and $\cos^{-1}(-0.5) = 240°$.

Check that
$\cos 120° = \cos 240° = -0.5$.

TRY SOME YOURSELF

4(i)   Find the two angles corresponding to each of the following. Give your answers in degrees:

Check that your answers lie in the right quadrants.

(a) $\cos^{-1}\dfrac{\sqrt{3}}{2}$ (b) $\cos^{-1}\left(-\dfrac{\sqrt{3}}{2}\right)$ (c) $\cos^{-1}0.707$

(d) $\cos^{-1}(-0.707)$.

(ii)   Find
(a) $\cos^{-1}0.4$ (b) $\cos^{-1}(-0.4)$.
Give your answers in radians.

(iii)   Find $\cos^{-1}0$.

(iv)   Find $\cos^{-1}(-1)$.

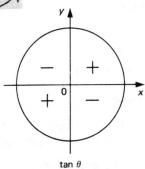

8.3(iv) TAN^{-1}

$$\tan\theta = \frac{\sin\theta}{\cos\theta}$$

We can therefore derive similar results for $\tan\theta$ from this definition.

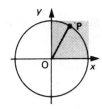 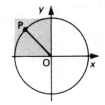 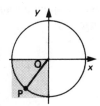

In the first quadrant ($0°$ to $90°$), both $\sin\theta$ and $\cos\theta$ are positive, so $\tan\theta$ is positive. In the second quadrant ($90°$ to $180°$) $\sin\theta$ is positive but $\cos\theta$ is negative, so $\tan\theta$ is negative. In the third quadrant ($180°$ to $270°$) both $\sin\theta$ and $\cos\theta$ are negative, so $\tan\theta$ is positive. In the fourth quadrant $\sin\theta$ is negative and $\cos\theta$ is positive, so $\tan\theta$ is negative.

This is also illustrated by the graph of $\tan\theta$.

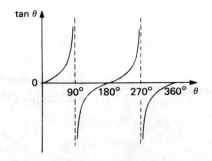

Notice that tan θ is positive when θ lies between $0°$ and $90°$, and between $180°$ and $270°$. Tan θ is negative when θ lies between $90°$ and $180°$, and between $270°$ and $360°$.

This suggests that

Similarly

$$tan\ (\pi - \theta) = -tan\ \theta$$
$$tan\ (\pi + \theta) = tan\ \theta$$
$$tan\ (2\pi - \theta) = -tan\ \theta$$

(i) $\tan (180° - \theta) = -\tan \theta$
(ii) $\tan (180° + \theta) = \tan \theta$
(iii) $\tan (360° - \theta) = -\tan \theta$
(iv) $\tan (-\theta) = -\tan \theta$.

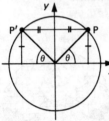

$\tan (180° - \theta) = -\tan \theta$

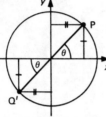

$\tan (180° + \theta) = \tan \theta$

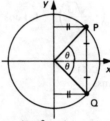

$\tan (360° - \theta) = -\tan \theta$
$\tan (-\theta) = -\tan \theta$

Thus, if the tangent is positive, there are two corresponding angles. One lies between $0°$ and $90°$; the other lies between $180°$ and $270°$ and is given by

The angles lie in the first and third quadrants.

$$\tan (180° + \theta) = \tan \theta.$$

Similarly, if the tangent is negative, the two corresponding angles can be derived from the basic angle θ, and are given by

The angles lie in the second and fourth quadrants.

$$\tan (180° - \theta) = -\tan \theta$$

and $\tan (360° - \theta) = -\tan \theta$.

EXAMPLE

Find

(i) $\tan^{-1} 1$

(ii) $\tan^{-1} (-1)$.

SOLUTION

(i) Using a calculator, $\tan^{-1} 1 = 45°$. This angle lies between $0°$ and $90°$, so it is the basic angle.

The angles lie in the first and third quadrants.

The second angle is given by

$$\tan (180° + \theta) = \tan \theta.$$

$\theta = 45°$, so

$$\tan (180° + 45°) = 1.$$

Hence $\tan^{-1} 1 = 45°$ and $\tan^{-1} 1 = 225°$.

Check that $\tan 45° = \tan 225° = 1$.

(ii) If the tangent is negative, most calculators will calculate the corresponding angle as a negative angle between $-90°$ and $0°$.

Try this on your calculator. Check with the maker's handbook. Your calculator may give the angle between $90°$ and $180°$.

Here, $\tan^{-1}(-1) = -45°$.

From above

$$\tan(-\theta) = -\tan\theta$$

so $\quad \tan(-45°) = -\tan 45°$.

This gives the basic angle, $\theta = 45°$.

The required angles are given by

$$\tan(180° - \theta) = -\tan\theta$$

and $\tan(360° - \theta) = -\tan\theta$.

The angles lie in the second and fourth quadrants.

$\theta = 45°$, so

$$\tan(180° - 45°) = -1$$

and $\tan(360° - 45°) = -1$.

Hence $\tan^{-1}(-1) = 135°$ and $\tan^{-1}(-1) = 315°$.

Check that $\tan 135° = \tan 45° = -1$.

TRY SOME YOURSELF

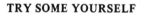

5(i) Find the two angles corresponding to each of the following. Give your answers in degrees:

Check that your answers lie in the right quadrants.

(a) $\tan^{-1} 1·732$ (b) $\tan^{-1}(-1·732)$ (c) $\tan^{-1}\dfrac{1}{\sqrt{3}}$

(d) $\tan^{-1}\left(-\dfrac{1}{\sqrt{3}}\right)$.

(ii) Find
(a) $\tan^{-1} 0·2$ (b) $\tan^{-1}(-0·2)$.
Give your answers in radians.

(iii) Find $\tan^{-1} 0$.

8.3(v) SUMMARY

We've introduced several new results in this section, but they *are* related.

The following diagrams show in which quadrants $\sin\theta$, $\cos\theta$ and $\tan\theta$ are positive and negative.

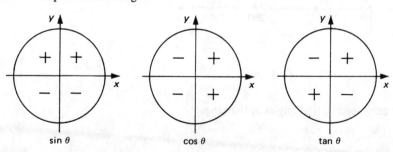

These may be summarised in one diagram. The letter in each quadrant indicates which trigonometric ratio is positive. You may find that this helps you to remember the results, which are listed below.

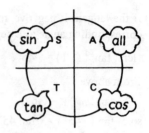

(i) *First quadrant*

All trigonometric ratios are positive.

(ii) *Second quadrant*

$$\sin (180° − θ) = \sin θ$$
$$\cos (180° − θ) = −\cos θ$$
$$\tan (180° − θ) = −\tan θ$$

sin positive
cos and tan
negative

(ш) *Third quadrant*

$$\sin (180° + θ) = −\sin θ$$
$$\cos (180° + θ) = −\cos θ$$
$$\tan (180° + θ) = \tan θ$$

sin and cos
negative
tan positive

(iv) *Fourth quadrant*

$$\sin (360° − θ) = −\sin θ$$
$$\cos (360° − θ) = \cos θ$$
$$\tan (360° − θ) = −\tan θ$$

sin negative
cos positive
tan negative

Negative angles correspond to clockwise angles. Thus

$$\sin (−θ) = −\sin θ$$
$$\cos (−θ) = \cos θ$$
$$\tan (−θ) = −\tan θ.$$

This is also illustrated by the graphs of sin θ, cos θ and tan θ.

In this section we have concentrated on angles lying between 0° and 360°. Generally, a given trigonometric ratio will have two corresponding angles. However, if we consider angles outside this range there are many more possibilities. For example, the graph of sin θ below indicates that there are many angles corresponding to $\sin^{-1} 0.5$.

Some exceptions:
$$\sin^{-1} 0 = 0° \text{ or } 180° \text{ or } 360°.$$
$$\tan^{-1} 0 = 0° \text{ or } 180° \text{ or } 360°.$$
$$\sin^{-1} (1) = 90°.$$
$$\sin^{-1} (−1) = 270°.$$
$$\cos^{-1} (−1) = 180°.$$

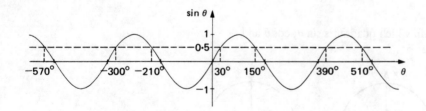

In practice you will usually only need to find angles in the range 0° to 360°.

After you have worked through this section you should be able to

a   Remember in which quadrants $\sin \theta$, $\cos \theta$ and $\tan \theta$ are positive and negative
b   Find the angles (between $0°$ and $360°$) corresponding to a given sine, cosine or tangent

Finally here are some exercises if you want more practice.

TRY SOME MORE YOURSELF

6(i)   Find each of the following. Give your answers in degrees, correct
to two decimal places:
(a) $\sin^{-1} 0{\cdot}3$ (b) $\cos^{-1} 0{\cdot}7$ (c) $\tan^{-1} 3{\cdot}2$ (d) $\sin^{-1}(-0{\cdot}6)$
(e) $\cos^{-1}(-0{\cdot}1)$ (f) $\tan^{-1}(-0{\cdot}4)$.

(ii)   Find each of the following. Give your answers in radians, correct
to two decimal places:
(a) $\sin^{-1} 0{\cdot}8$ (b) $\cos^{-1}(-0{\cdot}35)$ (c) $\tan^{-1}(-2)$ (d) $\cos^{-1} 0{\cdot}9$
(e) $\sin^{-1}(-0{\cdot}1)$ (f) $\tan^{-1} 5$.

(iii)   Rewrite each of the following in terms of the trigonometric ratio of
a positive angle: (For example, $\sin(-58°) = -\sin 58°$.)
(a) $\cos(-40°)$ (b) $\tan(-14°)$

(c) $\sin\left(-\dfrac{3\pi}{4}\right)$ (d) $\sin(-2\theta)$

(e) $\cos\left(-\dfrac{3\theta}{4}\right)$ (f) $\tan\left(-\dfrac{4\theta}{5}\right)$.

8.4 *Right Angled Triangles*

TRY THESE QUESTIONS FIRST

1   Find θ in $\triangle ABC$. Give your answer in degrees, correct to two
decimal places.

2   Find YZ in $\triangle XYZ$. Give your answer correct to two decimal places.

3   Solve $\triangle PQR$.

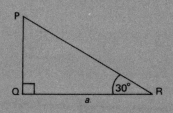

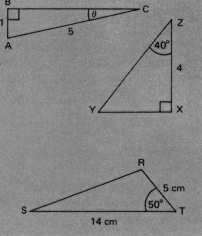

4   Find the area of $\triangle RTS$.

CHECK YOUR ANSWERS

1   $\sin \theta = \frac{1}{5}$, so $\theta = \sin^{-1} \frac{1}{5} = 11\cdot54°$.   *Section 8.4(i)*

2   $\dfrac{4}{YZ} = \cos 40°$, so $YZ = \dfrac{4}{\cos 40°} = 5\cdot22$.   *Section 8.4(ii)*

3   $Q\hat{P}R = 90° - 30° = 60°$ *Section 8.4(iii)*

    $\dfrac{QR}{PR} = \cos 30°$, so $\dfrac{a}{PR} = \dfrac{\sqrt{3}}{2}$, and $PR = \dfrac{2a}{\sqrt{3}}$.

    Using Pythagoras' theorem

$$PQ^2 = PR^2 - QR^2 = \frac{4a^2}{3} - a^2 = \frac{a^2}{3},$$

    so $PQ = \dfrac{a}{\sqrt{3}}$.

4   **Area** $= \frac{1}{2} \times RT \times ST \times \sin R\hat{T}S$ *Section 8.4(iv)*

            $= \frac{1}{2} \times 5 \times 14 \times \sin 50°$

            $= 26\cdot81 \text{ cm}^2$.

8.4(i)   FINDING UNKNOWN ANGLES

In Section 8.2 we discussed how to write down the trigonometric ratios in terms of the ratios of sides of a right angled triangle and in Section 8.3 we showed how to find the angle corresponding to a given trigonometric ratio. We now concentrate on finding unknown *angles* in a right angled triangle. Given the lengths of two sides we can write down one of the trigonometric ratios and so find the angle.

These angles will lie in the range $0°$ to $90°$. In this section we will measure all angles in degrees.

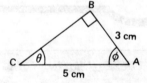

EXAMPLE

In $\triangle ABC$, $AB = 3$ cm and $AC = 5$ cm. Find θ and ϕ.

SOLUTION

We first find θ. The diagram shows that AB is the side opposite θ and AC is the hypotenuse. This suggests that we should consider the ratio $\sin \theta$.

$$\sin \theta = \frac{\text{opposite}}{\text{hypotenuse}} = \frac{AB}{AC} = \frac{3}{5} = 0\cdot6.$$

Now $\sin^{-1} 0\cdot6 = 36\cdot87°$ (correct to two decimal places).

Notice that we only need consider the angle between $0°$ and $90°$.

We could find ϕ by considering the ratio $\cos \phi$ since AB is the side adjacent to ϕ and AC is the hypotenuse. However it is easier to use the angle sum property of a triangle.

$$90° + \phi + \theta = 180°,$$

so
$$\phi = 180° - 90° - 36·87°$$
$$= 53·13°.$$

$$\cos \phi = \frac{AB}{AC} = \frac{3}{5}$$

Check that
$$\cos^{-1} \tfrac{3}{5} = 53·13°.$$

Notice that
$$\theta + \phi = 90°$$
so
$$\phi = 90° - \theta.$$

Once the trigonometric ratio is identified it is quite straightforward to find the corresponding angle. The hardest part is identifying the *right* ratio to use. You may find it helpful to label the sides opposite, adjacent and hypotenuse. The sides marked opposite and adjacent will depend upon which angle you need to refer to.

EXAMPLE

Find the remaining angles in $\triangle XYZ$.

SOLUTION

The hypotenuse is not given which indicates that we need to consider the tangent ratio. We can now find either $X\hat{Z}Y$ or $Z\hat{X}Y$; it's just a matter of choice. We choose to find $X\hat{Z}Y$.

$$\tan X\hat{Z}Y = \frac{\text{opposite}}{\text{adjacent}} = \frac{XY}{ZY} = \frac{5}{12}$$

so $X\hat{Z}Y = \tan^{-1} \tfrac{5}{12} = 22·62°.$

Now, $Z\hat{X}Y = 90° - X\hat{Z}Y = (90° - 22·62°) = 67·38°.$

Alternatively,
$$\tan Z\hat{X}Y = \frac{ZY}{XY} = \frac{12}{5}.$$

Check that
$$\tan^{-1} \tfrac{12}{5} = 67·38°.$$

TRY SOME YOURSELF

1   Find the missing angles in each of the following triangles. Give your answers correct to two decimal places:

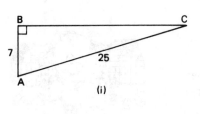

(i)

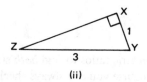

(ii)

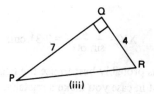

(iii)

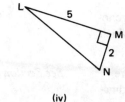

(iv)

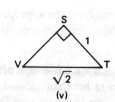

(v)

8.4(ii) FINDING UNKNOWN SIDES

Similarly, given one side and an angle, it is possible to find the unknown *sides*. Again, this depends on identifying the appropriate trigonometric ratio.

The triangle must of course be right angled.

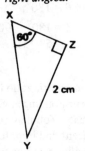

EXAMPLE

In $\triangle XYZ$, $Y\hat{X}Z = 60°$ and $YZ = 2$ cm. Find XZ and XY.

SOLUTION

We first find XZ. The diagram shows that XZ is the side adjacent to $Y\hat{X}Z$ and YZ is the side opposite $Y\hat{X}Z$. This suggests that we should consider the ratio $\tan 60°$.

$$\tan 60° = \frac{\text{opposite}}{\text{adjacent}} = \frac{YZ}{XZ} = \frac{2}{XZ}.$$

Hence

$$\tan 60° = \frac{2}{XZ}$$

so

$$XZ = \frac{2}{\tan 60°} = 1 \cdot 15 \text{ cm.}$$

Make XZ the subject of this equation by cross multiplying.

You should be able to calculate $\dfrac{2}{\tan 60°}$ directly using your calculator.

We could find XY using Pythagoras' theorem. Alternatively, we can consider the ratio $\sin 60°$, since YZ is the side opposite $Y\hat{X}Z$ and XY is the hypotenuse. Thus

$$\sin 60° = \frac{\text{opposite}}{\text{hypotenuse}} = \frac{YZ}{XY} = \frac{2}{XY}.$$

Hence

$$\sin 60° = \frac{2}{XY},$$

so

$$XY = \frac{2}{\sin 60°} = 2 \cdot 31 \text{ cm.}$$

$$XY^2 = XZ^2 + YZ^2$$
$$= (1 \cdot 15)^2 + (2)^2$$
$$= 5 \cdot 32$$
$$\text{so } XY = \sqrt{5 \cdot 32} = 2 \cdot 31.$$

It is probably best to use the trigonometric ratios to find *both* sides just in case you make a mistake. Of course you can always check your answers using Pythagoras' theorem.

Once again, the hardest part is identifying the appropriate trigonometric ratio to use. You should label the sides according to which angle is given.

If a triangle involves one of the common angles it is often more desirable to give the exact lengths rather than decimal approximations. This means leaving the answers in square root form. For example, in $\triangle XYZ$ above, $Y\hat{X}Z = 60°$.

See Section 8.2(iii).

Now, $XZ = \dfrac{2}{\tan 60°}$ and $XY = \dfrac{2}{\sin 60°}$.

But $\tan 60° = \sqrt{3}$ and $\sin 60° = \dfrac{\sqrt{3}}{2}$, so

$$XZ = \dfrac{2}{\sqrt{3}} \text{ cm and } XY = \dfrac{2}{\frac{\sqrt{3}}{2}} = \dfrac{4}{\sqrt{3}} \text{ cm.}$$

If the answers are left in square root form, then the answers are exact.

Notice too that
$$XZ^2 + YZ^2 = \left(\dfrac{2}{\sqrt{3}}\right)^2 + (2)^2$$
$$= \tfrac{4}{3} + 4$$
$$= \tfrac{16}{3}$$

so $\qquad XY = \sqrt{\dfrac{16}{3}} = \dfrac{4}{\sqrt{3}}.$

TRY SOME YOURSELF

2   Find the missing sides in each of the following triangles:

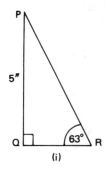
(i)

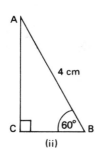
(ii)

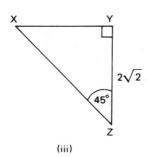
(iii)

In Part (i) give your answers correct to two decimal places.

Give exact answers to Parts (ii) and (iii).

Check your answers using Pythagoras' theorem.

8.4(iii) SOLVING RIGHT ANGLED TRIANGLES

The process of finding all the unknown sides *and* all the unknown angles of a right angled triangle is known as *solving the triangle*.

In Section 8.4(i) we showed that, given two sides, it is possible to find the unknown angles. The remaining side can be found using Pythagoras' theorem.

When the triangle is solved we know everything about it—all the angles and the lengths of all the sides.

EXAMPLE

Solve △ABC.

SOLUTION

Using Pythagoras' theorem
$$AC^2 = AB^2 + BC^2, \text{ so}$$
$$BC^2 = AC^2 - AB^2 = (3)^2 - (2)^2 = 9 - 4$$
$$= 5$$
so $BC = \sqrt{5} = 2·24$ (correct to two decimal places).

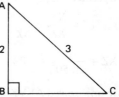

*Notice that we are not interested in the **actual** units of measurement; AC is 3 units and AB is 2 units.*

We now know all the sides. We can find $A\hat{C}B$ by considering the ratio, $\sin A\hat{C}B$, since AB is the side opposite $A\hat{C}B$ and AC is the hypotenuse. Hence

$$\sin A\hat{C}B = \frac{AB}{AC} = \frac{2}{3}$$

so $\quad A\hat{C}B = \sin^{-1}\frac{2}{3} = 41{\cdot}81°.$

Using the angle sum property

$$B\hat{A}C = 90° - 41{\cdot}81°$$
$$= 48{\cdot}19°.$$

It is probably better to consider the trigonometric ratio which involves the two sides which were given initially, just in case you make a mistake in calculating the third side.

We have now solved △ABC since we have found all the angles and the unknown side. The next example shows how to solve a triangle, given one side and one angle.

Alternatively we could have found $B\hat{A}C$ first by considering $\cos B\hat{A}C$. This gives the same answers.

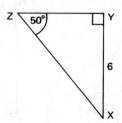

EXAMPLE

Solve △XYZ.

SOLUTION

We first find the remaining angle.

$$Y\hat{Z}X + Y\hat{X}Z = 90°$$

so $\quad\quad Y\hat{X}Z = 90° - 50° = 40°.$

Now, YZ is the side adjacent to $Y\hat{Z}X$, and XY is the side opposite $Y\hat{Z}X$. Hence

$$\tan 50° = \frac{XY}{YZ} = \frac{6}{YZ}$$

so $\quad YZ = \frac{6}{\tan 50°} = 5{\cdot}03.$

Similarly, since XZ is the hypotenuse

$$\sin 50° = \frac{XY}{XZ} = \frac{6}{XZ}$$

so $\quad XZ = \frac{6}{\sin 50°} = 7{\cdot}83.$

We have now solved △XYZ since we have found all the sides and the unknown angle.

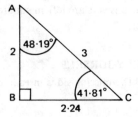

Again, it is better to use the original information just in case you make a mistake.

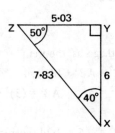

TRY SOME YOURSELF

3(i) Solve each of the following triangles. Give your answers correct to
two decimal places:

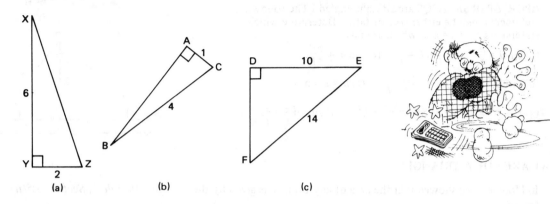

(a) (b) (c)

(ii) Solve each of the following triangles. Give your answers correct to
two decimal places:

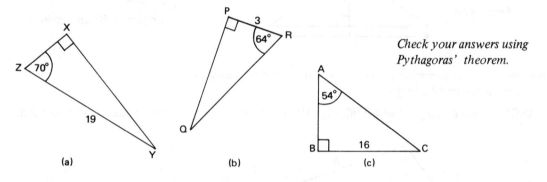

(a) (b) (c)

*Check your answers using
Pythagoras' theorem.*

So far we have only looked at numerical examples, but the same
techniques and principles apply if letters are used rather than
numbers.

TRY SOME YOURSELF

4(i) Use Pythagoras' theorem to find the unknown side, x, in each of
the following triangles:

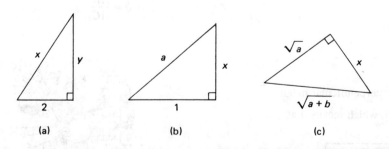

(a) (b) (c)

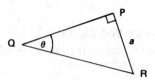

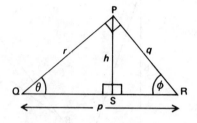

(ii)   In $\triangle PQR$ $PR = a$ and $P\hat{Q}R = \theta$. Find each of the following in terms of a and θ:
(a) PQ   (b) QR   (c) $P\hat{R}Q$.

(iii) $\triangle PQR$, $\triangle PSR$ and $\triangle PQS$ are all right angled. The following statements may be either true or false. Determine which statements are true and which are false:

(a) $\sin \theta = \dfrac{h}{r}$ (b) $\sin \theta = \dfrac{q}{p}$ (c) $\sin \theta = \dfrac{SR}{PR}$

(d) $\tan \phi = \dfrac{q}{r}$ (e) $\tan P\hat{S}Q = \dfrac{r}{h}$ (f) $h = q \sin \phi$

(g) $r^2 = p^2 + h^2$ (h) $SR^2 = q^2 - h^2$ (i) $\sin Q\hat{P}S = \dfrac{h}{q}$.

8.4(iv) AREA OF A TRIANGLE

In Module 5 we showed that the area of any triangle is given by the formula

See Module 5, Section 5.5(ii).

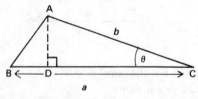

Area $= \frac{1}{2}bh$.

$b = base$

$h = perpendicular\ height$

We now derive an alternative formula in which it is not necessary to know the perpendicular height.

$\triangle ABC$ is a scalene triangle in which $BC = a$, $AC = b$ and $A\hat{C}B = \theta$.

See Module 5, Section 5.2(iii).

The perpendicular height is AD. Notice that AD intersects BC at right angles, producing two right angled triangles, $\triangle ABD$ and $\triangle ACD$.

Consider $\triangle ACD$. The hypotenuse is AC and $A\hat{C}D = \theta$. We can therefore express AD, the perpendicular height, in terms of b and $\sin \theta$.

AD is the side opposite θ.

$$\frac{AD}{b} = \sin \theta,$$

$\sin \theta = \dfrac{AD}{AC}$

so $AD = b \sin \theta$.

Now

area of $\triangle ABC = \frac{1}{2}$ base $\times$ perpendicular height

$= \frac{1}{2}a \times AD$, which means that

the area of $\triangle ABC = \frac{1}{2}ab \sin \theta$.

Thus the area of a triangle can be found in terms of the product of two sides multiplied by the sine of the included angle. This is a useful alternative formula since we don't always know the perpendicular height.

In fact the formula holds for any two sides and the included angle. Try it yourself.

EXAMPLE

Find the area of △PQR.

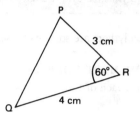

SOLUTION

PR = 3 cm and QR = 4 cm. The included angle, $\hat{PRQ}$ = 60°.

From above,

Area of △PQR = $\frac{1}{2}$ × PR × QR × sin $\hat{PRQ}$

$= \frac{1}{2}$ × 3 × 4 × $\frac{\sqrt{3}}{2}$

$= 3\sqrt{3}$ or 5·20 cm².

Remember that

$$sin\ 60° = \frac{\sqrt{3}}{2}.$$

TRY SOME YOURSELF

5(i) Find the area of each of the following triangles:

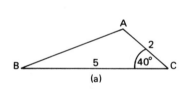

(a)

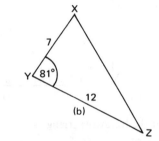

(b)

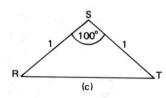

(c)

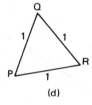

(d)

(ii) (a) Find the perpendicular height of △ABC.
      (b) Find the area of △ABC.

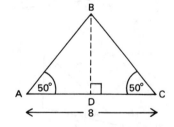

(iii) (a) Write down $\hat{XYZ}$.
       (b) Hence write down the area of △XYZ in terms of *p*, *q*, α and β.

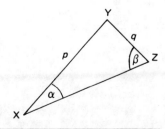

> **After you have worked through this section you should be able to**
>
> a Solve a right angled triangle, given two sides
> b Solve a right angled triangle, given one side and one angle other than the right angle
> c Find the area of a triangle given two sides and the included angle

Finally here are some exercises if you want more practice.

TRY SOME MORE YOURSELF

6(i) Solve each of the following triangles:

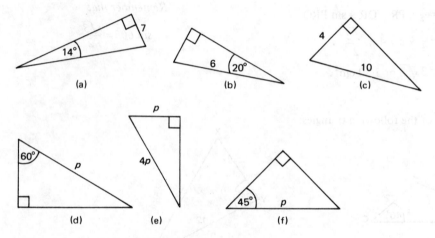

(a)   (b)   (c)

(d)   (e)   (f)

(ii) Find the area of each of the following triangles:

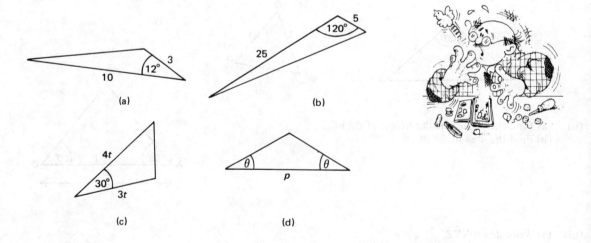

(a)   (b)

(c)   (d)

8.5 Investigations

In this section we invite you to explore the trigonometric ratios in a little more detail. The section consists solely of a set of structured exercises which allow you to investigate some well known results. We don't offer detailed explanations, but you should be able to verify the results for yourself as you work through the section. If you go on to study any further mathematics you will find that formal proofs are included in many courses and textbooks.

Most of the results are suggested by examining and comparing graphs.

TRY SOME YOURSELF

1(i) Use your calculator to complete the table below. Round your answers to one decimal place.

θ	$-\pi$	$-\dfrac{3\pi}{4}$	$-\dfrac{2\pi}{3}$	$-\dfrac{\pi}{2}$	$-\dfrac{\pi}{3}$	$-\dfrac{\pi}{6}$	0	$\dfrac{\pi}{6}$	$\dfrac{\pi}{3}$	$\dfrac{\pi}{2}$	$\dfrac{2\pi}{3}$	$\dfrac{3\pi}{4}$	π
$\sin\theta$													

Make sure your calculator is in the radian mode.

(ii) Use the table to plot the graph of $\sin\theta$ for θ ranging from $-\pi$ to π. (You may want to add some extra points.)

(iii) Draw up a similar table of values for $\cos\theta$ for θ ranging from $-\pi$ to π.

(iv) Plot the graph of $\cos\theta$ on the same axes you used for Part (ii).

(v) Write down the co-ordinates of the points of intersection of the two graphs.

(vi) To which equation do these co-ordinates give the solution?

It may help to mark off the horizontal axis in terms of π

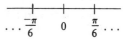

2(i) Without using a calculator write down $\sin 45°$.

(ii) Evaluate $2 \times \sin 45° \cos 45°$.

(iii) Now use a calculator to evaluate $2 \times \sin 45° \cos 45°$.

(iv) Use the same key sequence to complete the table of values below. Round your answers to one decimal place.

See Section 8.2(iii).

Make sure your calculator is in degree mode. Check your key sequence, using the answer to Part (ii) above.

θ	0°	15°	30°	45°	60°	75°	90°	105°	120°	135°	150°	165°	180°
$2\sin\theta\cos\theta$													

(v) Use the table to plot the graph of $2\sin\theta\cos\theta$ for values of θ lying between 0° and 180°.

(vi) You should recognise the shape of this graph.
(a) Write down the largest value of $2\sin\theta\cos\theta$ over this range.
(b) Write down the smallest value of $2\sin\theta\cos\theta$.

(vii)   Complete the table of values below.

θ	0°	20°	40°	60°	80°	100°	120°	140°	160°	180°
sin 2θ										

(viii) Plot the graph of sin 2θ on the same axes you used for Part (v).

(ix)   Suppose the range of values of θ is extended in both directions. Draw a sketch to show the rough shape of the corresponding graph of sin 2θ.

(x)   Write down the general result suggested by these graphs. Check the result using your calculator.

3(i)   Write down sin 30°.

(ii)   Without using a calculator, evaluate $1 - 2 (\sin 30°)^2$.

(iii) Investigate a key sequence to evaluate $1 - 2 (\sin 30°)^2$.

Check, using your answer to Part (ii).

(iv)   Use your calculator to complete the table below.

θ	0°	15°	30°	45°	60°	75°	90°	105°	120°	135°	150°	165°	180°
$1 - 2 (\sin \theta)^2$													

(v)   Use the table to plot the graph of $y = 1 - 2 (\sin \theta)^2$.

(vi)   You should recognise the shape of this graph.
(a) Write down the largest value of $1 - 2 (\sin \theta)^2$.
(b) Write down the smallest value of $1 - 2 (\sin \theta)^2$.

(vii) Without using a calculator, evaluate
(a) $2(\cos 60°)^2 - 1$ (b) $(\cos 90°)^2 - (\sin 90°)^2$.

(viii) Use your answers to Part (vii) to investigate key sequences for
(a) $2(\cos \theta)^2 - 1$ (b) $(\cos \theta)^2 - (\sin \theta)^2$.

(ix)   Draw up tables similar to that in Part (iv) for
(a) $2(\cos \theta)^2 - 1$ (b) $(\cos \theta)^2 - (\sin \theta)^2$.

(x)   Compare all three tables. What do you notice?

(xi)   Complete the table of values below and plot the graph of cos 2θ on the same axes you used for Part (v).

θ	0°	20°	40°	60°	80°	100°	120°	140°	160°	180°
cos 2θ										

(xii) Write down the general results suggested by this investigation. Check the results using your calculator.

4(i)   Complete the table of values below.

θ	0	$\frac{\pi}{6}$	$\frac{\pi}{4}$	$\frac{\pi}{3}$	$\frac{2\pi}{3}$	$\frac{5\pi}{6}$	π	$\frac{4\pi}{3}$	$\frac{5\pi}{3}$	2π	$\frac{7\pi}{3}$	$\frac{8\pi}{3}$	3π	$\frac{10\pi}{3}$	$\frac{11\pi}{3}$	4π
tan θ																

Make sure your calculator is in radian mode.

(ii)   (a) Which values of θ must be excluded in this range?
(b) Use the table to plot the graph of tan θ for θ ranging from 0 to 4π.

You may want to plot more points.

(iii) Use your graph to find the solutions to tan $\theta = 1$.

(iv) Now suppose the graph of $\tan \theta$ is extended indefinitely in both directions. This introduces more solutions to $\tan \theta = 1$. Write down the first six positive solutions.

(v) Part (iv) should suggest a definite pattern. Try writing down the nth positive solution to $\tan \theta = 1$.

5(i) (a) Without using a calculator, evaluate $\dfrac{2x}{1 - x^2}$ when $x = 3$.

(b) Repeat Part (a) for $x = \sqrt{3}$.

(ii) Investigate a key sequence to evaluate $\dfrac{2x}{1 - x^2}$.

Check using your answers to Part (i) (a) and Part (i) (b).

(iii) Now investigate a key sequence to evaluate $\dfrac{2 \tan 60°}{1 - (\tan 60°)^2}$.

$\tan 60° = \sqrt{3}$, so you can check your key sequences using your answers to Part (i) (b).

(iv) Use your calculator to complete the table below.

θ	0°	20°	40°	60°	80°	100°	120°	140°	160°	180°
$\dfrac{2 \tan \theta}{1 - (\tan \theta)^2}$										

(v) (a) What happens to $\dfrac{2 \tan \theta}{1 - (\tan \theta)^2}$ when $\theta = 45°$?

(b) Which other values of θ must be excluded in this range?

(vi) Use your solutions to Parts (iv) and (v) to plot the graph of

$$y = \frac{2 \tan \theta}{1 - (\tan \theta)^2}.$$

(vii) Draw up a table of values for $\tan 2\theta$ and plot the graph of $\tan 2\theta$ on the same axes you used for Part (vi).

(viii) Write down the general result suggested by these graphs.

6(i) Without using a calculator, write down
(a) $\sin 30°$ and (b) $\cos 60°$.
What do you notice?

See Section 8.2(iii). Use the appropriate right angled triangle.

(ii) Now write down
(a) $\sin 60°$ and (b) $\cos 30°$.

(iii) Show that, for any angle θ between 0° and 90°, $\sin \theta = \cos (90° - \theta)$ and $\cos \theta = \sin (90° - \theta)$.

Draw a right angled triangle and consider the appropriate ratios of sides.

7(i) Without using a calculator, evaluate
(a) $(\sin 30°)^2$ (b) $(\cos 30°)^2$ (c) $(\sin 30°)^2 + (\cos 30°)^2$.

(ii) Without using a calculator, show that $(\sin 60°)^2 + (\cos 60°)^2 = 1$.

(iii) Show that, for any angle θ between 0° and 90°, $(\sin \theta)^2 + (\cos \theta)^2 = 1$.

Draw a right angled triangle. Label the sides and use Pythagoras' theorem.

This section has been investigative in nature, so we do not expect you to be able to do any specific tasks, nor do we include any extra exercises! However, you should have had plenty of practice both in using a calculator to evaluate the trigonometric ratios, and in plotting graphs. This experience should be useful when you meet a more formal treatment of these results in your later studies of mathematics.

Countdown to Mathematics

Section 8.1 Solutions

1

(i) (a) $20° = \dfrac{20 \times 2\pi}{360} = 0·35$

(b) $78·3° = \dfrac{78·3 \times 2\pi}{360} = 1·37$

(c) First change the minutes to a decimal

$$-41° \, 21' = \dfrac{-41·35 \times 2\pi}{360} = -0·72.$$

(ii) (a) $\dfrac{\pi}{4} = \dfrac{\pi}{4} \times \dfrac{360}{2\pi} = 45°$

(b) $\dfrac{\pi}{8} = \dfrac{\pi}{8} \times \dfrac{360}{2\pi} = 22·5°$

(c) $\dfrac{2\pi}{3} = \dfrac{2\pi}{3} \times \dfrac{360}{2\pi} = 120°$

(d) $-1 = -1 \times \dfrac{360}{2\pi} = -57·30°$

2 (i)

θ	0°	10°	20°	30°	45°	60°	70°	80°	90°
$\cos\theta$	1·00	0·98	0·94	0·87	0·71	0·50	0·34	0·17	0·00

(ii)

θ	0	$\dfrac{\pi}{12}$	$\dfrac{\pi}{6}$	$\dfrac{\pi}{4}$	$\dfrac{\pi}{3}$	$\dfrac{5\pi}{12}$	$\dfrac{\pi}{2}$
$\cos\theta$	1·00	0·97	0·87	0·71	0·50	0·26	0·00

You may find, if you use the ⟨π⟩ key, that your calculator gives $\cos\dfrac{\pi}{2}$ as a very small number (such as 5×10^{-10}) rather than exactly zero. This is because the value of π is an approximation which introduces some rounding errors.

3

(i)

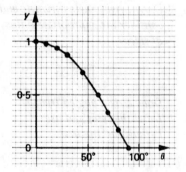

(ii)

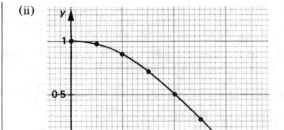

Notice that the shape of the graph depends upon the scales used.

4 (i)

θ	0°	10°	20°	30°	45°	60°	70°	80°	90°
$\sin\theta$	0·00	0·17	0·34	0·50	0·71	0·87	0·94	0·98	1·00

(ii)

θ	0	$\dfrac{\pi}{12}$	$\dfrac{\pi}{6}$	$\dfrac{\pi}{4}$	$\dfrac{\pi}{3}$	$\dfrac{5\pi}{12}$	$\dfrac{\pi}{2}$
$\sin\theta$	0·00	0·26	0·50	0·71	0·87	0·97	1·00

Notice that the table for $\sin\theta$ is very similar to that for $\cos\theta$. The values of $\sin\theta$ increase from left to right whereas the values of $\cos\theta$ decrease.

(iii) (a)

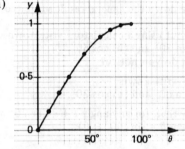

(b)

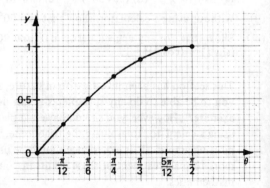

5

(i)

θ	120°	150°	210°	240°	300°	330°
$\cos\theta$	−0·5	−0·9	−0·9	−0·5	0·5	0·9

(ii)

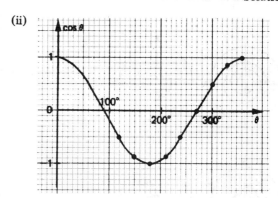

Notice that the scale of the vertical axis makes it difficult to plot the points to any greater accuracy than one decimal place.

6

(i)

θ	$\dfrac{2\pi}{3}$	$\dfrac{3\pi}{4}$	$\dfrac{5\pi}{6}$	π	$\dfrac{7\pi}{6}$	$\dfrac{5\pi}{4}$	$\dfrac{4\pi}{3}$	$\dfrac{3\pi}{2}$	$\dfrac{5\pi}{3}$	$\dfrac{7\pi}{4}$	$\dfrac{11\pi}{6}$	2π
$\cos\theta$	−0·5	−0·7	−0·9	−1	−0·9	−0·7	−0·5	0	0·5	0·7	0·9	1

(ii)

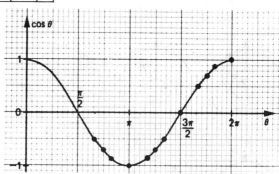

7

(i)

θ	120°	150°	210°	240°	300°	330°
$\sin\theta$	0·9	0·5	−0·5	−0·9	−0·9	−0·5

(ii)

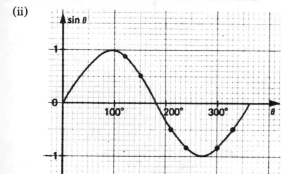

(iii) (b)

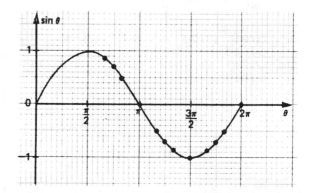

(iii) (a)

θ	$\dfrac{2\pi}{3}$	$\dfrac{3\pi}{4}$	$\dfrac{5\pi}{6}$	π	$\dfrac{7\pi}{6}$	$\dfrac{5\pi}{4}$	$\dfrac{4\pi}{3}$	$\dfrac{3\pi}{2}$	$\dfrac{5\pi}{3}$	$\dfrac{7\pi}{4}$	$\dfrac{11\pi}{6}$	2π
$\sin\theta$	0·9	0·7	0·5	0	−0·5	−0·7	−0·9	−1	−0·9	−0·7	−0·5	0

8

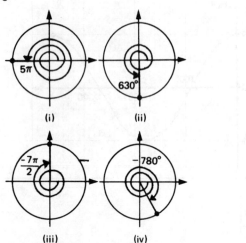

(i) (ii)

(iii) (iv)

9
(i)

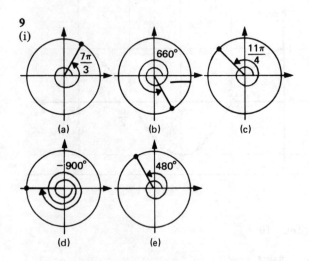

(a) (b) (c)

(d) (e)

(ii) (a) 0·5 (b) 0·5 (c) −0·71 (d) −1
(e) −0·5
(iii) (a) 0·87 (b) −0·87 (c) 0·71 (d) 0
(e) 0·87

Section 8.2 Solutions

1

(i) (a) $\sin \theta = \dfrac{\text{opposite}}{\text{hypotenuse}} = \dfrac{XY}{XZ} = \dfrac{12}{13} = 0.92$

(b) $\sin \theta = \dfrac{\text{opposite}}{\text{hypotenuse}} = \dfrac{AB}{AC} = \dfrac{4}{5} = 0.8$

(c) $\sin \theta = \dfrac{\text{opposite}}{\text{hypotenuse}} = \dfrac{DF}{EF}.$

DF is not given, but Pythagoras' theorem
states that $EF^2 = ED^2 + DF^2$,
so $DF^2 = EF^2 - ED^2 = 4 - 1 = 3$,
and $DF = \sqrt{3}$.

Hence $\sin \theta = \dfrac{\sqrt{3}}{2} = 0.87$.

(ii) (a) $\cos \theta = \dfrac{\text{adjacent}}{\text{hypotenuse}} = \dfrac{AC}{BC} = \dfrac{7}{25} = 0.28$

(b) $\cos \theta = \dfrac{\text{adjacent}}{\text{hypotenuse}} = \dfrac{XY}{YZ} = \dfrac{4}{5} = 0.8$

(c) $\cos \theta = \dfrac{\text{adjacent}}{\text{hypotenuse}} = \dfrac{PR}{QR}.$

PR is not given, but Pythagoras' theorem
states that $QR^2 = PQ^2 + PR^2$
so $PR^2 = QR^2 - PQ^2 = 9 - 1 = 8$
and $PR = \sqrt{8}$.

Hence $\cos \theta = \dfrac{\sqrt{8}}{3} = 0.94$.

2
(i)

θ	0°	10°	20°	30°	45°	60°	70°	80°
$\tan \theta$	0	0·177	0·364	0·577	1	1·732	2·749	5·661

(ii)

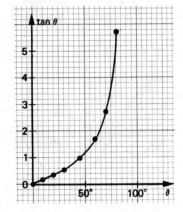

3 (i) tan 85° = 11·43   (ii) tan 89° = 57·29
(iii) tan 89·5° = 114·59
(iv) tan 89·9° = 572·96
Your calculator may give slightly different
values, but they should be of the same order
of magnitude as those given here.

4

(i)

θ	100°	120°	150°	210°	240°	260°	280°	300°	330°
$\tan\theta$	−5·7	−1·7	−0·6	0·6	1·7	5·7	−5·7	−1·7	−0·6

(ii) (a) $\tan 180° = \dfrac{\sin 180°}{\cos 180°} = \dfrac{0}{-1} = 0$

(b) $\tan 360° = \dfrac{\sin 360°}{\cos 360°} = \dfrac{0}{1} = 0$

(iii) $\cos 270° = 0$, so $\tan 270°$ is undefined.

(iv)

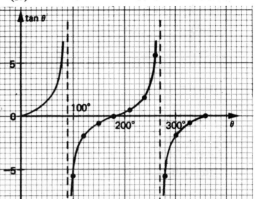

5

(i) $\tan\theta = \dfrac{\text{opposite}}{\text{adjacent}} = \dfrac{PQ}{PR} = \dfrac{7}{24} = 0\cdot29$

(ii) $\tan\theta = \dfrac{\text{opposite}}{\text{adjacent}} = \dfrac{XY}{YZ}$

Pythagoras' theorem states that
$XZ^2 = XY^2 + YZ^2$,

so $XY^2 = XZ^2 - YZ^2 = 25 - 9 = 16$

and $XY = \sqrt{16} = 4$.

Hence $\tan\theta = \frac{4}{3} = 1\cdot33$.

(iii) $\tan\theta = \dfrac{\text{opposite}}{\text{adjacent}} = \dfrac{PR}{PQ}$

Pythagoras' theorem states that
$QR^2 = PR^2 + PQ^2$,

so $PQ^2 = QR^2 - PR^2 = 4 - 1 = 3$

and $PQ = \sqrt{3}$.

Hence $\tan\theta = \dfrac{1}{\sqrt{3}} = 0\cdot58$.

6

(i) $\cos 30° = \dfrac{\text{adjacent}}{\text{hypotenuse}} = \dfrac{AD}{AB} = \dfrac{\sqrt{3}}{2}$

(ii) $\sin 30° = \dfrac{\text{opposite}}{\text{hypotenuse}} = \dfrac{BD}{AB} = \dfrac{1}{2}$

(iii) $\tan 30^c = \dfrac{\text{opposite}}{\text{adjacent}} = \dfrac{BD}{AD} = \dfrac{1}{\sqrt{3}}$

7

(i) (a)

θ	0	$\dfrac{\pi}{6}$	$\dfrac{\pi}{4}$	$\dfrac{\pi}{3}$	$\dfrac{2\pi}{3}$	$\dfrac{3\pi}{4}$	$\dfrac{5\pi}{6}$	π	$\dfrac{7\pi}{6}$	$\dfrac{5\pi}{4}$	$\dfrac{4\pi}{3}$	$\dfrac{5\pi}{3}$	$\dfrac{7\pi}{4}$	$\dfrac{11\pi}{6}$	2π
$\tan\theta$	0	0·6	1	1·7	−1·7	−1	−0·6	0	0·6	1	1·7	−1·7	−1	−0·6	0

In addition, notice that $\tan\theta$ is not defined
when $\theta = \dfrac{3\pi}{2}$, since $\cos\dfrac{3\pi}{2} = 0$.

(b)

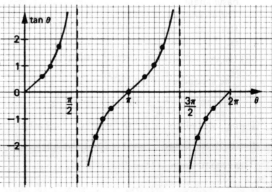

(ii) (a) $\sin\theta = 0\cdot85$, $\cos\theta = 0\cdot53$, $\tan\theta = 1\cdot59$
(b) $\sin\theta = 0\cdot24$, $\cos\theta = 0\cdot97$, $\tan\theta = 0\cdot25$
(c) $\sin\theta = \frac{1}{\sqrt{2}}$, $\cos\theta = \frac{1}{\sqrt{2}}$, $\tan\theta = 1$ $(\theta = 45°)$

(d) $\sin\theta = \frac{a}{\sqrt{a^2+b^2}}$, $\cos\theta = \frac{b}{\sqrt{a^2+b^2}}$,

$\tan\theta = \frac{a}{b}$

(e) $\sin\theta = \frac{1}{2}$, $\cos\theta = \frac{\sqrt{3}}{2}$, $\tan\theta = \frac{1}{\sqrt{3}}$ $(\theta = 30°)$.

(iii) (a) The triangle is isosceles, so it can be divided into 2 right angled triangles.

Hence $\sin\theta = \frac{\sqrt{7}}{4}$, $\cos\theta = \frac{3}{4} = 0\cdot75$,

$\tan\theta = \frac{\sqrt{7}}{3}$.

(b) $\sin\theta = \sqrt{1-x^2}$, $\cos\theta = x$,

$\tan\theta = \frac{\sqrt{1-x^2}}{x}$.

Section 8.3 Solutions

1

(i) (a) $\cos^{-1}1 = 0°$ (b) $\sin^{-1}1 = 90°$
(c) $\cos^{-1}0\cdot2 = 78\cdot46°$ (d) $\sin^{-1}0\cdot2 = 11\cdot54°$
(e) $\cos^{-1}0\cdot6 = 53\cdot13°$ (f) $\sin^{-1}0\cdot6 = 36\cdot87°$

(ii) (a) $\cos^{-1} = 0$ (b) $\sin^{-1}1 = 1\cdot57 \left(=\frac{\pi}{2}\right)$
(c) $\cos^{-1}0\cdot2 = 1\cdot37$ (d) $\sin^{-1}0\cdot2 = 0\cdot20$
(e) $\cos^{-1}0\cdot6 = 0\cdot93$ (f) $\sin^{-1}0\cdot6 = 0\cdot64$

(iii) A calculator will give an error message. $\sin\theta$ always lies between -1 and $+1$ so there is no meaning to $\sin^{-1}2$.

(iv) (a) $\tan^{-1}0\cdot2 = 0\cdot20$ (b) $\tan^{-1}2\cdot4 = 67\cdot38°$
(c) $\tan^{-1}7\cdot5 = 1\cdot44$
Notice that the tangent is not restricted to the ran -1 to $+1$.

2

(i) (a) Using a calculator, $\sin^{-1}0\cdot866 = 60°$. This angle lies between $0°$ and $90°$, so it is the basic angle.
The second angle is $(180° - 60°) = 120°$.
Hence $\sin^{-1}0\cdot866 = 60°$ and $\sin^{-1}0\cdot866 = 120°$.

(b) Using a calculator, $\sin^{-1}\frac{1}{\sqrt{2}} = 45°$.
The second angle is $(180° - 45°) = 135°$.
Hence $\sin^{-1}\frac{1}{\sqrt{2}} = 45°$ and $\sin^{-1}\frac{1}{\sqrt{2}} = 135°$.

(ii) Using a calculator, $\sin^{-1}0\cdot2 = 0\cdot20$. This angle lies between 0 and $\frac{\pi}{2}$, so it is the basic angle.
The second angle is $(\pi - 0\cdot2) = 2\cdot94$.

(iii) From the original definition of $\sin\theta$,
$\sin^{-1}(0) = 0°$, $\sin^{-1}0 = 180°$,
and $\sin^{-1}(0) = 360°$ $(0, \pi$ and $2\pi)$.
In each case the y-co-ordinate of the corresponding point on the unit circle is zero.

3

(i) (a) Using a calculator, $\sin^{-1}(-0\cdot866) = -60°$, so the basic angle is $60°$.
The required angles are therefore $(180° + 60°)$ and $(360° - 60°)$.
Hence $\sin^{-1}(-0\cdot866) = 240°$ and $\sin^{-1}(-0\cdot866) = 300°$.

(b) Using a calculator, $\sin^{-1}\left(-\frac{1}{\sqrt{2}}\right) = -45°$,
so the basic angle is $45°$.
The required angles are therefore $(180° + 45°)$ and $(360° - 45°)$.
Hence $\sin^{-1}\left(-\frac{1}{\sqrt{2}}\right) = 225°$ and $\sin^{-1}\left(-\frac{1}{\sqrt{2}}\right) = 315°$.

(ii) Using a calculator, $\sin^{-1}(-0\cdot4) = -0\cdot41$, so the basic angle is $0\cdot41$.
The required angles are therefore $(\pi + 0\cdot41)$ and $(2\pi - 0\cdot41)$.
Hence $\sin^{-1}(-0\cdot4) = 3\cdot55$ and $\sin^{-1}(-0\cdot4) = 5\cdot87$.

(iii) From the original definition of $\sin\theta$,
$\sin^{-1}(-1) = 270°$ $\left(=\frac{3\pi}{2}\right)$.

4

(i) (a) The angles lie in the first and fourth quadrants.
Using a calculator, $\cos^{-1}\frac{\sqrt{3}}{2} = 30°$.
The other angle is $(360° - 30°)$.
Hence $\cos^{-1}\frac{\sqrt{3}}{2} = 30°$ and $\cos^{-1}\frac{\sqrt{3}}{2} = 330°$.

(b) The angles lie in the second and third quadrants.
Using a calculator, $\cos^{-1}\left(-\frac{\sqrt{3}}{2}\right) = 150°$, one of the required angles.
The basic angle is $30°$ since, $\cos(180° - 30°) = -\cos30°$. The other angle is $(180° + 30°)$.
Hence $\cos^{-1}\left(-\frac{\sqrt{3}}{2}\right) = 150°$ and $\cos^{-1}\left(-\frac{\sqrt{3}}{2}\right) = 210°$.

(c) The angles lie in the first and fourth quadrants.
Using a calculator, $\cos^{-1} 0.707 = 45°$. The other angle is $(360° - 45°)$.
Hence $\cos^{-1} 0.707 = 45°$ and $\cos^{-1} 0.707 = 315°$.

(d) The angles lie in the second and third quadrants.
Using a calculator, $\cos^{-1}(-0.707) = 135°$, so the basic angle is $45°$. The other angle is $(180° + 45°)$.
Hence $\cos^{-1}(-0.707) = 135°$ and $\cos^{-1}(-0.707) = 225°$.

(ii) (a) The angles lie in the first and fourth quadrants.
Using a calculator, $\cos^{-1} 0.4 = 1.16$. The other angle is $(2\pi - 1.16)$.
Hence $\cos^{-1} 0.4 = 1.16$ and $\cos^{-1} 0.4 = 5.12$.

(b) The angles lie in the second and third quadrants.
Using a calculator $\cos^{-1}(-0.4) = 1.98$. The basic angle is 1.16 since $\cos(\pi - 1.16)$ $= -\cos 1.16 = \cos 1.98$. The other angle is $(\pi + 1.16)$.
Hence $\cos^{-1}(-0.4) = 1.98$ and $\cos^{-1}(-0.4) = 4.30$.

(iii) From the original definition of $\cos \theta$,
$\cos^{-1} 0 = 90°$ and $\cos^{-1} 0 = 270° \left(\dfrac{\pi}{2} \text{ and } \dfrac{3\pi}{2}\right)$.

(iv) From the original definition of $\cos \theta$,
$\cos^{-1}(-1) = 180° \ (= \pi)$.

5

(i) (a) The angles lie in the first and third quadrants.
Using a calculator, $\tan^{-1} 1.732 = 60°$. The other angle is $(180° + 60°)$.
Hence $\tan^{-1} 1.732 = 60°$ and $\tan^{-1} 1.732 = 240°$.

(b) The angles lie in the second and fourth quadrants.
Using a calculator, $\tan^{-1}(-1.732) = -60°$, so the basic angle is $60°$ and the required angles are $(180° - 60°)$ and $(360° - 60°)$.
Hence, $\tan^{-1}(-1.732) = 120°$ and $\tan^{-1}(-1.732) = 300°$.

(c) The angles lie in the first and third quadrants.
Using a calculator, $\tan^{-1}\left(-\dfrac{1}{\sqrt{3}}\right) = 30°$.
The other angle is $(180° + 30°)$.
Hence $\tan^{-1} \dfrac{1}{\sqrt{3}} = 30°$ and
$\tan^{-1}\left(\dfrac{1}{\sqrt{3}}\right) = 210°$.

(d) The angles lie in the second and fourth quadrants.
Using a calculator, $\tan^{-1}\left(-\dfrac{1}{\sqrt{3}}\right) = -30°$, so the basic angle is $30°$ and the required angles are $(180° - 30°)$ and $(360° - 30°)$.
Hence $\tan^{-1}\left(-\dfrac{1}{\sqrt{3}}\right) = 150°$ and
$\tan^{-1}\left(-\dfrac{1}{\sqrt{3}}\right) = 330°$.

(ii) (a) The angles lie in the first and third quadrants.
Using a calculator, $\tan^{-1} 0.2 = 0.20$. The other angle is $(\pi + 0.20)$.
Hence $\tan^{-1} 0.2 = 0.20$ and $\tan^{-1} 0.2 = 3.34$.

(b) The angles lie in the second and third quadrants.
Using a calculator, $\tan^{-1}(-0.2) = -0.20$, so the basic angle is 0.20. The required angles are therefore $(\pi - 0.20)$ and $(2\pi - 0.20)$.
Hence $\tan^{-1}(-0.2) = 2.94$ and $\tan^{-1}(-0.2) = 6.08$.

(iii) From the original definition of $\tan \theta$,
$\tan^{-1} 0 = 0°$, $\tan^{-1} 0 = 180°$ and $\tan^{-1} 0 = 360°$ $(0, \pi \text{ and } 2\pi)$.

6

(i) (a) $17.46°$, $162.54°$ (b) $45.57°$, $314.43°$
(c) $72.65°$, $252.65°$ (d) $216.87°$, $323.13°$
(e) $95.74°$, $264.26°$ (f) $158.20°$, $338.20°$

(ii) (a) 0.93, 2.21 (b) 1.93, 4.35 (c) 2.03, 5.18
(d) 0.45, 5.83 (e) 3.24, 6.18 (f) 1.37, 4.51

(iii) (a) $\cos(-40°) = \cos 40°$
(b) $\tan(-14°) = -\tan(14°)$
(c) $\sin\left(\dfrac{-3\pi}{4}\right) = -\sin\left(\dfrac{3\pi}{4}\right) = -\sin\dfrac{\pi}{4}$
(d) $\sin(-2\theta) = -\sin 2\theta$
(e) $\cos\left(\dfrac{-3\theta}{4}\right) = \cos\dfrac{3\theta}{4}$
(f) $\tan\left(\dfrac{-4\theta}{5}\right) = -\tan\dfrac{4\theta}{5}$.

Section 8.4 Solutions

1

(i) Consider $\hat{CAB}$.
$\cos \hat{CAB} = \dfrac{\text{adjacent}}{\text{hypotenuse}} = \dfrac{AB}{AC} = \dfrac{7}{25}$
so $\hat{CAB} = \cos^{-1} \dfrac{7}{25} = 73.74°$
and $\hat{ACB} = 90° - \hat{CAB} = (90° - 73.74°)$
$= 16.26°$.

(ii)   Consider $X\hat{Z}Y$.

$$\sin X\hat{Z}Y = \frac{\text{opposite}}{\text{hypotenuse}} = \frac{XY}{YZ} = \frac{1}{3}$$

so $X\hat{Z}Y = \sin^{-1} \frac{1}{3} = 19\cdot47°$

and $X\hat{Y}Z = 90° - X\hat{Y}Z = (90° - 19\cdot47°)$
$= 70\cdot53°$.

(iii)   Consider $Q\hat{R}P$.

$$\tan Q\hat{R}P = \frac{\text{opposite}}{\text{adjacent}} = \frac{QP}{QR} = \frac{7}{4}$$

so $Q\hat{R}P = \tan^{-1} \frac{7}{4} = 60\cdot26°$

and $Q\hat{P}R = 90° - Q\hat{R}P = 29\cdot74°$.

(iv)   Consider $L\hat{N}M$.

$$\tan L\hat{N}M = \frac{\text{opposite}}{\text{adjacent}} = \frac{LM}{MN} = \frac{5}{2},$$

so $L\hat{N}M = \tan^{-1} \frac{5}{2} = 68\cdot20°$

and $M\hat{L}N = 90° - L\hat{N}M = 21\cdot80°$.

(v)   Consider $S\hat{T}V$.

$$\cos S\hat{T}V = \frac{\text{adjacent}}{\text{hypotenuse}} = \frac{ST}{VT} = \frac{1}{\sqrt{2}}$$

so $S\hat{T}V = \cos^{-1} \frac{1}{\sqrt{2}} = 45°$

and $S\hat{V}T = 45°$.

You may have found the angles in a different order by considering different ratios. This doesn't matter; your answers should still agree with ours.

2

(i) $\frac{PQ}{QR} = \tan 63°$, so

$QR = \frac{PQ}{\tan 63°} = \frac{5}{\tan 63°} = 2\cdot55''.$

$\frac{PQ}{PR} = \sin 63°$, so

$PR = \frac{PQ}{\sin 63°} = \frac{5}{\sin 63°} = 5\cdot61''.$

(ii) $\frac{AC}{AB} = \sin 60°$, so

$AC = AB \sin 60° = 4 \frac{\sqrt{3}}{2} = 2\sqrt{3}.$

$\frac{BC}{AB} = \cos 60°$, so

$BC = AB \cos 60° = 4(\frac{1}{2}) = 2.$

(iii) $\frac{XY}{YZ} = \tan 45°$, so

$XY = YZ \tan 45° = 2\sqrt{2}(1) = 2\sqrt{2}.$

$\frac{YZ}{XZ} = \cos 45°$, so

$XZ = \frac{YZ}{\cos 45°} = 2\sqrt{2} \div \frac{1}{\sqrt{2}} = 4.$

3

(i)   (a) $XZ^2 = XY^2 + YZ^2 = 36 + 4 = 40$, so
    $XZ = \sqrt{40} = 6\cdot32.$

$\tan X\hat{Z}Y = \frac{XY}{YZ} = \frac{6}{2} = 3$, so

$\tan^{-1} X\hat{Z}Y = \tan^{-1} 3 = 71\cdot57°$
$Y\hat{X}Z = 90° - X\hat{Z}Y = 18\cdot43°.$

(b) $BC^2 = AB^2 + AC^2$, so $AB^2 = BC^2 - AC^2$
    $= 16 - 1 = 15$ and $AB = \sqrt{15} = 3\cdot87.$

$\cos A\hat{C}B = \frac{AC}{BC} = \frac{1}{4}$, so

$A\hat{C}B = \cos^{-1} 0\cdot25 = 75\cdot52°$ and
$A\hat{B}C = 90° - A\hat{C}B = 14\cdot48°.$

(c) $EF^2 = DE^2 + DF^2$, so $DF^2 = EF^2 - DE^2$
    $= (14)^2 - (10)^2 = 96$, and $DF = \sqrt{96} = 9\cdot80.$

$\sin D\hat{F}E = \frac{DE}{EF} = \frac{10}{14}$, so

$D\hat{F}E = \sin^{-1} (\frac{10}{14}) = 45\cdot58°$ and
$D\hat{E}F = 90° - D\hat{F}E = 44\cdot42°.$

Again, you may have obtained these ans rs in a different order; this doesn't matter as ig as your answers agree with ours.

(ii)   (a) $X\hat{Y}Z = 90° - 70° = 20°$.

$\frac{XZ}{YZ} = \cos 70°$, so $XZ = 19 \cos 70° = 6\cdot50$

$\frac{XY}{YZ} = \sin 70°$, so $XY = 19 \sin 70° = 17\cdot85.$

(b) $P\hat{Q}R = 90° - 64° = 26°$.

$\frac{PQ}{PR} = \tan 64°$, so $PQ = 3 \tan 64° = 6\cdot15$

$\frac{PR}{QR} = \cos 64°$, so $QR = \frac{3}{\cos 64°} = 6\cdot84.$

(c) $A\hat{C}B = 90° - 54° = 36°$.

$\frac{BC}{AB} = \tan 54°$, so $AB = \frac{16}{\tan 54°} = 11\cdot62$

$\frac{BC}{AC} = \sin 54°$, so $AC = \frac{16}{\sin 54°} = 19\cdot78.$

4

(i)   (a) $x^2 = y^2 + (2)^2$, so $x = \sqrt{y^2 + 4}.$
    (b) $a^2 = 1 + x^2$, so $x^2 = a^2 - 1$ and $x = \sqrt{a^2 - 1}.$
    (c) $a + b = a + x^2$, so $x^2 = b$ and $x = \sqrt{b}.$

(ii)   (a) $PQ = \frac{a}{\tan \theta}$ (b) $QR = \frac{a}{\sin \theta}$
    (c) $P\hat{R}Q = 90° - \theta.$

(iii)   (a) True; in $\triangle PSQ$ $\sin \theta = \frac{PS}{PQ} = \frac{h}{r}.$

(b) True; in $\triangle PQR$ $\sin \theta = \frac{PR}{QR} = \frac{q}{p}.$

(c) True; $\triangle PQR$ and $\triangle SPR$ are similar since $R\hat{S}P = R\hat{P}Q = 90°$ and $\hat{R}$ is common to both triangles. Hence $S\hat{P}R = \theta$ and

$\sin \theta = \frac{SR}{PR}.$

(d) False; in $\triangle$PQR $\tan \theta = \dfrac{PQ}{PR} = \dfrac{r}{q}$.

(e) False; $P\hat{S}Q = 90°$ and $\tan 90°$ is not defined.

(f) True; in $\triangle$PSR $\sin \phi = \dfrac{PS}{PR} = \dfrac{h}{q}$, so $h = q \sin \phi$.

(g) False; in $\triangle$PSQ $r^2 = PS^2 + QS^2 = h^2 + QS^2$, but $QS \neq p$.

(h) True; in $\triangle$PSR $q^2 = h^2 + SR^2$, so $SR^2 = q^2 - h^2$.

(i) True; $Q\hat{P}S = \phi$ and in $\triangle$PSR, $\sin \phi = \dfrac{h}{q}$.

5

(i) (a) Area $= \frac{1}{2}(AC)(BC) \sin A\hat{C}B$
$= (\frac{1}{2})(2)(5)(\sin 40°) = 3\cdot21$ sq. units.

(b) Area $= \frac{1}{2}(XY)(YZ) \sin X\hat{Y}Z$
$= (\frac{1}{2})(7)(12)(\sin 81°) = 41\cdot48$ sq. units.

(c) Area $= \frac{1}{2}(RS)(ST) \sin R\hat{S}T$
$= (\frac{1}{2})(1)(1)(\sin 100°) = 0\cdot49$ sq. units.

(d) $\triangle$PQR is equilateral, so $P\hat{Q}R = 60°$.
Area $= (\frac{1}{2})(1)(1)(\sin 60°) = \dfrac{\sqrt{3}}{4}$ sq. units.

(ii) (a) $\triangle$ABC is isosceles, so the perpendicular height BD bisects AC and $BD = 4 \tan 50°$.

(b) Area $= \frac{1}{2}(AC)(BD) = \frac{1}{2}(8)(4) \tan 50°$
$= 19\cdot07$ sq. units.

(iii) (a) $X\hat{Y}Z = 180° - (\alpha + \beta)$

(b) Area $= \frac{1}{2}(XY)(YZ) \sin X\hat{Y}Z$
$= \frac{1}{2}pq \sin (180° - (\alpha + \beta))$
$= \frac{1}{2}pq \sin (\alpha + \beta)$.

6

(i)

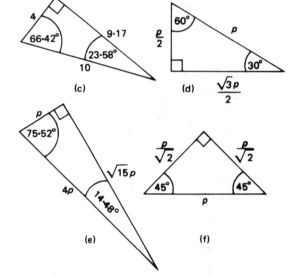

(ii) (a) $3\cdot12$ sq. units   (b) $54\cdot13$ sq. units

(c) $3t^2$ (d) $\dfrac{p^2}{4} \tan \theta$.

Section 8·5 Solutions

1

(i)

θ	$-\pi$	$\dfrac{-3\pi}{4}$	$\dfrac{-2\pi}{3}$	$\dfrac{-\pi}{2}$	$\dfrac{-\pi}{3}$	$\dfrac{-\pi}{6}$	0	$\dfrac{\pi}{6}$	$\dfrac{\pi}{3}$	$\dfrac{\pi}{2}$	$\dfrac{2\pi}{3}$	$\dfrac{3\pi}{4}$	π
$\sin \theta$	0	$-0\cdot7$	$-0\cdot9$	-1	$-0\cdot9$	$-0\cdot5$	0	$0\cdot5$	$0\cdot9$	1	$0\cdot9$	$0\cdot7$	0

(ii)

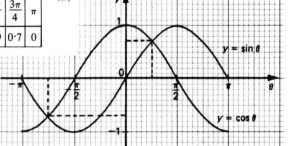

(iii)

θ	$-\pi$	$\dfrac{-3\pi}{4}$	$\dfrac{-2\pi}{3}$	$\dfrac{-\pi}{2}$	$\dfrac{-\pi}{3}$	$\dfrac{-\pi}{6}$	0	$\dfrac{\pi}{6}$	$\dfrac{\pi}{3}$	$\dfrac{\pi}{2}$	$\dfrac{2\pi}{3}$	$\dfrac{3\pi}{4}$	π
$\cos \theta$	-1	$-0\cdot7$	$-0\cdot5$	0	$0\cdot5$	$0\cdot9$	1	$0\cdot9$	$0\cdot5$	0	$-0\cdot5$	$-0\cdot7$	-1

(iv) See the graph above right.

(v)   The points are approximately $\left(\frac{\pi}{4}, 0{\cdot}7\right)$

and $\left(-\frac{3\pi}{4}, -0{\cdot}7\right)$.

(vi)   These co-ordinates give the solutions to

$\sin\theta = \cos\theta$ or $\dfrac{\sin\theta}{\cos\theta} = \tan\theta = 1$.

If the graphs are extended then there will be many more solutions. See Exercise 8.5(iv).

2

(i) $\sin 45° = \dfrac{1}{\sqrt{2}}$

(ii) $\cos 45° = \dfrac{1}{\sqrt{2}}$, so $2 \times \sin 45° \cos 45°$

$= 2 \times \dfrac{1}{\sqrt{2}} \times \dfrac{1}{\sqrt{2}} = \dfrac{2}{2} = 1$.

(iii)   Check that your key sequence gives
$2 \times \sin 45° \cos 45° = 1$.
You should be able to evaluate the expression as it is written, although you will have to enter the angle first before finding the sine or cosine. Try the sequence

$\boxed{2}\ \boxed{\times}\ \boxed{45}\ \boxed{\sin}\ \boxed{\times}\ \boxed{45}\ \boxed{\cos}\ \boxed{=}$.

(iv)

θ	0°	15°	30°	45°	60°	75°	90°	105°	120°	135°	150°	165°	180°
$2\sin\theta\cos\theta$	0	0·5	0·9	1	0·9	0·5	0	−0·5	−0·9	−1	−0·9	−0·5	0

(v)

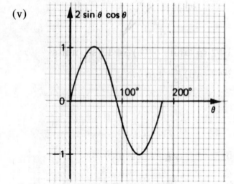

(vi)   (a) The largest value is +1.
(b) The smallest value is −1.
In fact the graph looks like the graph of $\sin\theta$ but it repeats every 180° rather than every 360°.

(vii)

θ	0°	20°	40°	60°	80°	100°	120°	140°	160°	180°
$\sin 2\theta$	0	0·6	1	0·9	0·3	−0·3	−0·9	−1	−0·6	0

(viii) The graph of $\sin 2\theta$ lies exactly on top of the graph of $2\sin\theta\cos\theta$. See Part (v).

(ix)

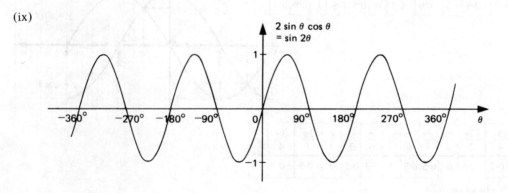

(x) The general result suggested by these graphs is
$\sin 2\theta = 2 \sin \theta \cos \theta$. Check this by
substituting values for θ.
Notice that the graph of $\sin 2\theta$ is very similar
to the graph of $\sin \theta$ but it repeats every $180°$
rather than every $360°$, which makes it appear
more squashed.

3

(i) $\sin 30° = \frac{1}{2}$

(ii) $1 - 2(\sin 30°)^2 = 1 - 2(\frac{1}{2})^2 = 1 - 2(\frac{1}{4}) = \frac{1}{2}$ or $0·5$.

(iii) First of all investigate a sequence to evaluate
$1 - 2x^2$ and check it by substituting $x = 0·5$.
Now replace x with $\sin 30°$. You may be
able to evaluate the expression as it is written
but you may need to insert brackets as in
$1 - (2(\sin 30°)^2)$.

(iv)

θ	0°	15°	30°	45°	60°	75°	90°	105°	120°	135°	150°	165°	180°
$1 - 2(\sin \theta)^2$	1	0·9	0·5	0	-0·5	-0·9	-1	-0·9	-0·5	0	0·5	0·9	1

(v)

(vi) (a) The largest value is $+1$.
(b) The smallest value is -1.
In fact the graph looks like the graph of $\cos \theta$
but it repeats every $180°$ rather than every
$360°$.

(vii) (a) $2(\cos 60°)^2 - 1 = 2(0·5)^2 - 1 = -0·5$
(b) $(\cos 90°)^2 - (\sin 90°)^2 = 0 - 1 = -1$

(viii) First investigate key sequences for
$2x^2 - 1$ and $x^2 - y^2$.
Now put $x = \cos \theta$ and $y = \sin \theta$.
Again, you should be able to evaluate the
expressions as they are written although you
may need to use brackets.

(ix) (a)

θ	0°	15°	30°	45°	60°	75°	90°	105°	120°	135°	150°	165°	180°
$2(\cos \theta)^2 - 1$	1	0·9	0·5	0	-0·5	-0·9	-1	-0·9	-0·5	0	0·5	0·9	1

(b)

θ	0°	15°	30°	45°	60°	75°	90°	105°	120°	135°	150°	165°	180°
$(\cos \theta)^2 - (\sin \theta)^2$	1	0·9	0·5	0	-0·5	-0·9	-1	-0·9	-0·5	0	0·5	0·9	1

(x) The three tables are identical, so
$1 - 2(\sin \theta)^2 = 2(\cos \theta)^2 - 1 = (\cos \theta)^2 - (\sin \theta)^2$.

(xi)

θ	0°	20°	40°	60°	80°	100°	120°	140°	160°	180°
$\cos 2\theta$	1	0·8	0·2	-0·5	-0·9	-0·9	-0·5	0·2	0·8	1

The graph of $\cos 2\theta$ lies exactly on top of the
graph of $1 - 2(\sin \theta)^2$. See Part (v) above.

Countdown to Mathematics

(xii) The graphs suggest that $\cos 2\theta = 1 - 2(\sin \theta)^2$,
and Part (x) indicates that

$$\cos 2\theta = 1 - 2(\sin \theta)^2$$
$$\cos 2\theta = 2(\cos \theta)^2 - 1$$
$$\cos 2\theta = (\cos \theta)^2 - (\sin \theta)^2.$$

Check by substituting values for θ.
Notice that the graph of $\cos 2\theta$ is very similar
to the graph of $\cos \theta$, but it repeats every $180°$
rather than every $360°$, which makes it appear
more squashed.

4

(i)

θ	0	$\frac{\pi}{6}$	$\frac{\pi}{4}$	$\frac{\pi}{3}$	$\frac{2\pi}{3}$	$\frac{5\pi}{6}$	π	$\frac{4\pi}{3}$	$\frac{5\pi}{3}$	2π	$\frac{7\pi}{3}$	$\frac{8\pi}{3}$	3π	$\frac{10\pi}{3}$	$\frac{11\pi}{3}$	4π
$\tan \theta$	0	0·6	1	1·7	−1·7	−0·6	0	1·7	−1·7	0	1·7	−1·7	0	1·7	−1·7	0

(ii) (a) $\theta = \frac{\pi}{2}, \frac{3\pi}{2}, \frac{5\pi}{2}, \frac{7\pi}{2}$. For each of these values
of θ, $\cos \theta = 0$ and so $\tan \theta$ is undefined.

(b)

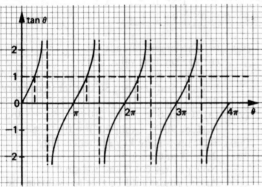

(iii) $\theta = \frac{\pi}{4}, \frac{5\pi}{4}, \frac{9\pi}{4}, \frac{13\pi}{4}$.

(iv) $\frac{\pi}{4}, \frac{5\pi}{4}, \frac{9\pi}{4}, \frac{13\pi}{4}, \frac{17\pi}{4}, \frac{21\pi}{4}$.

(v) The first solution is $\frac{\pi}{4}$.

The second solution is $\frac{\pi}{4} + \pi = \frac{\pi}{4} + (2 - 1)\pi$.

The third solution is $\frac{\pi}{4} + 2\pi = \frac{\pi}{4} + (3 - 1)\pi$.

The fourth solution is $\frac{\pi}{4} + 3\pi = \frac{\pi}{4} + (4 - 1)\pi$.

The nth solution is therefore $\frac{\pi}{4} + (n - 1)\pi$ or
$\frac{(4n - 3)}{4}\pi$.

5

(i) (a) $\frac{2(3)}{1 - 3^2} = -\frac{6}{8} = -\frac{3}{4}$ or $-0·75$.

(b) $\frac{2(\sqrt{3})}{1 - (\sqrt{3})^2} = \frac{2\sqrt{3}}{-2} = -\sqrt{3} = -1·732$

(ii) Remember that $\frac{2x}{1 - x^2}$ is the same as
$2x \div (1 - x^2)$.

(iii) You may need to take more care here. If in
doubt, insert extra brackets. Try substituting
$\theta = 0$ as an extra check.

(v) (a) When $\theta = 45°$ $\tan \theta = 1$ and $1 - (\tan \theta)^2$
$= 1 - 1 = 0$.

The denominator is zero, so $\frac{2 \tan \theta}{1 - (\tan \theta)^2}$ is
undefined at $\theta = 45°$.

(b) Similarly, when $\theta = 135°$, $\tan \theta = -1$ and
$1 - (\tan \theta)^2 = 0$, so $\theta = 135°$ must also be
excluded.

(iv)

θ	0°	20°	40°	60°	80°	100°	120°	140°	160°	180°
$\dfrac{2 \tan \theta}{1 - (\tan \theta)^2}$	0	0·8	5·7	−1·7	−0·4	0·4	1·7	−5·7	−0·8	0

(vi)

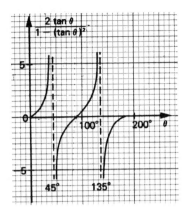

(vii)

θ	0°	20°	40°	60°	80°	100°	120°	140°	160°	180°
tan 2θ	0	0·8	5·7	−1·7	−0·4	0·4	1·7	−5·7	−0·8	0

The graph of tan 2θ lies exactly on top of the graph of $\dfrac{2 \tan \theta}{1 - (\tan \theta)^2}$. See Part (vi) above.

(viii) The graphs suggest that $\tan 2\theta = \dfrac{2 \tan \theta}{1 - (\tan \theta)^2}$.

Check this by substituting values for θ.
Notice that the graph of tan 2θ is very similar to the graph of tan θ, but it repeats every 90° rather than every 180°.

6

(i) (a) $\sin 30° = 0·5$ (b) $\cos 60° = 0·5$, so $\sin 30° = \cos 60°$.

(ii) (a) $\sin 60° = \dfrac{\sqrt{3}}{2}$ (b) $\cos 30° = \dfrac{\sqrt{3}}{2}$

(iii)

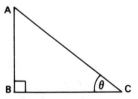

$\triangle ABC$ is right angled and $A\hat{C}B = \theta$. Hence $B\hat{A}C = 90° - \theta$.

Now, $\sin A\hat{C}B = \dfrac{AB}{AC} = \sin \theta$ and $\cos B\hat{A}C = \dfrac{AB}{AC} = \sin \theta$.

Hence $\cos (90° - \theta) = \sin \theta$.

Similarly, $\cos \theta = \dfrac{BC}{AC} = \sin B\hat{A}C$, so $\sin (90° - \theta) = \cos \theta$.

7

(i) (a) $\sin 30° = \frac{1}{2}$, so $(\sin 30°)^2 = (\frac{1}{2})^2 = \frac{1}{4}$.

(b) $\cos 30° = \dfrac{\sqrt{3}}{2}$, so $(\cos 30°)^2 = \left(\dfrac{\sqrt{3}}{2}\right)^2 = \dfrac{3}{4}$.

(c) $(\sin 30°)^2 + (\cos 30°)^2 = \frac{1}{4} + \frac{3}{4} = 1$

(ii) $\sin 60° = \dfrac{\sqrt{3}}{2}$ and $\cos 60° = \dfrac{1}{2}$, so

$$(\sin 60°)^2 + (\cos 60°)^2 = \left(\dfrac{\sqrt{3}}{2}\right)^2 + \left(\dfrac{1}{2}\right)^2$$
$$= \dfrac{3}{4} + \dfrac{1}{4} = 1.$$

(iii)

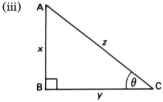

$AB = x$, $BC = y$ and $AC = z$.

$\sin \theta = \dfrac{AB}{AC} = \dfrac{x}{z}$ and $\cos \theta = \dfrac{BC}{AC} = \dfrac{y}{z}$,

so

$$(\sin \theta)^2 + (\cos \theta)^2 = \left(\dfrac{x}{z}\right)^2 + \left(\dfrac{y}{z}\right)^2 = \dfrac{x^2 + y^2}{z^2}.$$

Pythagoras' theorem states that
$AC^2 = AB^2 + BC^2$, so $z^2 = x^2 + y^2$.

Hence

$$(\sin \theta)^2 + (\cos \theta)^2 = \dfrac{x^2 + y^2}{z^2} = \dfrac{z^2}{z^2} = 1.$$

MODULE ⑨

9.1 Indices

9.2 Logarithms

9.3 Square Roots

9.4 Indices (II)

9.5 Factorisation

9.1 Indices

TRY THESE QUESTIONS FIRST

1   Use the y^x key on your calculator to evaluate $(-3)^{-5}$.

2   Simplify $x^4 \times x^2 \div x^{-3} \times x^{-7} \div x^3 \times x$.

3   Simplify $(y^{-4})^{-2}$.

4   Evaluate $\left(\dfrac{4}{9}\right)^{5/2}$ without using a calculator.

9.1(i) INDICES

You should already be familiar with power notation. It was first introduced in Module 1 when we discussed scientific notation and in Module 2 and Module 6 we used it to simplify algebraic expressions. Just to remind you:

Module 1, Section 1.3(iii).
Module 2, Section 2.2(iii).
Module 6, Section 6.4(ii).

   positive powers correspond to multiplication

For example,

$$x^9 = \underbrace{x\,x\,x\,x\,\ldots\,x\,x}_{9\ times}$$

   negative powers correspond to division

$$x^{-9} = \frac{1}{\underbrace{x\,x\,x\,x\,\ldots\,x\,x}_{9\ times}}$$

and to complete the pattern, anything to the power zero is equal to one.

So $2^0 = 1$, $6^0 = 1$ and $x^0 = 1$, for any value of x.

In this section we examine power notation, or *index notation* as it is often called, in more detail. We begin by giving you some practice in evaluating numerical powers. You should be able to do this using the y^x key on your calculator. This key can be used to find positive and negative powers. Investigate your calculator by evaluating $(2)^3$ and $(-2)^3$.

x^5 power or index

If your calculator displays an error message when you try to calculate $(-2)^3$ you will need to apply some mathematical reasoning. Remember

   if m is odd, $(-a)^m = -(a^m)$

   if n is even, $(-a)^n = a^n$.

Check your answer by working out $(2)^3$ and $(-2)^3$ on paper.

See Module 7, Section 7.3(i).

EXAMPLE

Evaluate (i) $(-2)^5$

(ii) $(-3)^{-4}$.

SOLUTION

(i) The index is odd, so $(-2)^5 = -(2^5)$.
Since $2^5 = 32$, $(-2)^5 = -(2^5) = -32$.

The index or power is 5, and 5 is an odd number.

(ii) The index is even, so, using a calculator, $(-3)^{-4} = 3^{-4} = 0\cdot0123$.

It doesn't matter whether the index is positive or negative.

TRY SOME YOURSELF

1   Use the y^x key on your calculator to evaluate each of the
following:
(i)   (a) 5^3 (b) 3^5 (c) 5^{-2} (d) 2^{-5} (e) $(-2)^5$ (f) $(-5)^2$
(ii)   (a) $(1\cdot147)^9$ (b) $(2\cdot7)^{-4}$ (c) $(-5\cdot73)^6$ (d) $(-2\cdot49)^{-3}$.

You should be able to check your answers to Part (i) without using a calculator.

9.1(ii) MULTIPLYING AND DIVIDING

We can demonstrate how to multiply two powers by writing out the calculations in full. For example,

$$a^2 \times a^5 = \overbrace{a \times a}^{2\ times} \times \overbrace{a \times a \times a \times a \times a}^{5\ times}$$
$$\underbrace{\qquad\qquad\qquad\qquad}_{7\ times}$$

$$= a^7.$$

Thus $a^2 \times a^5 = a^{(2 + 5)} = a^7$.

This suggests that to multiply two powers you need only add the indices. The rule works for both positive and negative indices, since, for example

Of course, the powers must involve the same symbol. You can simplify $a^2 \times a^5$ using this rule, but not $a^2 \times b^5$.

$$a^{-2} \times a^{-5} = \frac{1}{a \times a} \times \frac{1}{a \times a \times a \times a \times a} = \frac{1}{a^7} = a^{-7} = a^{(-2) + (-5)}$$

and

$$a^{-2} \times a^5 = \frac{1}{a \times a} \times a \times a \times a \times a \times a = \frac{\not{a} \times \not{a} \times a \times a \times a}{\not{a} \times \not{a}}$$

$$= a \times a \times a = a^3 = a^{(-2) + 5}.$$

The result is given below in its most general form.

$$\boxed{a^m \times a^n = a^{(m + n)}}$$

Here, m and n stand for any whole numbers.

$$\underbrace{(a \times \ldots \times a)}_{m \text{ times}} \times \underbrace{(a \times \ldots \times a)}_{n \text{ times}}$$

The next example illustrates how this rule can be used to multiply any number of terms.

EXAMPLE

Simplify $x^2 \times x^5 \times x^{-3} \times x^{-1} \times x$.

SOLUTION

$$x^2 \times x^5 \times x^{-3} \times x^{-1} \times x = x^{2 + 5 + (-3) + (-1) + 1}$$

$$= x^4$$

Remember that $x = x^1$.

TRY SOME YOURSELF

2(i) Evaluate each of the following without using a calculator:
(a) $2^2 \times 2^3$ (b) $3^2 \times 3^{-3}$ (c) $(-2)^4 \times (-2)$ (d) $2^{-2} \times 2^{-3}$
(e) $5^2 \times 5^{-3} \times 5^4 \times 5^{-1}$.

You can check your answers using a calculator.

(ii) Simplify each of the following:
(a) $b^2 \times b^9$ (b) $y^{-4} \times y^5$ (c) $z^4 z^{-3} z^2$ (d) $cc^4 c^{-9} c^4$.

Dividing

Division of one power by another is also illustrated by writing out the expression. For example,

$$a^6 \div a^4 = \frac{a^6}{a^4} = \frac{\not{a} \times \not{a} \times \not{a} \times \not{a} \times a \times a}{\not{a} \times \not{a} \times \not{a} \times \not{a}}$$

Reduce the fraction to its simplest form by cancelling.

$$= a \times a = a^2.$$

Thus $a^6 \div a^4 = a^{(6 - 4)} = a^2$.

This suggests that to divide one power by another you need only subtract the second index from the first. This rule also works for positive and negative indices, although you will need to take particular care when dividing by a negative power.

Again, the powers must involve the same symbols. You can simplify $a^6 \div a^4$ but not $a^6 \div b^4$.

EXAMPLE

Simplify $a^3 \div a^{-7}$.

SOLUTION

$$a^3 \div a^{-7} = a^{3-(-7)} = a^{3+7} = a^{10}$$

This can be illustrated by writing out the expression.

$$a^3 \div a^{-7} = (a \times a \times a) \div \frac{1}{a \times a \times a \times a \times a \times a \times a}$$

$$= (a \times a \times a) \times (a \times a \times a \times a \times a \times a \times a)$$

$$= a^{10}$$

To divide by a fraction, multiply by the reciprocal. The reciprocal of $\frac{1}{x}$ is just x.

Again, we give the result in its most general form.

$$a^m \div a^n = \frac{a^m}{a^n} = a^{(m-n)}$$

m and n stand for any whole numbers.

In fact this rule is essentially the same as the rule for multiplication, since

$$\frac{a^m}{a^n} = a^m \times \frac{1}{a^n} = a^m \times a^{-n} = a^{m+(-n)} = a^{(m-n)}.$$

We can now attach a meaning to the power zero. Notice that

$$\frac{2}{2} = 1, \quad \frac{987}{987} = 1, \quad \frac{a}{a} = 1, \quad \frac{a^2}{a^2} = 1, \quad \frac{a^3}{a^3} = 1$$

and in general,

$$\frac{a^m}{a^m} = 1.$$

Using the rule for division,

$$\frac{a^m}{a^m} = a^{(m-m)} = a^0.$$

This holds true for any value of a apart from a = 0. Remember that division by zero is not allowed.

Hence $a^0 = 1$.

The next examples combine multiplication and division.

EXAMPLE

Evaluate $2^2 \times 2^4 \div 2 \times 2^{-3} \div 2^{-4}$.

SOLUTION

The indices are added or subtracted depending upon whether the term is multiplied or divided.

$$2^2 \times 2^4 \div 2 \times 2^{-3} \div 2^{-4}$$

$$= 2^{2+4-1+(-3)-(-4)}$$

$$= 2^6 = 64$$

Remember, $2 = 2^1$.

EXAMPLE

Simplify $z^2 \times z^{-3} \div z^{-4} \times z^5$.

SOLUTION

$z^2 \times z^{-3} \div z^{-4} \times z^5 = z^{2 + (-3) - (-4) + 5} = z^8$

TRY SOME YOURSELF

3(i) Evaluate each of the following without using a calculator:
(a) $3^2 \div 3^5$ (b) $2^{-2} \div 2^4$ (c) $4^{-2} \div 4^{-5}$
(d) $3^4 \times 3^{-2} \div 3^{-4} \div 3^5 \times 3$ (e) $106^{11} \times 106^{-3} \div 106^8$.

(ii) Simplify each of the following:
(a) $a^2 \div a^9$ (b) $z^{-4} \div z^6$ (c) $q^3 \div q^{-4}$
(d) $a^2 \times a^{-3} \div a^4$ (e) $c \div c^{-4} \times c^2 \times 1$.

You may want to check your answers using a calculator.

9.1(iii) POWERS OF POWERS

We now investigate how to simplify an expression such as $(b^4)^3$.
You already know that

$$a^2 = a \times a$$

so if we put $a = 2^3$, then

$$(2^3)^2 = 2^3 \times 2^3 = 2^{3+3} = 2^6 = 2^{3 \times 2},$$

and if $a = b^4$, then

$$(b^4)^2 = b^4 \times b^4 = b^{4+4} = b^8 = b^{4 \times 2}.$$

Substitute $a = 2^3$ into $a^2 = a \times a$.

Similarly, since

$$a^3 = a \times a \times a$$
$$(2^3)^3 = 2^3 \times 2^3 \times 2^3 = 2^{3+3+3} = 2^9 = 2^{3 \times 3}$$

and

$$(b^4)^3 = b^4 \times b^4 \times b^4 = b^{4+4+4} = b^{12} = b^{4 \times 3}.$$

This suggests that to simplify powers of powers you need only multiply the indices. Again, the rule works for positive and negative indices.

EXAMPLE

Simplify (i) $(a^{-4})^2$

(ii) $(x^{-3})^{-4}$.

You can check these solutions by writing out each expression:

SOLUTION

(i) $(a^{-4})^2 = a^{(-4) \times 2} = a^{-8}$

(ii) $(x^{-3})^{-4} = x^{(-3) \times (-4)} = x^{12}$.

$$(a^{-4})^2 = (a^{-4}) \times (a^{-4}) = a^{-8}$$

$$(x^{-3})^{-4} = \frac{1}{x^{-3} \times x^{-3} \times x^{-3} \times x^{-3}}$$

$$= \frac{1}{x^{-12}} = x^{12}$$

The general result is

$$(a^m)^n = a^{mn}.$$

Where m and n stand for any whole numbers.

TRY SOME YOURSELF

4(i)   Evaluate each of the following without using a calculator:
(a) $(2^2)^2$ (b) $(2^3)^{-2}$ (c) $(3^2)^4$ (d) $(4^{-5})^{-2}$.

(ii)   Simplify each of the following:
(a) $(a^{12})^3$ (b) $(z^{-2})^{-3}$ (c) $(e^4)^{-2}$ (d) $(e^{-3})^4$.

9.1(iv)   FRACTIONAL INDICES

Up until now, all the indices we have considered have been whole numbers and it was possible to write out each power as a product. But it is not so easy to attach a meaning to a fractional index. For example, what is meant by an expression such as $a^{1/n}$?

For example,

$$a^n = \underbrace{a \times a \times \ldots \times a}_{n \text{ times}}$$

We now investigate the meaning of fractional indices.

TRY SOME YOURSELF

5   Use the y^x key on your calculator to evaluate each of the following:
(i) $4^{0 \cdot 5}$ (ii) $9^{0 \cdot 5}$ (iii) $16^{0 \cdot 5}$.

This exercise shows that for any positive a,

$$a^{1/2} = \sqrt{a}.$$

Notice that $a = (\sqrt{a})^2 = (a^{1/2})^2 = a^{1/2} \times a^{1/2} = a^{1/2 + 1/2} = a^1$.
This suggests that the rules for multiplying and dividing powers also apply to fractional indices. Thus,

$$(a^{1/3})^3 = a^{1/3} \times a^{1/3} \times a^{1/3} = a^1 = a$$
$$(a^{1/4})^4 = a^{1/4} \times a^{1/4} \times a^{1/4} \times a^{1/4} = a^1 = a$$
$$(a^{1/5})^5 = a^{1/5} \times a^{1/5} \times a^{1/5} \times a^{1/5} \times a^{1/5} = a^1 = a.$$

This means that $a^{1/3}$ is the cube root of a, since

$$(a^{1/3})^3 = a.$$

The cube root of a is sometimes written as $\sqrt[3]{a}$.

Similarly

$a^{1/4}$ is the fourth root of a

$a^{1/5}$ is the fifth root of a

and, in general, $a^{1/n}$ is the nth root of a, since

$$(a^{1/n})^n = a.$$

Written as $\sqrt[4]{a}$.

Written as $\sqrt[5]{a}$.

Written as $\sqrt[n]{a}$.

The following exercise enables you to verify this result for yourself using your calculator. Your calculator may have a key which evaluates roots. Alternatively, you may be able to use the y^x key. Otherwise you will just have to convert each fraction to a decimal and round off your answers accordingly.

Check with the maker's handbook how to find $\sqrt[x]{y}$ or $y^{1/x}$.

TRY SOME YOURSELF

6   Use your calculator to evaluate each of the following:
(i) $27^{1/3}$ (ii) $64^{1/6}$ (iii) $625^{1/4}$
(iv) $\left(\frac{1}{4}\right)^{1/2}$ (v) $\left(\frac{8}{27}\right)^{1/3}$.

Try finding $(-4)^{1/2}$ using your calculator. You will find that it is impossible. Notice however, that

$$(-2)^3 = -8, \text{ so } (-8)^{1/3} = -2.$$

$(-4)^{1/2} = \sqrt{-4}$. We've already shown that the square root of a negative number does not exist.

This indicates that you need to take care when working with fractional powers of negative numbers. In general,

> if n is even then the nth root of a negative number does not exist,

> but if n is odd then it is possible to find the nth root of any number, positive or negative.

You may still have difficulty if you do this on your calculator. Try finding $(-8)^{1/3}$.

At this stage we do not need to go into any further explanation since we will be concerned only with powers of positive numbers.

The rules for manipulating indices also work for fractional indices, so

$$a^m \times a^n = a^{m+n}$$
$$a^m \div a^n = a^{m-n}$$
$$(a^m)^n = a^{mn}.$$

for any value of m and n, positive, negative or zero, whole number or fraction.

Notice that
$$a^0 \times a^n = 1 \times a^n = a^n = a^{0+n}$$
etc.

Other fractional indices can be built up from $a^{1/n}$ using the rule

$$(a^m)^n = a^{mn}.$$

For example,

$$(a^{1/n})^2 = a^{1/n \times 2} = a^{2/n}$$
$$(a^{1/n})^3 = a^{1/n \times 3} = a^{3/n}$$
$$(a^{1/n})^m = a^{1/n \times m} = a^{m/n}.$$

We now consider some numerical examples.

EXAMPLE

Evaluate $8^{5/3}$.

SOLUTION

$$8^{5/3} = (8^{1/3})^5 = 2^5 = 32$$

Remember that $8^{1/3} = 2$ since $2^3 = 8$.

EXAMPLE

Evaluate $27^{2/3}$.

SOLUTION

$$27^{2/3} = (27^{1/3})^2 = 3^2 = 9$$

$27^{1/3} = 3$ since $3^3 = 27$.

TRY SOME YOURSELF

7   Use the answers to Exercise 6 to evaluate each of the following:
(i) $27^{4/3}$ (ii) $64^{-5/6}$ (iii) $625^{-3/4}$
(iv) $\left(\dfrac{1}{4}\right)^{5/2}$ (v) $\left(\dfrac{8}{27}\right)^{2/3}$.

It is probably easier to simplify an expression if it is expressed completely in terms of indices.

EXAMPLE

Simplify $(x^3)^{5/3}$.

SOLUTION

Using the rule $(a^m)^n = a^{mn}$
$$(x^3)^{5/3} = x^{3 \times 5/3} = x^5.$$

Multiply the indices:
$3 \times \frac{5}{3} = 5.$

TRY SOME YOURSELF

8   Simplify each of the following:
(i) $(b^5)^{3/5}$ (ii) $(c^4)^{5/2}$ (iii) $(d^{-6})^{4/3}$ (iv) $(f^{-4})^{-5/2}$.

By now you should be able to recognise some of the powers of 2, 3, 4 and 5.

For example,
$$4 = 2^2, \quad 8 = 2^3, \quad 16 = 2^4, \quad 32 = 2^5, \quad 64 = 2^6 \text{ etc.}$$
and
$$9 = 3^2, \quad 27 = 3^3, \quad 81 = 3^4 \text{ etc.}$$

This helps when evaluating numerical powers.

EXAMPLE

Evaluate $8^{5/3}$.

SOLUTION

$$8^{5/3} = (2^3)^{5/3} = 2^5 = 32$$

Compare this with the solution in the example above. Which is easier?

EXAMPLE

Evaluate $16^{5/4}$.

SOLUTION

$$16^{5/4} = (2^4)^{5/4} = 2^5 = 32$$

Multiply the indices:
$4 \times \frac{5}{4} = 5.$

EXAMPLE

Evaluate $27^{-2/3}$ without using a calculator.

260

SOLUTION

$$27^{-2/3} = (3^3)^{-2/3} = 3^{-2} = \frac{1}{3^2} = \frac{1}{9}$$

Multiply the indices:
$$3 \times \frac{(-2)}{3} = -2.$$

TRY SOME YOURSELF

9 Simplify each of the following without using a calculator:
(i)   (a) $81^{3/4}$ (b) $9^{5/2}$ (c) $16^{-3/4}$ (d) $(125)^{-2/3}$

You will need to recognise the number as a power of 2, 3 or 5.

     (e) $\left(\dfrac{1}{27}\right)^{4/3}$ (f) $\left(\dfrac{1}{8}\right)^{-2/3}$

(ii)   (a) $\left(\dfrac{8}{27}\right)^{-4/3}$ (b) $\left(\dfrac{16}{81}\right)^{3/2}$ (c) $\left(\dfrac{125}{8}\right)^{-4/3}$ (d) $\left(\dfrac{9}{4}\right)^{5/2}$.

After you have worked through this section you should be able to

a Evaluate numerical powers using a calculator
b Use the rules $a^m \times a^n = a^{m+n}$ and $a^m \div a^n = a^{m-n}$ to simplify numerical and algebraic expressions
c Use the rule $(a^m)^n = a^{mn}$ to simplify numerical and algebraic expressions
d Find the nth root of a number using your calculator
e Apply the rule $(a^m)^n$ to simplify expressions involving fractional indices

---

Finally here are some exercises if you want more practice.

TRY SOME MORE YOURSELF

10 (i) Evaluate each of the following using the y^x key on your calculator. Give your answers correct to three significant figures:
    (a) $(2 \cdot 173)^4$ (b) $(1 \cdot 321)^{-10}$ (c) $(5 \cdot 741)^3$ (d) $(-1 \cdot 321)^{-7}$.

(ii)   Simplify each of the following:
    (a) $2^3 \times 2^{-7} \div 2^{-10} \times 2^{-2} \times 2$ (b) $3^2 \div 3^{-2} \times 3^{10} \times 3^{-4} \div 3^6$
    (c) $a^{-4} \div a^{-4} \times a^{-9} \div a^3 \times a^5$ (d) $x^2 \div x^{-7} \times x^{-12} \div x^{-4}$.

(iii)   Simplify each of the following:
    (a) $(4^2)^{-8}$ (b) $(2^{-4})^3$ (c) $(a^5)^6$ (d) $(y^{-2})^{-4}$.

(iv)   Simplify each of the following:
    (a) $(z^{12})^{3/4}$ (b) $(x^{21})^{4/7}$ (c) $(2^{10})^{3/5}$
    (d) $(32)^{3/5}$ (e) $\left(\dfrac{27}{64}\right)^{-2/3}$ (f) $\left(\dfrac{4}{9}\right)^{-3/2}$.

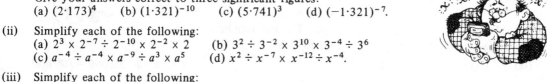

9.2 Logarithms

9.2(i) POWERS OF 10

In this section we show how the rule

$$a^n \times a^m = a^{n + m}$$

can be used to convert multiplication of any two numbers to addition. We start by considering an easy example which you should be able to do in your head, 100×1000. The two numbers can be converted immediately to powers of 10 to give

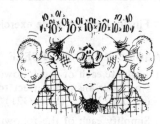

$$100 \times 1000 \qquad\qquad 100\,000$$
$$\downarrow \qquad\quad \downarrow \qquad\qquad\qquad \uparrow$$
$$10^2 \times 10^3 = 10^{2 + 3} = 10^5.$$

Check $100 \times 1000 = 100\,000$.

This suggests a method for multiplying any two numbers.

> (i)   Convert the numbers to powers of ten
> (ii)   Add the indices
> (iii)   Convert back to a number

TRY SOME YOURSELF

1   Use the method above to find each of the following:
(i) 10×10 (ii) 10×100 (iii) $1000 \times 10\,000$.

You can check your answers in your head.

The same method can even be used to find 1×1000.

$$1 \times 1000 \qquad\qquad 1000$$
$$\downarrow \qquad \downarrow \qquad\qquad \uparrow$$
$$10^0 \times 10^3 = 10^{(0+3)} = 10^3$$

We now show how the process can be extended. The table below was built up using the y^x key on a calculator.

x	10^x	Number
0	10^0	1·0000
0·1	$10^{0·1}$	1·2589
0·2	$10^{0·2}$	1·5849
0·3	$10^{0·3}$	1·9953
0·4	$10^{0·4}$	2·5119
0·5	$10^{0·5}$	3·1623
0·6	$10^{0·6}$	3·9811
0·7	$10^{0·7}$	5·0119
0·8	$10^{0·8}$	6·3096
0·9	$10^{0·9}$	7·9433
1·0	$10^{1·0}$	10·000

Check this yourself by finding $10^{0·1}$, $10^{0·2}$ etc. on your calculator. You should find that
$$10^{0·1} = 1·2589$$
$$10^{0·2} = 1·5849$$
and so on.

Notice that $1·5849 = 10^{0·2}$ and $1·9953 = 10^{0·3}$. Hence, using the method above,

Convert the numbers to powers of 10

$$1·5849 \times 1·9953 \qquad\qquad 3·1623$$
$$\downarrow \qquad\qquad \downarrow \qquad\qquad\qquad \uparrow$$
$$10^{0·2} \times 10^{0·3} = 10^{0·2+0·3} = 10^{0·5}$$

Add indices

Convert back using the table

Check this using a calculator.
1·5849 x 1·9953 = 3·1623.

TRY SOME YOURSELF

2 Use the table given to evaluate each of the following:
   (i) $1·5849 \times 2·5119$ (ii) $1·2589 \times 1·9953$
   (iii) $5·0119 \times 1·5849$.

Check using a calculator.

In fact the table can be used more extensively, as the next example illustrates.

EXAMPLE

Use the table to evaluate $5·0119 \times 6·3096$.

SOLUTION

$$5·0119 \times 6·3096 \qquad\qquad \boxed{?}$$
$$\downarrow \qquad\qquad \downarrow \qquad\qquad\qquad \uparrow$$
$$10^{0·7} \times 10^{0·8} = 10^{0·7+0·8} = 10^{1·5}$$

An estimate is given by 5 x 6 = 30.

CHECK YOUR ANSWERS

1 $25 \cdot 119 = 10 \times 2 \cdot 5119 = 10^{1 \cdot 4}$ *Section 9.2(i)*

    $0 \cdot 39811 = 10^{-1} \times 3 \cdot 9811 = 10^{-1} \times 10^{0 \cdot 6} = 10^{-0 \cdot 4}$

    $10^{1 \cdot 4} \times 10^{-0 \cdot 4} = 10^{1} = 10$, so $25 \cdot 119 \times 0 \cdot 39811 = 10$.

2 (i) $800 = 10^{2} \times 8$, so $\log_{10} 800 = 2 + 0 \cdot 9031 = 2 \cdot 9031$.   *Section·9.2(ii)*

  (ii) $-1 \cdot 0969 = -2 + 0 \cdot 9031$ so antilog $-1 \cdot 0969 = 10^{-2} \times 8 = 0 \cdot 08$.

3 (i) $3 \log_{10} 2 - \log_{10} 4 = \log_{10} 8 - \log_{10} 4$.   *Section 9.2(iii)*

                      $= \log_{10} \left(\frac{8}{4}\right) = \log_{10} 2$.

  (ii) $27 = 3^{3}$, so $\log_{3} 27 = 3$.

There is no entry in the table for $x = 1 \cdot 5$, but notice that
$$10^{1 \cdot 5} = 10^{1 + 0 \cdot 5} = 10 \times 10^{0 \cdot 5}.$$

From the table $10^{0 \cdot 5} = 3 \cdot 1623$, so
$$10^{1 \cdot 5} = 10 \times 3 \cdot 1623 = 31 \cdot 623.$$

Hence $5 \cdot 0119 \times 6 \cdot 3096 = 31 \cdot 623$.   *This agrees with the estimate.*

Using the y^{x} key, $10^{1 \cdot 5} = 31 \cdot 623$.

You may like to check this using your calculator. There may be some error since we have rounded everything to five significant figures, but you should find that the answers agree to this level of accuracy.

TRY SOME YOURSELF

3   Use the table to evaluate each of the following:
(i) $3 \cdot 9811 \times 3 \cdot 1623$ (ii) $7 \cdot 9433 \times 2 \cdot 5119$
(iii) $6 \cdot 3096 \times 7 \cdot 9433$

Thus, the table can be used to convert to and from numbers which are larger than 10.

EXAMPLE

Use the table to evaluate $158 \cdot 49 \times 39 \cdot 811$.

SOLUTION

Although $158 \cdot 49$ does not appear on the table,
$$158 \cdot 49 = 1 \cdot 5849 \times 100 = 1 \cdot 5849 \times 10^{2}.$$

Now, from the table, $1 \cdot 5849 = 10^{0 \cdot 2}$.

Hence $158 \cdot 49 = 10^{0 \cdot 2} \times 10^{2} = 10^{2 \cdot 2}$.   *Check by finding $10^{2 \cdot 2}$ on your calculator.*

Similarly,

$$39{\cdot}811 = 3{\cdot}9811 \times 10 = 10^{0{\cdot}6} \times 10^1 = 10^{1{\cdot}6}.$$

Check by finding $10^{1{\cdot}6}$ on your calculator.

Thus

$$\begin{array}{ccc} 158{\cdot}49 & \times & 39{\cdot}811 \\ \downarrow & & \downarrow \\ 10^{2{\cdot}2} & \times & 10^{1{\cdot}6} \end{array} = 10^{2{\cdot}2 + 1{\cdot}6} = 10^{3{\cdot}8}.$$

$10^{3{\cdot}8} = 10^3 \times 10^{0{\cdot}8} = 1000 \times 10^{0{\cdot}8}$, and from the table, $10^{0{\cdot}8} = 6{\cdot}3096$, so $10^{3{\cdot}8} = 6309{\cdot}6$.

Hence $158{\cdot}49 \times 39{\cdot}811 = 6309{\cdot}6$.

Check the answer using your calculator.

TRY SOME YOURSELF

4   Use the table to evaluate each of the following:
(i) $25{\cdot}119 \times 50{\cdot}119$ (ii) $125{\cdot}89 \times 31{\cdot}623$
(iii) $1584{\cdot}9 \times 39{\cdot}811$.

These exercises show that the table can be used to evaluate products of numbers which are larger than 10. The same table can also be used when the calculation involves numbers which are less than 1.

EXAMPLE

Use the table to evaluate $0{\cdot}15849 \times 0{\cdot}25119$.

SOLUTION

Notice that

$$0{\cdot}15849 = 1{\cdot}5849 \times 10^{-1}.$$

From the table, $1{\cdot}5849 = 10^{0{\cdot}2}$, so

$$0{\cdot}15849 = 10^{0{\cdot}2} \times 10^{-1} = 10^{0{\cdot}2 \, - \, 1} = 10^{-0{\cdot}8}.$$

The principle is exactly the same as that used to convert numbers to scientific notation: write each number as a number between 1 and 10 multiplied by a power of 10.

Similarly,

$$0{\cdot}25119 = 2{\cdot}5119 \times 10^{-1} = 10^{0{\cdot}4} \times 10^{-1} = 10^{-0{\cdot}6}.$$

Now

$$\begin{array}{ccc} 0{\cdot}15849 & \times & 0{\cdot}25119 \\ \downarrow & & \downarrow \\ 10^{-0{\cdot}8} & \times & 10^{-0{\cdot}6} \end{array} = 10^{-0{\cdot}8 + (-0{\cdot}6)} = 10^{-1{\cdot}4}.$$

In order to use the table we need to rewrite $10^{-1{\cdot}4}$ in terms of a *positive* power between 0 and 1. This is the most difficult part. It's tempting to write

$$10^{-1{\cdot}4} = 10^{-1} \times 10^{-0{\cdot}4}$$

but this doesn't help, since the powers are all negative. In fact

Take care. It's easy to get into difficulties with negative numbers. Notice that $-1 + 0{\cdot}4 = -0{\cdot}6$ and $-1 - 0{\cdot}4 = -1{\cdot}4$.

Countdown to Mathematics

$$10^{-1\cdot4} = 10^{-2} \times 10^{0\cdot6}$$
$$= 10^{-2} \times 3\cdot9811$$
$$= 0\cdot039811.$$

Check by adding the indices
$-2 + 0\cdot6 = -1\cdot4.$

Hence $0\cdot15849 \times 0\cdot25119 = 0\cdot039811.$

Check this using a calculator.

TRY SOME YOURSELF

5   Use the table to evaluate each of the following:
(i) $0\cdot19953 \times 0\cdot31623$ (ii) $0\cdot050119 \times 0\cdot63096$
(iii) $0\cdot079433 \times 0\cdot12589 \times 1\cdot9953.$

*Check your answers using a
calculator.*

The same principle can be used to divide one number by another
since

$$a^n \div a^m = \frac{a^n}{a^m} = a^n \times a^{-m} = a^{n-m}$$

but rather than add the indices we must subtract one index from
the other.

EXAMPLE

Use the table to evaluate $5\cdot0119 \times 0\cdot31623 \div 12\cdot589.$

SOLUTION

First convert each number to a power of 10.
$$5\cdot0119 = 10^{0\cdot7}$$
$$0\cdot31623 = 3\cdot1623 \times 10^{-1} = 10^{0\cdot5} \times 10^{-1} = 10^{-0\cdot5}$$
$$12\cdot598 = 1\cdot2598 \times 10^{1} = 10^{0\cdot1} \times 10^{1} = 10^{1\cdot1}$$

Add or subtract indices.
$$10^{0\cdot7} \times 10^{-0\cdot5} \div 10^{1\cdot1} = 10^{0\cdot7 - 0\cdot5 - 1\cdot1} = 10^{-0\cdot9}$$

Convert $10^{-0\cdot9}$ back to a number.
$$10^{-0\cdot9} = 10^{-1} \times 10^{0\cdot1}$$
$$= 10^{-1} \times 1\cdot2598 = 0\cdot12598$$

*Check this answer using a
calculator. Remember that there
may be some discrepancy because
we have rounded all the numbers
to five significant figures.*

TRY SOME YOURSELF

6   Use the table to evaluate each of the following:
(i) $0\cdot19953 \times 794\cdot33 \div 630\cdot96$ (ii) $0\cdot25119 \div 7\cdot9433 \times 63\cdot096$
(iii) $251\cdot19 \div 7943\cdot3 \times 0\cdot012589$
(iv) $31\cdot623 \div 63\cdot096 \div 0\cdot15849.$

9.2(ii) LOGARITHMS

When a number is expressed as a power of 10 the index is called the
logarithm (or just *log*) of the number. For example, $1\cdot9533 = 10^{0\cdot3}$,
so the logarithm of $1\cdot9533$ is $0\cdot3$. This is written as

*More precisely the power of 10
is the logarithm to base 10.*

$\log_{10} 1 \cdot 9533 = 0 \cdot 3.$

This indicates that the log is a power of 10

Similarly

$\log_{10} 1 \cdot 5849 = 0 \cdot 2$

$\log_{10} 10 = 1$

$\log_{10} 15 \cdot 849 = 1 \cdot 2.$

$1 \cdot 5849 = 10^{0 \cdot 2}$

$10 = 10^1$

$15 \cdot 849 = 10^{1 \cdot 2}$

The process of converting a power of 10 back to a number is called *finding the antilogarithm* (or *antilog*). For example,

$10^{0 \cdot 3} = 1 \cdot 9533$, so antilog $0 \cdot 3 = 1 \cdot 9533.$

This is the reverse process to finding the log; in a sense it 'undoes' the log. You may like to think of it as 'finding the number whose log is . . .'.

Similarly

antilog $0 \cdot 2 = 10^{0 \cdot 2} = 1 \cdot 5849$

antilog $1 \quad = 10^1 \quad = 10$

antilog $1 \cdot 2 = 10^{1 \cdot 2} = 15 \cdot 849.$

The method we have used in this section for multiplying and dividing numbers can now be written in terms of logs.

To multiply or divide

(i)	Find the logs of the numbers
(ii)	Add or subtract the logs
(iii)	Find the antilog

We can now reproduce the table from page 263 in terms of logs and antilogs.

x	$\log x$		y	antilog y
1·0000	0		0	1·0000
1·2589	0·1		0·1	1·2589
1·5849	0·2		0·2	1·5849
1·9953	0·3		0·3	1·9953
2·5119	0·4		0·4	2·5119
3·1623	0·5		0·5	3·1623
3·9811	0·6		0·6	3·9811
5·0119	0·7		0·7	5·0119
6·3096	0·8		0·8	6·3096
7·9433	0·9		0·9	7·9433
10·000	1		1	10·000

In addition

$100 = 10^2$, so

$\log_{10} 100 = 2.$

Similarly

$\log_{10} 1000 = 3,$

$\log_{10} 10000 = 4,$

$\log_{10} 0 \cdot 1 = -1,$

etc.

Also

antilog 2 = 100,

antilog 3 = 1000,

antilog −1 = 0·1

etc.

The table on the left is a simple log table. You may be used to using log tables for calculations. Such tables usually provide a comprehensive list of logs of numbers between 1 and 10, starting at 1·0000 and going up in steps of 0·0001 to 10.

Logs to base 10 are often called common logs because they are used so frequently.

It is not necessary to know antilogs of all values of x since any positive number (x) can be expressed in the form

$$x = a \times 10^m$$

where a is a number between 1 and 10 and m is a whole number. If the original number is larger than 10, then m is positive; if the original number is less than 1 then m is negative. For example,

$$15\cdot849 = 1\cdot5849 \times 10^1$$

and

$$0\cdot15849 = 1\cdot5849 \times 10^{-1}.$$

$$\{x\} = \{a\} \times \{10^m\}$$

The log of a can be looked up in the table, so

$$\log_{10} x = m + \log_{10} a.$$

Thus

$$\log_{10} 15\cdot849 = 1 + \log_{10} 1\cdot5849 = 1 + 0\cdot2 = 1\cdot2$$

and

$$\log_{10} 0\cdot15849 = -1 + \log_{10} 1\cdot5849 = -1 + 0\cdot2 = -0\cdot8.$$

If you have used logs before you may have expected us to use '*bar logs*' for numbers less than 1. Using this convention we would write

$$\log_{10} 0\cdot15849 = \bar{1}\cdot2$$

where the 'bar' indicates that m is negative. This notation was adopted to make calculations involving logs more methodical. However, since we assume you have a calculator, we do not expect you to carry out calculations using log tables. The calculator is much quicker and more accurate as well! Consequently we are concerned with the *principles* involved in using logarithms rather than how to perform the calculations and where necessary we will always express logs using negative numbers.

TRY SOME YOURSELF

7    $\log_{10} 3 = 0\cdot4771$. Write down each of the following:
(i)   (a) $\log_{10} 30$ (b) $\log_{10} 3000$ (c) $\log_{10} 0\cdot03$ (d) $\log_{10} 0\cdot00003$.
(ii)   (a) antilog $2\cdot4771$ (b) antilog $4\cdot4771$ (c) antilog $-3\cdot5229$.

Your calculator may have a log key which automatically evaluates the log of a number. Try finding $\log_{10} 10$, $\log_{10} 100$ and $\log_{10} 0\cdot1$ using your calculator. You will find that your calculator also expresses logs using negative numbers rather than 'bar logs'.

Notice that logarithms are only defined for positive numbers.

This is just scientific notation.

From above
$$log_{10}\, 0\cdot15849 = -1 + log_{10}\, 1\cdot5849.$$
$$bar\ 1 \qquad 0\cdot2$$
Hence
$$log_{10}\, 0\cdot15849 = \bar{1}\cdot2.$$

So we will write
$$log_{10}\, 0\cdot15849 = -1 + 0\cdot2$$
$$= -0\cdot8.$$

Check with the maker's handbook how to find $log_{10}\, x$ or 'common logs'.

The table on the right on page 267 is an antilog table. Again, if you are used to using log tables for calculations then you will have seen more comprehensive tables than this one. The antilog converts a power of 10 back to a number between 1 and 10. You could use the y^x key on your calculator to find antilogs; alternatively, since the antilog 'undoes' the log, you may be able to use the inverse key in conjunction with the log key. Try finding $antilog_{10} 1$, $antilog_{10} 2$ and $antilog_{10} -1$ using your calculator.

Remember that antilog $x = 10^x$.

Check with the maker's handbook. This is similar to finding sin^{-1}, cos^{-1} and tan^{-1} etc.

We include the next example just to demonstrate the principles involved in using logarithms.

EXAMPLE

Use logs to evaluate $31 \cdot 5 \times 7 \cdot 6$.

SOLUTION

Using a calculator,

$$\log_{10} 31 \cdot 5 = 1 \cdot 4983 \text{ and } \log_{10} 7 \cdot 6 = 0 \cdot 8808.$$

To multiply two numbers we must add the logs, so

$$1 \cdot 4983 + 0 \cdot 8808 = 2 \cdot 3791.$$

Now we convert back to a number by finding the antilog.

Using a calculator

$$antilog_{10} 2 \cdot 3791 = 239 \cdot 4.$$

Hence $31 \cdot 5 \times 7 \cdot 6 = 239 \cdot 4$.

(i) First find the logs of the numbers.

(ii) Add or subtract logs.

(iii) Find antilog.

Check the answer using a calculator.

TRY SOME YOURSELF

8 Use logs to evaluate each of the following:
   (i) $57 \cdot 6 \div 28 \cdot 4$ (ii) $17 \cdot 6 \times 4 \cdot 3$ (iii) $0 \cdot 023 \times 14 \cdot 17 \div 0 \cdot 142$.

9.2(iii) THEORY OF LOGS

You may think that logs have little practical use now that calculators remove the drudgery from calculations. However, logs actually turn up in a variety of situations. Because of this, we feel that it is worthwhile examining the theory involved. We have concentrated on logs to base 10, where the log corresponds to the power of 10. Thus, if $x = 10^y$ then $y = \log_{10} x$.

For example, log graphs are often useful in displaying experimental data.

Now, if $x_1 = 10^{y_1}$ and $x_2 = 10^{y_2}$, then $\log_{10} x_1 = y_1$ and $\log_{10} x_2 = y_2$.

The product $x_1 x_2 = 10^{y_1} 10^{y_2} = 10^{y_1 + y_2}$, so

$$\log_{10} x_1 x_2 = y_1 + y_2$$
$$= \log_{10} x_1 + \log_{10} x_2.$$

This demonstrates the first rule for manipulating logs.

$$\log_{10} x_1 x_2 = \log_{10} x_1 + \log_{10} x_2 \qquad \textit{Rule 1}$$

Similarly,

$$\frac{x_1}{x_2} = x_1 \div x_2 = 10^{y_1} \div 10^{y_2} = 10^{y_1 - y_2}$$

$$\text{so } \log_{10} \left(\frac{x_1}{x_2} \right) = y_1 - y_2 = \log_{10} x_1 - \log_{10} x_2.$$

This gives a second rule for manipulating logs.

$$\log_{10} \left(\frac{x_1}{x_2} \right) = \log_{10} x_1 - \log_{10} x_2 \qquad \textit{Rule 2}$$

We now consider the power of a number.

If $x = 10^y$, then $\log_{10} x = y$.

Now $x^n = (10^y)^n$
$$= 10^{yn} \text{ or } 10^{ny} \qquad \textit{Using the rule } (a^m)^n = a^{mn}.$$

so $\log_{10} (x^n) = ny = n \log_{10} x.$

This gives a third rule.

$$\log_{10} (x^n) = n \log_{10} x \qquad \textit{Rule 3}$$

These rules allow logarithms to be manipulated without actually evaluating anything. The next examples show how expressions involving several logarithms can be simplified to a single log.

EXAMPLE

Simplify $\log_{10} 6 + \log_{10} 5$.

SOLUTION

$$\log_{10} 6 + \log_{10} 5 = \log_{10} (6 \times 5) = \log_{10} 30. \qquad \textit{Using Rule 1.}$$

EXAMPLE

Simplify $3 \log_{10} 2 - \log_{10} 4$.

SOLUTION

Consider the term $3 \log 2$.
$$3 \log_{10} 2 = \log_{10} 2^3 = \log_{10} 8. \qquad \textit{Using Rule 3.}$$

Now
$$\log_{10} 8 - \log_{10} 4 = \log_{10} \left(\frac{8}{4} \right) = \log_{10} 2. \qquad \textit{Using Rule 2.}$$

TRY SOME YOURSELF

9   Express each of the following as a single logarithm:

(i) $\log_{10} 2 + \log_{10} 6$ (ii) $\log_{10} 12 - \log_{10} 4$ (iii) $1 - \log_{10} 2 + \log_{10} 3$

(iv) $3 \log_{10} 2 - 2 \log_{10} 4$ (v) $2 \log_{10} a - \log_{10} b$.   *Remember that $10 = 10^1$.*

Other bases

In this section we have concentrated on common logarithms, based upon powers of 10, but the principle applies more generally and logarithms may be based upon the powers of any positive number.

For example,

$$8 = 2^3 \quad \text{(a power of 2)}$$

and $\log_2 8 = 3$ (log to base 2).   *The log to base 2 is the power of 2.*

Similarly

$$81 = 3^4 \quad \text{(a power of 3)}$$

and $\log_3 81 = 4$ (log to base 3).   *The log to base 3 is the power of 3.*

In general, if a number is expressed as a power of a then the logarithm to base a is given by the index. Thus

> if $x = a^n$
> then $\log_a x = n$.

TRY SOME YOURSELF

10   Write down each of the following:

(i) $\log_5 125$ (ii) $\log_3 9$ (iii) $\log_4 64$ (iv) $\log_3 \frac{1}{9}$

(v) $\log_2 \frac{1}{32}$ (vi) $\log_3 3$ (vii) $\log_3 1$.

The three rules we have introduced in this section actually apply to logs in any base. However, having outlined the principles involved for logs to base 10, we feel that any further investigation is best left to your future studies in mathematics.

After you have worked through this section you should be able to

a Multiply and divide numbers by
      (i)   expressing the numbers as powers of 10
      (ii) adding or subtracting the indices
      (iii) converting back to a number

b Express any positive number (x) in the form $x = a \times 10^m$ and hence find $\log x$ in terms of $\log a$ and m.
    In fact, $\log x = m + \log a$

c Find logarithms and antilogarithms using a calculator

d Multiply and divide numbers by adding or subtracting their logs

e Simplify expressions involving logarithms to a single term using the rules

    (1) $\log_{10} (x_1 x_2) = \log_{10} x_1 + \log_{10} x_2$

    (2) $\log_{10} \left(\dfrac{x_1}{x_2} \right) = \log_{10} x_1 - \log_{10} x_2$

    (3) $\log_{10} (x^n) = n \log_{10} x$

Finally, here are some exercises if you want more practice.

TRY SOME MORE YOURSELF

11(i) Use the table on page 263 to evaluate each of the following:

(a) $630 \cdot 96 \div 79433$ (b) $0 \cdot 12598 \times 0 \cdot 0019953 \div 0 \cdot 063096$

(c) $79 \cdot 433 \div 251 \cdot 19$ (d) $501 \cdot 19 \times 0 \cdot 079433 \div 15 \cdot 849$.

(ii) Given that $\log_{10} 4 = 0 \cdot 6021$ write down each of the following:

(a) $\log_{10} 40$ (b) $\log_{10} 400$ (c) $\log_{10} 0 \cdot 4$ (d) $\log_{10} 0 \cdot 004$

(e) antilog $3 \cdot 6021$ (f) antilog $-2 \cdot 3979$.

(iii) Express each of the following as a single logarithm:

(a) $\log_{10} 4 + \log_{10} 5$ (b) $\log_{10} 49 - 2 \log_{10} 7$

(c) $4 \log_{10} 2 - \log_{10} 8 + 2 \log_{10} 4$ (d) $1 + \log_{10} 6 - \log_{10} 1$.

9.3 Square Roots

TRY THESE QUESTIONS FIRST

1 Simplify $\sqrt{96}$.

2 Simplify each of the following:

(i) $3\sqrt{96} - 4\sqrt{54} + 2\sqrt{24}$

(ii) $(3\sqrt{3} + 5\sqrt{2})(\sqrt{6} - 3)$.

3 Rationalise $\dfrac{\sqrt{2} - \sqrt{5}}{2\sqrt{2} - \sqrt{5}}$.

9.3(i) SIMPLIFYING SQUARE ROOTS

In most cases, if a calculation involves a square root, then it is best to evaluate the square root using a calculator. However, there are instances where it is more accurate and more convenient to leave the answer in square root form. For example, it's often easier to work with sines, cosines and tangents in square root form (such as $\sin 60° = \dfrac{\sqrt{3}}{2}$, and $\cos 45° = \dfrac{1}{\sqrt{2}}$ etc.). Indeed, in mathematics it is often necessary to work with *exact* numbers, in which case it is essential to leave the quantity as a square root. In this section we consider how to manipulate square roots. You will find that they can be handled just like algebraic symbols, using the same rules and techniques.

See Module 8, Section 8.2(iii).

First of all we need to introduce another property of indices. Notice that

$$2^2 \times 3^2 = 4 \times 9 = 36 = 6^2 = (2 \times 3)^2$$

and

$$2^3 \times 3^3 = 8 \times 27 = 216 = 6^3 = (2 \times 3)^3.$$

Similarly

$$2^2 \times 5^2 = 4 \times 25 = 100 = 10^2 = (2 \times 5)^2$$

and

$$2^3 \times 5^3 = 8 \times 125 = 1000 = 10^3 = (2 \times 5)^3.$$

This suggests the rule

$$\boxed{a^n \times b^n = (ab)^n.}$$

In particular

$$(a^{1/2} \times b^{1/2})^2 = (a^{1/2})^2 \times (b^{1/2})^2 = ab$$

so

$$a^{1/2} \times b^{1/2} = (ab)^{1/2}$$

or

$$\sqrt{a} \times \sqrt{b} = \sqrt{ab}.$$

You can check this for yourself using a calculator with your own choice of numbers for a and b.

Sometimes it is possible to recognise the square root immediately (for example, $\sqrt{4} = 2$). You may also be able to identify square roots which cannot be simplified without a calculator (for example, $\sqrt{7}$). However there are many situations where it is difficult to 'spot' the square root immediately. In the next examples we use the rule

$$\sqrt{ab} = \sqrt{a} \times \sqrt{b}$$

to reduce square roots to their simplest form.

Remember that only positive numbers have square roots.

EXAMPLE

Simplify $\sqrt{12}$.

SOLUTION

Since $12 = 4 \times 3$

$$\sqrt{12} = \sqrt{4 \times 3}$$

$$= \sqrt{4} \times \sqrt{3}$$

$$= 2\sqrt{3}.$$

The expression is now in its simplest form since $\sqrt{3}$ cannot be simplified any further.

Using the rule $\sqrt{ab} = \sqrt{a} \times \sqrt{b}$.

$\sqrt{3}$ cannot be evaluated without a calculator, so it is left in square root form.

CHECK YOUR ANSWERS

1 $\sqrt{96} = \sqrt{16 \times 6} = 4\sqrt{6}$ — *Section 9.3(i)*

2 (i) $3\sqrt{96} - 4\sqrt{54} + 2\sqrt{24} = 12\sqrt{6} - 12\sqrt{6} + 4\sqrt{6}$ — *Section 9.3(ii)*

$= 4\sqrt{6}$

(ii) $(3\sqrt{3} + 5\sqrt{2})(\sqrt{6} - 3)$

$= (3\sqrt{3} \times \sqrt{6}) - (3 \times 3\sqrt{3}) + (5\sqrt{2} \times \sqrt{6}) - (5\sqrt{2} \times 3)$

$= 9\sqrt{2} - 9\sqrt{3} + 10\sqrt{3} - 15\sqrt{2}$

$= \sqrt{3} - 6\sqrt{2}$

3 $\dfrac{\sqrt{2} - \sqrt{5}}{2\sqrt{2} - \sqrt{5}} = \dfrac{(\sqrt{2} - \sqrt{5})(2\sqrt{2} + \sqrt{5})}{(2\sqrt{2} - \sqrt{5})(2\sqrt{2} + \sqrt{5})}$ — *Section 9.3(iii)*

$= \dfrac{(\sqrt{2} - \sqrt{5})(2\sqrt{2} + \sqrt{5})}{3}$

$= \dfrac{4 - 2\sqrt{10} - 5 + \sqrt{10}}{3}$

$= \dfrac{-1 - \sqrt{10}}{3}$

EXAMPLE

Simplify $\sqrt{72}$.

SOLUTION

We need to express 72 as a product of a *perfect square* and another factor.

A perfect square is a number whose square root is a whole number. For example, 4 (= 2^2), 9 (= 3^2), 16 (= 4^2) and 25 (= 5^2) are perfect squares.

$72 = 9 \times 8$, so

$\sqrt{72} = \sqrt{9 \times 8} = \sqrt{9} \times \sqrt{8}$

$= 3\sqrt{8}.$

But $\sqrt{8}$ can be simplified further by repeating the process.

$3\sqrt{8} = 3\sqrt{4 \times 2}$

$= 3(\sqrt{4} \times \sqrt{2}) = 3(2\sqrt{2})$

$= 6\sqrt{2}$

Of course, we could have written 72 = 36 x 2 immediately; the answer is exactly the same.

The expression is now in its simplest form, since $\sqrt{2}$ cannot be simplified any further.

These examples suggest a method for simplifying square roots.

> (i) Write the number under the square root as a product of a perfect square and another factor
> (ii) Now consider the other factor and repeat the process
> (iii) Eventually this process will give either a product of perfect squares (in which case the answer will be a whole number) or a square root which cannot be simplified (in which case the answer will be in terms of this square root)

The square root of the perfect square can be written down immediately.

TRY SOME YOURSELF

1 Write each of the following expressions in its simplest form:
(i) $\sqrt{18}$ (ii) $\sqrt{27}$ (iii) $\sqrt{80}$ (iv) $\sqrt{32}$ (v) $\sqrt{300}$
(vi) $\sqrt{576}$.

If you want, you can check your answers with a calculator.

A common application is found in the formula method for solving quadratic equations.

See Module 6, Section 6.5(i).

EXAMPLE

Solve $x^2 - 2x - 1 = 0$.

SOLUTION

Using the formula

$$x = \frac{2 \pm \sqrt{(-2)^2 - (4)(1)(-1)}}{2}$$

$$= \frac{2 \pm \sqrt{8}}{2}$$

$$= \frac{2 \pm \sqrt{4}\sqrt{2}}{2} = \frac{2 \pm 2\sqrt{2}}{2}$$

$$= 1 \pm \sqrt{2}.$$

The formula method states that the solutions to $ax^2 + bx + c = 0$ are given by

$$x = \frac{-b \pm \sqrt{b^2 - 4ac}}{2a}.$$

TRY SOME YOURSELF

2 Use the formula method to solve each of the following equations. Leave your answers in square root form:
(i) $y^2 - y - 1 = 0$ (ii) $2z^2 - 4z - 4 = 0$ (iii) $x^2 - 6x - 6 = 0$.

9.3(ii) ARITHMETIC OF SQUARE ROOTS

Adding and subtracting

Square roots are treated just like algebraic symbols in that only like terms can be added or subtracted. Thus, $\sqrt{2} + \sqrt{2} = 2\sqrt{2}$, but $\sqrt{2} + \sqrt{3}$ cannot be simplified any further.

Countdown to Mathematics

Expressions which involve two or more different roots can therefore be simplified by collecting like terms.

EXAMPLE

Simplify $3\sqrt{2} - 5\sqrt{3} + 7\sqrt{2} + 4\sqrt{3}$.

SOLUTION

$$3\sqrt{2} - 5\sqrt{3} + 7\sqrt{2} + 4\sqrt{3} = (3\sqrt{2} + 7\sqrt{2}) + (-5\sqrt{3} + 4\sqrt{3})$$
$$= 10\sqrt{2} - \sqrt{3}$$

Group like terms together then add or subtract as necessary.

However, it is not always so easy to identify like terms, as you may need to simplify the square roots first.

EXAMPLE

Simplify $\sqrt{27} - \sqrt{12}$.

SOLUTION

At first sight it looks as though this expression can't be simplified. However

$$\sqrt{27} = \sqrt{9 \times 3} = 3\sqrt{3}$$

and

$$\sqrt{12} = 2\sqrt{3}.$$

So $\sqrt{27} - \sqrt{12} = 3\sqrt{3} - 2\sqrt{3} = \sqrt{3}$.

TRY SOME YOURSELF

3   Simplify each of the following:
(i) $3\sqrt{5} - 2\sqrt{7} + 7\sqrt{5} - 3\sqrt{7}$ (ii) $\sqrt{32} + \sqrt{18}$
(iii) $2\sqrt{75} - 3\sqrt{48}$ (iv) $\sqrt{27} + 2\sqrt{48} + 2\sqrt{20} - \sqrt{12} - \sqrt{45}$.

Multiplication

The rule

$$\sqrt{a}\sqrt{b} = \sqrt{ab}$$

is used to multiply expressions involving square roots. Treat the square roots like algebraic symbols to multiply out the expressions initially, then simplify the square roots.

EXAMPLE

Simplify $\sqrt{2}(\sqrt{12} + 2\sqrt{2} + \sqrt{3})$.

SOLUTION

Multiply each of the terms inside the brackets by $\sqrt{2}$.

$$\sqrt{2}(\sqrt{12} + 2\sqrt{2} + \sqrt{3})$$
$$= (\sqrt{2} \times \sqrt{12}) + (\sqrt{2} \times 2\sqrt{2}) + (\sqrt{2} \times \sqrt{3})$$
$$= \sqrt{24} + 2\sqrt{4} + \sqrt{6}$$
$$= 2\sqrt{6} + 4 + \sqrt{6}$$
$$= 3\sqrt{6} + 4$$

Using the rule $\sqrt{a}\sqrt{b} = \sqrt{ab}$.

TRY SOME YOURSELF

4 Simplify each of the following:
(i) $\sqrt{6} \times \sqrt{3}$ (ii) $2\sqrt{15} \times 3\sqrt{5}$ (iii) $\sqrt{20} \times \sqrt{12} \times \sqrt{45}$
(iv) $\sqrt{2}(\sqrt{6} + 3\sqrt{3})$ (v) $\sqrt{3}(2\sqrt{2} - 4\sqrt{6} + \sqrt{18})$.

The same principle is used to multiply out more complicated expressions.

EXAMPLE

Simplify $(\sqrt{2} + \sqrt{3})(2\sqrt{2} + \sqrt{3})$.

SOLUTION

$$(\sqrt{2} + \sqrt{3})(2\sqrt{2} + \sqrt{3})$$

Multiply out the brackets just like $(a + b)(c + d)$.

$$(\sqrt{2} \times 2\sqrt{2}) + (\sqrt{2} \times \sqrt{3}) + (\sqrt{3} \times 2\sqrt{2}) + (\sqrt{3} \times \sqrt{3})$$
$$= 2\sqrt{4} + \sqrt{6} + 2\sqrt{6} + \sqrt{9}$$
$$= 4 + \sqrt{6} + 2\sqrt{6} + 3$$
$$= 7 + 3\sqrt{6}$$

Simplify square roots and collect like terms.

TRY SOME YOURSELF

5 Simplify each of the following:
(i) $(1 + \sqrt{2})(1 + 2\sqrt{2})$ (ii) $(1 + \sqrt{2})(2 + \sqrt{3})$
(iii) $(\sqrt{5} + \sqrt{2})(\sqrt{10} - 2\sqrt{2})$ (iv) $(\sqrt{3} - \sqrt{2})(\sqrt{3} + \sqrt{2})$.

9.3(iii) FRACTIONS INVOLVING SQUARE ROOTS

In the same way that $(ab)^n = a^n b^n$, so

$$\left(\frac{a}{b}\right)^n = \frac{a^n}{b^n}.$$

Check this for yourself by investigating $\frac{3^2}{2^2}$, $\frac{4^3}{3^3}$ etc.

In particular

$$\left(\frac{\sqrt{a}}{\sqrt{b}}\right)^2 = \frac{a}{b}, \text{ so } \sqrt{\frac{a}{b}} = \frac{\sqrt{a}}{\sqrt{b}}.$$

We now show how this property can be used to simplify fractions involving square roots.

EXAMPLE

Simplify $\dfrac{2\sqrt{18}}{3\sqrt{6}}$.

SOLUTION

$$\frac{2\sqrt{18}}{3\sqrt{6}} = \frac{2}{3}\sqrt{\frac{18}{6}} = \frac{2\sqrt{3}}{3}$$

Alternatively, $\sqrt{18} = 3\sqrt{2}$, so

$$\frac{2\sqrt{18}}{3\sqrt{6}} = \frac{2 \times 3\sqrt{2}}{3\sqrt{6}} = \frac{2\sqrt{2}}{\sqrt{6}} = 2\sqrt{\frac{2}{6}} = 2\sqrt{\frac{1}{3}} \text{ or } \frac{2}{\sqrt{3}}.$$

This shows that $\dfrac{2\sqrt{3}}{3} = \dfrac{2}{\sqrt{3}}$.

One of these expressions $\left(\dfrac{2}{\sqrt{3}}\right)$ perhaps looks neater, but it involves a square root in the denominator. $\dfrac{2\sqrt{3}}{3}$ may look a little more complicated but the square root is now in the numerator. It's often desirable to express a fraction in a form where the denominator involves no square roots. If the denominator originally contains a square root then the fraction must be rewritten so that the only square roots occur in the numerator. This process is known as *rationalisation*.

$\sqrt{1} = 1$, so

$$\sqrt{\frac{1}{3}} = \frac{1}{\sqrt{3}}$$

$$\frac{2\sqrt{3}}{3} = 2\sqrt{\frac{3}{9}} = 2\sqrt{\frac{1}{3}} = \frac{2}{\sqrt{3}}.$$

EXAMPLE

Rationalise $\dfrac{2}{\sqrt{3}}$.

SOLUTION

To get rid of the $\sqrt{3}$ in the denominator we need to multiply it by $\sqrt{3}$. But this means we must also multiply the numerator by $\sqrt{3}$. Thus

$$\frac{2}{\sqrt{3}} = \frac{2 \times \sqrt{3}}{\sqrt{3} \times \sqrt{3}} = \frac{2\sqrt{3}}{\sqrt{9}} = \frac{2\sqrt{3}}{3}.$$

The denominator now contains no square roots so the fraction is rationalised.

In general, to rationalise a fraction of the form $\dfrac{a}{\sqrt{b}}$, multiply the numerator and denominator by $\sqrt{b}$. Thus

$$\frac{a}{\sqrt{b}} = \frac{a \times \sqrt{b}}{\sqrt{b} \times \sqrt{b}} = \frac{a\sqrt{b}}{b}.$$

Notice that $\sqrt{b} \times \sqrt{b} = \sqrt{b^2} = b.$

TRY SOME YOURSELF

6   Simplify each of the following. Give your answers in rationalised form:

(i) $\dfrac{10}{\sqrt{12}}$ (ii) $\dfrac{\sqrt{5}}{\sqrt{2}}$ (iii) $5\sqrt{2} + \dfrac{2}{\sqrt{2}}$ (iv) $\dfrac{1}{\sqrt{5}} + \dfrac{1}{\sqrt{20}}$.

Each answer must consist of a single fraction. The denominator contains no square roots.

We now consider how to rationalise fractions in which the denominators consist of more than one term.

We have already shown that

$$(\sqrt{3} - \sqrt{2})(\sqrt{3} + \sqrt{2}) = 3 - 2 = 1.$$

See Exercise 5(iv) above.

This is a special case of the general result

$$(a - b)(a + b) = a^2 - b^2.$$

Check this by multiplying out the brackets.

For the moment we will be concerned with this result in the form

$$(\sqrt{a} - \sqrt{b})(\sqrt{a} + \sqrt{b}) = a - b.$$

This can be used to rationalise a fraction in which the denominator has the form $(\sqrt{a} + \sqrt{b})$ or $(\sqrt{a} - \sqrt{b})$.

EXAMPLE

Rationalise $\dfrac{1}{\sqrt{3} - \sqrt{2}}$.

SOLUTION

Since $(\sqrt{3} - \sqrt{2})(\sqrt{3} + \sqrt{2}) = 3 - 2 = 1$, we can remove the square roots from the denominator by multiplying it by $(\sqrt{3} + \sqrt{2})$. This means that the numerator must also be multiplied by $(\sqrt{3} + \sqrt{2})$. Thus

$$\frac{1}{\sqrt{3} - \sqrt{2}} = \frac{1}{(\sqrt{3} - \sqrt{2})} \times \frac{(\sqrt{3} + \sqrt{2})}{(\sqrt{3} + \sqrt{2})} = \frac{\sqrt{3} + \sqrt{2}}{1}$$

$$= \sqrt{3} + \sqrt{2}.$$

If you want, you can check that
$$\frac{1}{\sqrt{3} - \sqrt{2}} = \sqrt{3} + \sqrt{2} \text{ using a}$$
calculator.

EXAMPLE

Rationalise $\dfrac{1 - \sqrt{3}}{2\sqrt{5} + \sqrt{3}}$.

SOLUTION

Since $(2\sqrt{5} + \sqrt{3})(2\sqrt{5} - \sqrt{3}) = 20 - 3 = 17$, we can remove the square roots from the denominator by multiplying the fraction by $\dfrac{(2\sqrt{5} - \sqrt{3})}{(2\sqrt{5} - \sqrt{3})}$. Thus

$(a - b)(a + b) = a^2 - b^2$, where $a = 2\sqrt{5}$ and $b = \sqrt{3}$.

$$\frac{1-\sqrt{3}}{2\sqrt{5}+\sqrt{3}} = \frac{(1-\sqrt{3})}{(2\sqrt{5}+\sqrt{3})} \times \frac{(2\sqrt{5}-\sqrt{3})}{(2\sqrt{5}-\sqrt{3})}$$

$$= \frac{(1-\sqrt{3})(2\sqrt{5}-\sqrt{3})}{17}$$

$$= \frac{2\sqrt{5}-(\sqrt{3}\times2\sqrt{5})-\sqrt{3}+(\sqrt{3}\times\sqrt{3})}{17}$$

Multiply out the numerator, and simplify the square roots.

$$= \frac{2\sqrt{5}-2\sqrt{15}-\sqrt{3}+3}{17}.$$

Notice that the denominator now contains no square roots.

EXAMPLE

Rationalise $\dfrac{\sqrt{3}-\sqrt{2}}{3\sqrt{2}+2\sqrt{3}}$.

SOLUTION

We need to multiply by $\dfrac{3\sqrt{2}-2\sqrt{3}}{3\sqrt{2}-2\sqrt{3}}$.

$$\frac{\sqrt{3}-\sqrt{2}}{3\sqrt{2}+2\sqrt{3}} = \frac{(\sqrt{3}-\sqrt{2})}{(3\sqrt{2}+2\sqrt{3})} \times \frac{(3\sqrt{2}-2\sqrt{3})}{(3\sqrt{2}-2\sqrt{3})}$$

(3√2 + 2√3)(3√2 − 2√3)
= (9 x 2) − (4 x 3)
= 18 − 12 = 6

$$= \frac{(\sqrt{3}-\sqrt{2})(3\sqrt{2}-2\sqrt{3})}{6}$$

$$= \frac{(\sqrt{3}\times3\sqrt{2})-(\sqrt{3}\times2\sqrt{3})-(\sqrt{2}\times3\sqrt{2})+(\sqrt{2}\times2\sqrt{3})}{6}$$

Multiply out the numerator and simplify.

$$= \frac{3\sqrt{6}-6-6+2\sqrt{6}}{6}$$

$$= \frac{5\sqrt{6}-12}{6}$$

Again, there are no square roots in the denominator.

TRY SOME YOURSELF

7   Rationalise each of the following fractions:

(i) $\dfrac{\sqrt{2}}{\sqrt{3}-\sqrt{2}}$ (ii) $\dfrac{21}{\sqrt{18}+\sqrt{11}}$ (iii) $\dfrac{2\sqrt{5}-\sqrt{2}}{\sqrt{5}-\sqrt{2}}$

(iv) $\dfrac{19-7\sqrt{10}}{3\sqrt{5}-\sqrt{2}}$.

After you have worked through this section you should be able to

a   Reduce a square root to its simplest form
b   Add, subtract and multiply numerical expressions involving square roots
c   Rationalise a fraction by removing the square roots from the denominator

Finally, here are some exercises if you want more practice.

TRY SOME MORE YOURSELF

8(i)   Simplify each of the following:
    (a) $\sqrt{60}$ (b) $\sqrt{160}$ (c) $\sqrt{432}$.

(ii)   Solve each of the following equations. Leave your answers in square root form.
    (a) $4x^2 - 2x - 1 = 0$ (b) $y^2 + 8y - 4 = 0$ (c) $2c^2 + 2c - 1 = 0$.

(iii)   Simplify each of the following:
    (a) $\sqrt{48} - \sqrt{12}$ (b) $\sqrt{8} + \sqrt{32} - 2\sqrt{2}$ (c) $2\sqrt{3}(3 + \sqrt{3})$
    (d) $(2\sqrt{5} + 1)(\sqrt{2} - \sqrt{5})$ (e) $(\sqrt{5} + \sqrt{3})(2\sqrt{3} - \sqrt{5})$.

(iv)   Rationalise each of the following:

(a) $\dfrac{3 + \sqrt{3}}{\sqrt{2}}$ (b) $\dfrac{\sqrt{3}}{\sqrt{2} - \sqrt{3}}$ (c) $\dfrac{7}{\sqrt{9} + \sqrt{5}}$ (d) $\dfrac{2\sqrt{3} - 3\sqrt{5}}{\sqrt{5} - \sqrt{3}}$.

9.4 Indices (II)

TRY THESE QUESTIONS FIRST

1   Simplify

$$\frac{(x^2 y^{-1})^3}{(x^{1/3} y)^{1/2}} \times (x^{1/6} y^{-1/2})^{-5}.$$

2   Simplify $(3\sqrt{a} + 2\sqrt{b})(\sqrt{a} - 7\sqrt{b})$.

3   Expand $(3x^2 y + 4y^2)(2xy^3 + 4xy^5)$.

9.4(i) MANIPULATING INDICES IN ALGEBRAIC EXPRESSIONS

We now consider how to simplify more complicated expressions involving indices. The techniques required are exactly the same as those used in Sections 9.1 and 9.3; the rules are summarised here for easy reference.

CHECK YOUR ANSWERS

1 $\dfrac{(x^2y^{-1})^3}{(x^{1/3}y)^{1/2}} \times (x^{1/6}y^{-1/2})^{-5}$ *Section 9.4(i)*

$= (x^2y^{-1})^3(x^{1/3}y)^{-1/2}(x^{1/6}y^{-1/2})^{-5}$

$= (x^6y^{-3})(x^{-1/6}y^{-1/2})(x^{-5/6}y^{5/2})$

$= x^5y^{-1} = \dfrac{x^5}{y}$

2 $(3\sqrt{a} + 2\sqrt{b})(\sqrt{a} - 7\sqrt{b})$

$= 3a + 2\sqrt{ab} - 21\sqrt{ab} - 14b$ *Section 9.4(ii)*

$= 3a - 19\sqrt{ab} - 14b$

3 $(3x^2y + 4y^2)(2xy^3 + 4xy^5)$ *Section 9.4(iii)*

$= 6x^3y^4 + 12x^3y^6 + 8xy^5 + 16xy^7$

$a^m a^n = a^{(m+n)}$

$(a^m)^n = a^{mn}$

$(ab)^n = a^n b^n$

$\left(\dfrac{a}{b}\right)^n = \dfrac{a^n}{b^n}$

These rules hold for any values of m and n, positive or negative, whole number or fraction. The last two rules are particularly useful in that they allow complicated expressions to be broken down into simpler components.

EXAMPLE

Simplify $(2x^3y^2)^2$.

SOLUTION

Using the rule $(ab)^n = a^n b^n$

$$(2x^3y^2)^2 = 2^2((x^3)^2)((y^2)^2)$$
$$= 4x^{(3\times 2)}y^{(2\times 2)}$$
$$= 4x^6y^4.$$

Split up the expression so that each symbol can be treated separately.

In the next example we show that there are two approaches that are suitable for simplifying fractions.

EXAMPLE

Simplify $\left(\dfrac{z^3}{x^2}\right)^{-4}$.

SOLUTION

$$\frac{z^3}{x^2} = z^3 x^{-2}$$

$$\text{so} \left(\frac{z^3}{x^2}\right)^{-4} = (z^3 x^{-2})^{-4}$$

$$= ((z^3)^{-4})((x^{-2})^{-4})$$

$$= z^{-12} x^8 = \frac{x^8}{z^{12}}.$$

Since $\frac{1}{x^2} = x^{-2}$ the fraction can be converted to a product, which is easier to handle.

Alternatively,

$$\left(\frac{z^3}{x^2}\right)^{-4} = \frac{(z^3)^{-4}}{(x^2)^{-4}} = \frac{z^{-12}}{x^{-8}}$$

$$= \frac{1}{z^{12}} \div \frac{1}{x^8} = \frac{x^8}{z^{12}}.$$

This second approach often leads to more complicated manipulation (as in this example). Consequently it is probably good practice to convert the fraction to a product before simplifying.

$$(x^2)^{-4}$$

TRY SOME YOURSELF

1 Simplify each of the following:

(i) (a) $(a^2)^5$ (b) $(x^{-4})^3$ (c) $(z^{-2})^{-3}$

(ii) (a) $(x^2 y)^3$ (b) $(3xz^{-1})^{-1}$ (c) $\left(\frac{a}{b}\right)^{-2}$ (d) $\left(\frac{ab^2}{c^3}\right)^2$

(e) $\left(\frac{3x^{-1}}{x^2}\right)^2$.

Use whichever method you find easiest.

We now consider some examples in which the indices are fractions. The expressions can be simplified using the same rules, but the manipulation is probably more complicated just because fractions are harder to handle than whole numbers.

EXAMPLE

Simplify (i) $a^{2/3} a^{-4/3}$

(ii) $(a^{2/3})^{-4/3}$.

SOLUTION

(i) $a^{2/3} a^{-4/3} = a^{2/3 + (-4/3)} = a^{-2/3}$

(ii) $(a^{2/3})^{-4/3} = a^{2/3 \times (-4/3)} = a^{-8/9}$

$a^m a^n = a^{m+n}$

$(a^m)^n = a^{mn}$

TRY SOME YOURSELF

2   Simplify each of the following:

(i)   (a) $16^{1/2} \times 16^{1/4}$ (b) $9^{1/2} \times 9^{-1/4}$ (c) $a^{1/5}a^{1/6}$

(d) $\dfrac{a^{1/4}}{a^{1/2}}$.

(ii)   (a) $(4^{1/2})^{1/3}$ (b) $(b^{1/3})^{-1/4}$ (c) $(c^{-1/3})^{3/2}$.

EXAMPLE

Simplify $(16a^4b^{-1/2})^{-1/2}$.

SOLUTION

$$(16a^4b^{-1/2})^{-1/2} = (16)^{-1/2}(a^4)^{-1/2}(b^{-1/2})^{-1/2}$$

$$= (2^4)^{-1/2}a^{-2}b^{1/4}$$

$$= 2^{-2}a^{-2}b^{1/4}$$

$$= \frac{b^{1/4}}{4a^2}$$

Split up the expression so that each symbol is handled separately. Write 16 as 2^4 in order to simplify.

Finally, write in terms of positive indices only.

The next example shows how the product of two or more expressions can be simplified, using the same approach. Again, it is probably easiest to break the expressions down so that you can handle each symbol separately.

EXAMPLE

Simplify $(3a^{-1/2}b^{1/3})^{-3} \times 2(ab^2)^{-3/2}$.

SOLUTION

First consider $(3a^{-1/2}b^{1/3})^{-3}$.

$$(3a^{-1/2}b^{1/3})^{-3} = ((3)^{-3})((a^{-1/2})^{-3})((b^{1/3})^{-3})$$

$$= 3^{-3}a^{3/2}b^{-1}$$

Consider each expression separately.

Leave the expression as a product.

Similarly

$$2(ab^2)^{-3/2} = 2(a)^{-3/2}(b^2)^{-3/2}$$

$$= 2a^{-3/2}b^{-3}.$$

Notice that 2 is not in the brackets, so it must be left as it is.

Now

$$(3a^{-1/2}b^{1/3})^{-3} \times 2(ab^2)^{-3/2} = (3^{-3}a^{3/2}b^{-1}) \times (2a^{-3/2}b^{-3})$$

$$= (3^{-3} \times 2)(a^{3/2}a^{-3/2})(b^{-1}b^{-3})$$

$$= \frac{2a^0b^{-4}}{3^3}$$

$$= \frac{2}{27b^4}.$$

Rearrange the expression so that the coefficients and like symbols are next to each other.

Remember that $a^0 = 1$.

Write the answer in terms of positive indices only.

With practice you will be able to simplify expressions like this more quickly, for you may not need to consider each expression separately, and you may be able to carry out several steps at once. However, if you do get into difficulties you will find that it helps to break the expressions down and proceed in a methodical manner, one step at a time.

TRY SOME YOURSELF

3   Simplify each of the following. Give your answers in terms of positive indices only:

(i) $(a^3 x^{-3} y^{-1})^2 \times (y x^3)^3$ (ii) $(a^{1/3} b^{2/3})^2 \times (a^4 b^{-1})^{1/3}$

(iii) $(x^{2/3} y^{-1/2})^{3/4} (x^{2/3} y^{3/4})^{1/2}$ (iv) $(16 a^2)^{-1/4} (27 a^3)^{1/3}$.

It is probably best to convert fractions to products since this makes the manipulation a bit easier.

EXAMPLE

Simplify $\dfrac{(a^2 b)^{1/2}}{(a b^{-2})^2}$.

(ab^{-2})

SOLUTION

$$\frac{(a^2 b)^{1/2}}{(a b^{-2})^2} = (a^2 b)^{1/2} \times (a b^{-2})^{-2}$$

$$= (a^{2 \times 1/2})(b^{1/2}) \times (a^{-2})(b^{-2 \times -2})$$

$$= a^1 b^{1/2} a^{-2} b^4$$

$$= a a^{-2} b^{1/2} b^4$$

$$= a^{-1} b^{9/2}$$

$$= \frac{b^{9/2}}{a}$$

$\dfrac{1}{(ab^{-2})^2} = (ab^{-2})^{-2}$.

Treat each symbol separately.

Simplify indices.

Put like symbols together and simplify.

Write the answer in terms of positive indices only.

TRY SOME YOURSELF

4   Simplify each of the following. Give your answers in terms of positive indices only:

(i) $\left(\dfrac{1}{ab}\right)^{-2}$ (ii) $\dfrac{(3x^{-1})^2}{x}$ (iii) $\dfrac{(3x^{-1})^2}{(x^2)^{-1}}$ (iv) $\dfrac{a^{1/2} a^{1/3}}{(a^{1/2})^{1/3}}$

(v) $\dfrac{(8x^2 y)^{1/3}}{(16 x^{1/3} y)^{1/2}}$ (vi) $\dfrac{(a^2 b^{-3/2})^3 (a^{-2} b^6)^{1/2}}{(a^4 b)^{1/2}}$.

9.4(ii) SQUARE ROOTS

In Section 9.3 we were concerned with the square roots of numbers. In many ways it is easier to work with square roots of algebraic expressions since it is easier to identify exact squares. For example, it is possible to write down $\sqrt{a^2b^2c}$ immediately $(ab\sqrt{c})$ but it is less obvious that $\sqrt{108} = 6\sqrt{3}$.

$\sqrt{a^2} = a \text{ and } \sqrt{b^2} = b$
$\sqrt{108} = \sqrt{9 \times 4 \times 3}$

Square roots of algebraic symbols are manipulated just like the symbols themselves.

EXAMPLE

Simplify $(\sqrt{a} + \sqrt{b})(\sqrt{a} + \sqrt{b})$.

SOLUTION

$$(\sqrt{a} + \sqrt{b})(\sqrt{a} + \sqrt{b}) = (\sqrt{a})^2 + 2\sqrt{a}\sqrt{b} + (\sqrt{b})^2$$

$$= a + 2\sqrt{ab} + b$$

Compare this with
$(x + y)^2 = x^2 + 2xy + y^2.$

EXAMPLE

Rationalise $\dfrac{2}{3\sqrt{p} + 2\sqrt{q}}$.

See Section 9.3(iii).

SOLUTION

To remove the square roots from the denominator we must multiply by $\dfrac{3\sqrt{p} - 2\sqrt{q}}{3\sqrt{p} - 2\sqrt{q}}$. Thus

$$\frac{2}{3\sqrt{p} + 2\sqrt{q}} = \frac{2}{(3\sqrt{p} + 2\sqrt{q})} \times \frac{(3\sqrt{p} - 2\sqrt{q})}{(3\sqrt{p} - 2\sqrt{q})}$$

$$= \frac{2(3\sqrt{p} - 2\sqrt{q})}{9p - 4q}$$

$$= \frac{6\sqrt{p} - 4\sqrt{q}}{9p - 4q}.$$

$(3\sqrt{p} + 2\sqrt{q})(3\sqrt{p} - 2\sqrt{q})$
$= 9p - 4q$
which contains no square roots.

TRY SOME YOURSELF

5(i) Simplify each of the following:
  (a) $\sqrt{x^2yz^2}$ (b) $\sqrt{r}(\sqrt{r} + \sqrt{rs})$ (c) $(1 + \sqrt{b})(3 - \sqrt{b})$
  (d) $(2\sqrt{c} + \sqrt{d})(\sqrt{c} - 3\sqrt{d})$.

(ii) Rationalise each of the following:
  (a) $\dfrac{x}{\sqrt{2y}}$ (b) $\dfrac{1}{\sqrt{a} - \sqrt{b}}$ (c) $\dfrac{3\sqrt{m} + 2\sqrt{n}}{\sqrt{m} - 3\sqrt{n}}$.

9.4(iii) EXPANDING BRACKETS

Finally we return to the manipulation of algebraic expressions.

We now investigate how to expand brackets which involve more complicated terms, using the rules for manipulating indices.

See Module 2, Section 2.3(iii) and Module 6, Section 1.1(iii).

You should be able to expand $(a + b)^2$ without any trouble:

$$(a + b)^2 = a^2 + 2ab + b^2.$$

But it's not so easy to expand $(3p^2 + 4q^3)^2$.

This can be done by substitution, putting $a = 3p^2$ and $b = 4q^3$, in which case

$$(a + b)^2 = (3p^2 + 4q^3)^2$$

and

$$
\begin{aligned}
a^2 + 2ab + b^2 &= (3p^2)^2 + 2(3p^2)(4q^3) + (4q^3)^2 \\
&= 3^2((p^2)^2) + 2(3)(4)p^2q^3 + (4)^2((q^3)^2) \\
&= 9p^4 + 24p^2q^3 + 16q^6.
\end{aligned}
$$

Thus $(3p^2 + 4q^3)^2 = 9p^4 + 24p^2q^3 + 16q^6$.

Again, you'll probably find it easiest to work step by step rather than trying to take short cuts.

TRY SOME YOURSELF

The   The following exercise provides some practice in substitution.

TRY SOME YOURSELF

6(i)   If $x = 2a$ and $y = 5a$, express each of the following expressions in terms of a:

(a) $2x^2y$ (b) $2x + 8y^2 + 3xy$ (c) $(3x^2)^2 - (2y^2)^3$.

(ii)   If $a = 2t^2$ and $b = 4s^3$, express each of the following expressions in terms of s and t:

(a) $(4ab)^2$ (b) $a^2 + 2ab + b^2$ (c) $2a^2b + 3ab^2 + (ab)^2$.

(iii)   Use the result

$$(a + b)^2 = a^2 + 2ab + b^2$$

to expand each of the following:

(a) $(x + 2y)^2$ (b) $(v^2w + 3v)^2$ (c) $(3x^2 + 2y^2)^2$.

However, substitution doesn't necessarily make the manipulation any easier, and in the next example it's best to multiply out the brackets immediately.

EXAMPLE

Expand $(3x^2 + 2y)(x^4 + 6y^5)$.

Countdown to Mathematics

SOLUTION

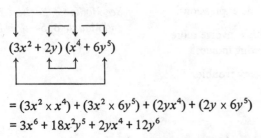

$$= (3x^2 \times x^4) + (3x^2 \times 6y^5) + (2yx^4) + (2y \times 6y^5)$$
$$= 3x^6 + 18x^2y^5 + 2yx^4 + 12y^6$$

Multiply out the brackets then simplify.

When the algebra becomes lengthy and tedious it is often tempting to take short cuts, but, unless you are absolutely confident in what you are doing, short cuts can be disastrous and it is better to take the long-winded approach which is more likely to lead to the correct answer. Consequently you should tackle the solution step by step, considering each term separately. This will help you to avoid unnecessary mistakes.

It is also true that practice makes the manipulation become easier. So, if you find it's hard work, you should try as many examples as you can.

TRY SOME YOURSELF

7   Expand each of the following:
   (i) $(q^2 + 3r^2)(4q + 5r^4)$ (ii) $(4p^4 + pq^2)(p^3 + 2q^2)$
   (iii) $(2x^3 + y^{-4})(3x^{-2} + y^2)$ (iv) $(a^2 + 3b)(a^4 + 2b^3 + b^2)$.

After you have worked through this section you should be able to

a   Use the following rules to simplify algebraic expressions
   $$a^m a^n = a^{(m+n)}$$
   $$(a^m)^n = a^{mn}$$
   $$(ab)^n = a^n b^n$$
   $$\left(\frac{a}{b}\right)^n = \frac{a^n}{b^n}$$

   where m and n may be positive or negative, whole numbers or fractions
b   Simplify an algebraic expression involving square roots, giving the answer in its simplest form
c   Expand brackets involving powers of symbols

Finally, here are some exercises if you want more practice.

TRY SOME MORE YOURSELF

8(i)   Simplify each of the following:
   (a) $(p^2 q^3)^4$ (b) $(p^2 q^3)^{3/4}$ (c) $\left(\frac{c^4 d}{d^{3/4}}\right)^4$.

(ii)   Simplify each of the following:

(a) $\dfrac{a^{3/2}b^{1/2}}{a^{1/2}b^{-5/2}}$ (b) $(3a^{1/2}b)^2 \times (4a^2b^8)^{1/2}$

(c) $\dfrac{(2x^{1/2}y)^2}{x^3y} \times (8xy)^{2/3}$ (d) $\dfrac{(3x^{5/4}y^{-4})^2}{(x^{-1/6}y)^3} \div (2x^2y^{-3})^2$.

(iii)   Rationalise each of the following:

(a) $\dfrac{2+\sqrt{a}}{2\sqrt{a}-1}$ (b) $\dfrac{2\sqrt{a}+1}{3+2\sqrt{a}}$ (c) $\dfrac{3\sqrt{a}+2\sqrt{b}}{\sqrt{b}-2\sqrt{a}}$.

(iv)   Expand each of the following:
(a) $(3x^4 - 2y^2)^2$ (b) $(2y^4 - 3y^2)(2y^4 + 3y^2)$
(c) $(6x^2 + 2y^3)(3x^2 + 4y^3)$ (d) $(2 + 3a^3)(1 + a + a^4)$.

9.5 *Factorisation*

TRY THESE QUESTIONS FIRST

1   Factorise $81a^2b^4 - 16a^2c^6$.

2   Factorise $3p^2 - 4pq - 4q^2$.

3   Completely factorise the expression $x^3y(xy + 12) + 35x^2$.

9.5(i) DIFFERENCE OF TWO SQUARES

In this section we consider how to factorise expressions which involve two or more different symbols. Hopefully, now that you have had some practice in manipulating powers of symbols, you will find that you can feel your way through the solutions. You will need to be quite systematic as it is easy to miss out a factor.

We start with a relatively easy situation.

In Sections 9.3 and 9.4 we used the result

$$(a - b)(a + b) = a^2 - b^2$$

to rationalise fractions.

We now consider the reverse process, namely rewriting $a^2 - b^2$ as a product of the factors $(a - b)(a + b)$. An expression such as $a^2 - b^2$ is called the *difference of two squares* and the difference of two squares always factorises into a product of the form

$$(a - b)(a + b).$$

Sometimes you can spot the squares immediately but it's not always so obvious.

Notice that the symbols are the same in each factor, just the sign is different.

EXAMPLE

Factorise $9y^2 - 4z^2$.

SOLUTION

$$9y^2 = (3y)^2$$

and $4z^2 = (2z)^2.$

So $9y^2 - 4z^2$ is the difference of two squares and

$$9y^2 - 4z^2 = (3y - 2z)(3y + 2z).$$

It's more difficult to spot the squares if fractions are involved.

EXAMPLE

Factorise $\dfrac{1}{4} - \dfrac{a^2}{9}$.

SOLUTION

$\dfrac{1}{4} = \left(\dfrac{1}{2}\right)^2$ and $\dfrac{a^2}{9} = \left(\dfrac{a}{3}\right)^2$, so

$$\frac{1}{4} - \left(\frac{a}{9}\right)^2 = \left(\frac{1}{2} - \frac{a}{3}\right)\left(\frac{1}{2} + \frac{a}{3}\right).$$

You may find it easier to rewrite $\dfrac{1}{4}$ as 2^{-2} and $\dfrac{a^2}{9}$ as (a^23^{-2}).

TRY SOME YOURSELF

1 Factorise each of the following expressions:
   (i) $25 - t^2$ (ii) $9x^2 - 4y^2$ (iii) $64 - p^4$ (iv) $a^4 - 16b^6$
   (v) $(x + y)^2 - (x - y)^2$.

Sometimes you may need to remove a common factor before spotting the difference of two squares. For example, at first sight the expression $5 - 125c^2$ does not appear to be a difference of two squares. But if the common factor, 5, is removed first, we get $5(1 - 25c^2)$, which can now be factorised to give

$$5(1 - 5c)(1 + 5c).$$

$1 = 1^2$ and $25c^2 = (5c)^2$.

TRY SOME YOURSELF

2 Factorise each of the following:
  (i) $18 - 2y^2$ (ii) $a^3 - 4a$ (iii) $3bx^2 - 12b$
  (iv) $5(x + y)^2 - 5$ (v) $12y^5 - 3y^3$.

Take out all the common factors first.

9.5(ii) FACTORISING QUADRATICS INVOLVING TWO SYMBOLS

In Module 6 we discussed how to factorise a quadratic expression of the form

$$ax^2 + bx + c.$$

Such an expression involves only one symbol, x. We now look at expressions which involve two symbols. The first problem is how to determine whether or not such an expression can be factorised. A quadratic expression in one symbol factorises into a product of the form

$$(ax + b)(cx + d).$$

Check by multiplying out the brackets.

Similarly, a quadratic expression involving two symbols, say, x and y, factorises into a product of the form

$$(ax + by)(cx + dy).$$

The simplest possible case is

$$(x + y)(x + y)$$

which corresponds to $x^2 + 2xy + y^2$.

This suggests that a quadratic expression must have a particular form if it is to be factorised. It must contain:

  (i) a term involving the square of one symbol.

x^2

It may also contain:

  (ii) a term involving the square of the other symbol

y^2

  (iii) a term involving the product of the two symbols.

$2xy$

Notice, however, that the coefficients of these terms may be zero.

It must contain NO OTHER TERMS.

For example, it may be possible to factorise

$$2x^2 + 3xy + y^2$$

as a quadratic but it is not possible to factorise

$$2x^2 + 3xy + y^2 + 3x + y$$

because of the terms $3x$ and y.

Of course, even if the expression has the right form it may not be possible to factorise; that depends upon the coefficients.

TRY SOME YOURSELF

3   Determine whether or not each of the following expressions could be factorised as a quadratic:
(i) $3x^2 - 4xy - y^2$ (ii) $2x^2 - 2y^2$ (iii) $a^2 + 2ab + b^2 + 1$
(iv) $a^2 + ab + b$.

Look at the form of the expression. Does it contain the right type of terms?

The following examples show that the method for factorising quadratics in two symbols is essentially the same as the method used for expressions involving one symbol. It, too, relies on inspection of the coefficients.

See Module 6, Section 6.2 and 6.3.

EXAMPLE

Factorise $a^2 + 3ab + 2b^2$.

SOLUTION

Consider factors of the form
$$(a + \square)(a + \square).$$

1   The coefficient of a^2 is 1 as required.

1 $a^2 + 3ab + 2b^2$

2   Now look at the term involving b^2.

$a^2 + 3ab + 2b^2$

$$(a + \square)(a + \square)$$

Since each bracket must contain a term involving b, there is only one possibility

$$(a + b)(a + 2b).$$

Look at the factors of $2b^2$. If each factor contains b, there is only one possibility, $b \times 2b$.

3   Check the coefficient of ab.

$$(a + b)(a + 2b)$$

$a^2 + 3ab + 2b^2$

Hence $a^2 + 3ab + 2b^2 = (a + b)(a + 2b)$.

In fact, if the quadratic has the form outlined above, then it must be factorised into the form

$$(a + \square b)(a + \square b)$$

in which case it is only necessary to look at the coefficients.

You can check that the process is the same by putting $b = 1$, in which case
$$a^2 + 3a + 2 = (a + 1)(a + 2)$$

EXAMPLE

Factorise $6y^2 + 5yz + z^2$.

SOLUTION

1   The quadratic has the right form. To ensure that the coefficient
    of y^2 is 6 there are two possibilities to consider

    $(6y + \square z)(y + \square z)$ and $(3y + \square z)(2y + \square z)$.

$\boxed{6}\, y^2 + 5yz + z^2$

2   Look at the coefficient of z^2. The coefficient is one, which
    means the factors must be

    $(6y + z)(y + z)$ or $(3y + z)(2y + z)$.

$6y^2 + 5yz \;\boxed{+}\; z^2$

3   Check the coefficient of yz.

    In $(6y + z)(y + z)$ the coefficient of yz is 7.

    In $(3y + z)(2y + z)$ the coefficient of yz is 5.

    Hence $6y^2 + 5yz + z^2 = (3y + z)(2y + z)$.

$6y^2 \;\boxed{+\,5}\; yz + z^2$

Check by multiplying out the brackets.

TRY SOME YOURSELF

4   Factorise each of the following expressions:
    (i) $a^2 + 3ab + 2b^2$ (ii) $5x^2 + 6xy + y^2$ (iii) $p^2 + 5pq + 4q^2$
    (iv) $30b^2 + 13bc + c^2$.

Check your answers by multiplying out the brackets.

The same analogy can be used when one or more of the coefficients
is negative.

See Module 6, Section 6.2.

EXAMPLE

Factorise $a^2 - 5ab + 6b^2$.

SOLUTION

The quadratic has the right form, and the coefficient of a^2 is one, so
it factorises into a product of the form

$(a + \square b)(a + \square b)$.

We need to find two numbers which multiply together to give 6
and whose sum is -5. This indicates that both factors are
negative, giving -2 and -3.

Hence $a^2 - 5ab + 6b^2 = (a - 2b)(a - 3b)$.

Again, you can check that the method is the same as that for factorising expressions involving one symbol by putting $b = 1$, in which case the quadratic is $a^2 - 5a + 6$.

Check by multiplying out the brackets.

EXAMPLE

Factorise $a^2 - ab - 6b^2$.

SOLUTION

Consider $(a + \square b)(a + \square b)$.

The coefficient of a^2 is one as required. We need to find two
numbers which multiply together to give -6 and whose sum is -1.
This indicates that one factor must be positive and the other
negative, giving -3 and 2.

Hence $a^2 - ab - 6b^2 = (a - 3b)(a + 2b)$.

Check by multiplying out the brackets.

TRY SOME YOURSELF

5   Factorise each of the following:
(i) $a^2 - ab - 2b^2$ (ii) $x^2 - 3xy + 2y^2$ (iii) $b^2 - 7bc - 8c^2$
(iv) $b^2 - 4bc + 4c^2$.

Check your answers by mutliplying out the brackets.

More complicated expressions in two symbols can also be
factorised by looking at the coefficients.

EXAMPLE

Factorise $3a^2 + 7ab + 2b^2$.

See Module 6, Section 6.3.

SOLUTION

Consider $(\square a + \square b)(\square a + \square b)$.

Put b = 1 and compare the solution to that for $3a^2 + 7a + 2$.

We need to find two numbers which multiply together to give
$3 \times 2 = 6$, and whose sum is 7. Trial and error produces the
numbers 6 and 1. Now consider the two pairs of numbers
$(3, 6)$ and $(3, 1)$.

The highest common factor of 3 and 6 is 3, so the two pairs reduce
to $(1, 2)$ and $(3, 1)$.

Hence $3a^2 + 7ab + 2b^2 = (a + 2b)(3a + b)$.

Check by multiplying out the brackets.

The next example is as difficult as any you are likely to meet.

EXAMPLE

Factorise $16x^2 + 14xy - 15y^2$.

Compare this with $16x^2 + 14x - 15$.

SOLUTION

Look at the coefficients.

We need to find two numbers which multiply together to give
-16×15 and whose sum is 14. Trial and error produces the
numbers -24 and 10.

Now consider the two pairs of numbers $(16, -24)$ and $(16, 10)$.

Divide each pair of numbers by its highest common factor.

These reduce to $(2, -3)$ and $(8, 5)$.

Hence $16x^2 + 14xy - 15y^2 = (2x + 3y)(8x - 5y)$.

Check by multiplying out the brackets.

TRY SOME YOURSELF

6   Factorise each of the following:
(i) $4b^2 + 8bc + 3c^2$ (ii) $2p^2 - 5pq - 12q^2$ (iii) $6a^2 - 7ab + 2b^2$.

Check your answers by multiplying out the brackets.

There is another common form of expression related to the quadratic
which involves two symbols. This is perhaps easier to deal with than
the case we have just considered.

EXAMPLE

Factorise $x^2y^2 + 5xy + 4$.

SOLUTION

The easiest way to deal with this is to put $t = xy$, in which case the expression becomes

$$t^2 + 5t + 4.$$

This can be factorised immediately to give

$$(t + 1)(t + 4).$$

We can now substitute back to get

$$(xy + 1)(xy + 4).$$

With practice you will be able to spot the factors without substituting, but you may find it helps to substitute at first.

TRY SOME YOURSELF

7   Factorise each of the following:
(i) $2a^2b^2 + 3ab - 2$ (ii) $x^2y^2 + 7xy + 12$ (iii) $a^4b^2 - 4a^2b - 12$.

Check your answers by multiplying out the brackets.

9.5(iii) COMPLETE FACTORISATION

We have now considered several techniques for factorisation: taking out a common factor; the difference of two squares, and the factorisation of quadratics. Quite often, in order to factorise an expression *completely*, it is necessary to apply more than one technique. As a general rule you should always look for common factors first.

EXAMPLE

Factorise $a^2b + 2ab^2 - 3b^3$.

SOLUTION

b is a common factor, and

$$a^2b + 2ab^2 - 3b^3 = b(a^2 + 2ab - 3b^2).$$

Now $a^2 + 2ab - 3b^2$ is a quadratic and factorises into

$$(a + 3b)(a - b).$$

Hence

$$a^2b + 2ab^2 - 3b^3 = b(a + 3b)(a - b).$$

The expression is now completely factorised.

TRY SOME YOURSELF

8   Completely factorise each of the following:
(i) $x^2y^2 - 8x^2y - 20x^2$ (ii) $a^2x^2 - 2a^2x + a^2$
(iii) $a^2 - 2a^3b + a^4b^2$.

Look for common factors first.

Sometimes the expression must be multiplied out before it can be factorised.

EXAMPLE

Factorise $x(x + 1) + 6(x - 5)$.

SOLUTION

$$x(x + 1) + 6(x - 5) = x^2 + x + 6x - 30$$
$$= x^2 + 7x - 30$$
$$= (x + 10)(x - 3)$$

Multiply out the brackets first, then factorise.

TRY SOME YOURSELF

9   Factorise each of the following:
(i) $x(x + 1) + 6(x + 2)$ (ii) $3x(x + 1) - 2(3x + 3)$
(iii) $xy(4x + 3y) + x(y^2 + x^2)$.

Finally, we include an example just for completeness. We do not expect *you* to be able to factorise such expressions, but you should be able to follow our method.

Sometimes an expression may not have any common factors, but can be arranged into groups of terms involving common factors. This sometimes means that the expression *can* be factorised. However, the process involves trial and error and you may well find it difficult at the moment.

This example illustrates that the technique depends largely upon being able to spot factors. Consequently, it requires considerable experience, and luck!

EXAMPLE

Factorise $3xy - 3ab + 9bx - ay$.

SOLUTION

Your immediate reaction might be that this cannot possibly be factorised.

However, the expression can be rearranged as

$$3xy + 9bx - 3ab - ay.$$

Here, the expression has been written in a different order.

Now consider the two groups

$$(3xy + 9bx) \text{ and } (-3ab - ay)$$

$3x$ is a common factor of $3xy$ and $9bx$ and a is a common factor of $-3ab$ and $-ay$.

Look at the common factors of the two pairs of terms.

Thus

$$3xy + 9bx - 3ab - ay = 3x(y + 3b) - a(3b + y)$$
$$= 3x(y + 3b) - a(y + 3b).$$

$(y + 3b)$ is now a common factor, so

$$3x(y + 3b) - a(y + 3b) = (y + 3b)(3x - a).$$

Check by multiplying out the brackets.

Notice that the original expression consists of four terms, all different. The technique consists of splitting the expression into two pairs and then taking out a common factor of each pair. Hopefully you should then be able to spot another common factor which allows the expression to be written as a product of factors.

*The difficulty lies in splitting the expression up into the **right** pairs. This is where trial and error, and experience are required.*

After you have worked through this section you should be able to

a Factorise the difference of two squares
b Factorise a quadratic involving two symbols
c Completely factorise an expression by
      (i)   taking out any common factors
      (ii) multiplying out the brackets if necessary and simplifying
      (iii) factorising the resulting expression

Finally here are some exercises if you want more practice.

TRY SOME MORE YOURSELF

10   Completely factorise each of the following expressions:
(i)   (a) $a^4 - a^2$ (b) $(2x + 3y)^2 - 4(x + y)^2$
       (c) $(x - y - 1)^2 - (x - 2y)^2$

(ii)   (a) $a^2 - 5ab + 4b^2$ (b) $x^2 + 2xy - 8y^2$ (c) $y^2 - 10yz + 16z^2$
       (d) $a^2 + 4ab - 12b^2$ (e) $y^2 - yz - 12z^2$ (f) $a^2 - 9ab + 20b^2$

(iii)   (a) $x^2 + (m + n)x + mn$ (b) $abx^2 + (a + b)x + 1$
       (c) $abx^2 + c(a + b)x + c^2$

(iv)   (a) $16y^2 - 8xy - 3x^2$ (b) $4y^2 - 21yz + 5z^2$
       (c) $6a^2 + 13ab + 6b^2$

(v)   (a) $t^4 - 5t^3 - 14t^2$ (b) $kp^2 - 4kp - 12k$
       (c) $5x^2y^2 - 2x^3y - 2xy^3$ (d) $4a^2b^2 - 6ab^3 - 4b^4$

(vi)   (a) $x(2x + 7y) + 3y^2$ (b) $3x(x + 3y) - y(x - 5y)$
       (c) $2p(1 + pq) + p^2q(1 - 2pq).$

Section 9.1 Solutions

1
(i)   (a) 125 (b) 243 (c) 0·04 ($\frac{1}{25}$)
       (d) 0·03125 ($\frac{1}{32}$) (e) -32 (f) 25

(ii)   These answers are given correct to three significant figures.
       (a) 3·44 (b) 0·0188 (c) 35 400 (d) $-0·0648$

2
(i)   (a) $2^2 \times 2^3 = 2^{2 + 3} = 2^5 = 32$
       (b) $3^2 \times 3^{-3} = 3^{2 + (-3)} = 3^{2 - 3} = 3^{-1} = \frac{1}{3}$
       (c) $(-2)^4 \times (-2) = (-2)^4 \times (-2)^1$
           $= (-2)^{4 + 1} = (-2)^5 = -(2^5) = -32$
       (d) $2^{-2} \times 2^{-3} = 2^{(-2) + (-3)} = 2^{-5} = \frac{1}{2^5} = \frac{1}{32}$
       (e) $5^2 \times 5^{-3} \times 5^4 \times 5^{-1} = 5^{2 + (-3) + 4 + (-1)}$
           $= 5^2 = 25$

Solutions

(ii)   (a) $b^2 \times b^9 = b^{2+9} = b^{11}$
       (b) $y^{-4} \times y^5 = y^{-4+5} = y^1 = y$
       (c) $z^4z^{-3}z^2 = z^{4+(-3)+2} = z^3$
       (d) $cc^4c^{-9}c^4 = c^{1+4+(-9)+4} = c^0 = 1$

3

(i)   (a) $3^2 \div 3^5 = 3^{2-5} = 3^{-3} = \dfrac{1}{3^3} = \dfrac{1}{27}$

       (b) $2^{-2} \div 2^4 = 2^{-2-4} = 2^{-6} = \dfrac{1}{2^6} = \dfrac{1}{64}$

       (c) $4^{-2} \div 4^{-5} = 4^{-2-(-5)} = 4^3 = 64$
       (d) $3^4 \times 3^{-2} \div 3^{-4} \div 3^5 \times 3 = 3^{4-2-(-4)-5+1}$
$$= 3^2 = 9$$
       (e) $106^{11} \times 106^{-3} \div 106^8 = 106^{11+(-3)-8}$
$$= 106^0 = 1$$

(ii)   (a) $a^2 \div a^9 = a^{2-9} = a^{-7}$
       (b) $z^{-4} \div z^6 = z^{-4-6} = z^{-10}$
       (c) $q^3 \div q^{-4} = q^{3-(-4)} = q^7$
       (d) $a^2 \times a^{-3} \div a^4 = a^{2-3-4} = a^{-5}$
       (e) $c \div c^{-4} \times c^2 \times 1 = c^{1-(-4)+2+0} = c^7$

4

(i)   (a) $(2^2)^2 = 2^{2 \times 2} = 2^4 = 16$
       (b) $(2^3)^{-2} = 2^{3 \times (-2)} = 2^{-6} = \frac{1}{64}$
       (c) $(3^2)^4 = 3^{2 \times 4} = 3^8$
       (d) $(4^{-5})^{-2} = 4^{(-5) \times (-2)} = 4^{10}$

(ii)   (a) $(a^{12})^3 = a^{12 \times 3} = a^{36}$
       (b) $(z^{-2})^{-3} = z^{(-2) \times (-3)} = z^6$
       (c) $(e^4)^{-2} = e^{4 \times (-2)} = e^{-8}$
       (d) $(e^{-3})^4 = e^{(-3) \times 4} = e^{-12}$

5

(i) 2   (ii) 3   (iii) 4

6

(i) 3   (ii) 2   (iii) 5
(iv) $0 \cdot 5(\frac{1}{2})$ (v) $0 \cdot 67(\frac{2}{3})$

7

(i) $27^{4/3} = (27^{1/3})^4 = 3^4 = 81$
(ii) $64^{-5/6} = (64^{1/6})^{-5} = 2^{-5} = \frac{1}{32}$
(iii) $(625)^{-3/4} = (625^{1/4})^{-3} = 5^{-3} = \frac{1}{125}$
(iv) $\left(\dfrac{1}{4}\right)^{5/2} = \left(\left(\dfrac{1}{4}\right)^{1/2}\right)^5 = \left(\dfrac{1}{2}\right)^5 = \dfrac{1}{32}$
(v) $\left(\dfrac{8}{27}\right)^{2/3} = \left(\left(\dfrac{8}{27}\right)^{1/3}\right)^2 = \left(\dfrac{2}{3}\right)^2 = \dfrac{4}{9}$

8

(i) $(b^5)^{3/5} = b^{5 \times 3/5} = b^3$
(ii) $(c^4)^{5/2} = c^{4 \times 5/2} = c^{10}$
(iii) $(d^{-6})^{4/3} = d^{(-6) \times 4/3} = d^{-8}$
(iv) $(f^{-4})^{-5/2} = f^{(-4) \times (-5/2)} = f^{10}$

9

(i)   (a) $81^{3/4} = (3^4)^{3/4} = 3^3 = 27$
       (b) $9^{5/2} = (3^2)^{5/2} = 3^5 = 243$
       (c) $16^{-3/4} = (2^4)^{-3/4} = 2^{-3} = \frac{1}{8}$
       (d) $125^{-2/3} = (5^3)^{-2/3} = 5^{-2} = \frac{1}{25}$
       (e) $\left(\dfrac{1}{27}\right)^{4/3} = \left(\dfrac{1}{3^3}\right)^{4/3} = (3^{-3})^{4/3} = 3^{-4} = \frac{1}{81}$
       (f) $\left(\dfrac{1}{8}\right)^{-2/3} = \left(\dfrac{1}{2^3}\right)^{-2/3} = (2^{-3})^{-2/3} = 2^2 = 4$

(ii)   (a) $\left(\dfrac{8}{27}\right)^{-4/3} = \left(\left(\dfrac{2}{3}\right)^3\right)^{-4/3} = \left(\dfrac{2}{3}\right)^{-4} = \dfrac{1}{(2/3)^4}$
$$= \dfrac{81}{16}$$

       (b) $\left(\dfrac{16}{81}\right)^{3/2} = \left(\left(\dfrac{2}{3}\right)^4\right)^{3/2} = \left(\dfrac{2}{3}\right)^6 = \dfrac{64}{729}$

       (c) $\left(\dfrac{125}{8}\right)^{-4/3} = \left(\left(\dfrac{5}{2}\right)^3\right)^{-4/3} = \left(\dfrac{5}{2}\right)^{-4} = \dfrac{1}{(5/2)^4}$
$$= \dfrac{16}{625}$$

       (d) $\left(\dfrac{9}{4}\right)^{5/2} = \left(\left(\dfrac{3}{2}\right)^2\right)^{5/2} = \left(\dfrac{3}{2}\right)^5 = \dfrac{243}{32}$

10

(i)   (a) $22 \cdot 3$ (b) $0 \cdot 0618$ (c) 189   (d) $-0 \cdot 142$
(ii)   (a) $2^5 = 32$ (b) $3^4 = 81$ (c) a^{-7} (d) x
(iii)   (a) 4^{-16} (b) 2^{-12} (c) a^{30} (d) y^8
(iv)   (a) z^9 (b) x^{12} (c) $2^6 = 64$ (d) $2^3 = 8$
      (e) $\frac{16}{9}$ (f) $\frac{27}{8}$

Section 9.2 Solutions

1

(i) $10 \times 10 = 10^1 \times 10^1 = 10^2 = 100$
(ii) $10 \times 100 = 10^1 \times 10^2 = 10^3 = 1000$
(iii) $1000 \times 10\,000 = 10^3 \times 10^4 = 10^7$
$$= 10\,000\,000$$

2

(i) $1 \cdot 5849 \times 2 \cdot 5119 = 3 \cdot 9811$
       $10^{0 \cdot 2} \times 10^{0 \cdot 4} = 10^{0 \cdot 6}$

(ii) $1 \cdot 2589 \times 1 \cdot 9953 = 2 \cdot 5119$
       $10^{0 \cdot 1} \times 10^{0 \cdot 3} = 10^{0 \cdot 4}$

(iii) $5 \cdot 0119 \times 1 \cdot 5849 = 7 \cdot 9433$
       $10^{0 \cdot 7} \times 10^{0 \cdot 2} = 10^{0 \cdot 9}$

3

(i) $3 \cdot 9811 \times 3 \cdot 1623 = 10^{0 \cdot 6} \times 10^{0 \cdot 5} = 10^{1 \cdot 1}$
       $= 10 \times 10^{0 \cdot 1} = 10 \times 1 \cdot 2589 = 12 \cdot 589$
(ii) $7 \cdot 9433 \times 2 \cdot 5119 = 10^{0 \cdot 9} \times 10^{0 \cdot 4} = 10^{1 \cdot 3}$
       $= 10 \times 10^{0 \cdot 3} = 10 \times 1 \cdot 9953 = 19 \cdot 953$
(iii) $6 \cdot 3096 \times 7 \cdot 9433 = 10^{0 \cdot 8} \times 10^{0 \cdot 9} = 10^{1 \cdot 7}$
       $= 10 \times 10^{0 \cdot 7} = 50 \cdot 119$

4

(i) $25 \cdot 119 = 10 \times 2 \cdot 5119 = 10^{1 \cdot 4}$ and
$50 \cdot 119 = 10 \times 5 \cdot 0119 = 10^{1 \cdot 7}.$
So $25 \cdot 119 \times 50 \cdot 119 = 10^{1 \cdot 4} \times 10^{1 \cdot 7} = 10^{3 \cdot 1}$
$= 10^3 \times 10^{0 \cdot 1} = 1258 \cdot 9.$

(ii) $125 \cdot 89 \times 31 \cdot 623 = 10^{2 \cdot 1} \times 10^{1 \cdot 5} = 10^{3 \cdot 6}$
$= 10^3 \times 10^{0 \cdot 6} = 3981 \cdot 1$

(iii) $1584 \cdot 9 \times 39 \cdot 811 = 10^{3 \cdot 2} \times 10^{1 \cdot 6} = 10^{4 \cdot 8}$
$= 10^4 \times 10^{0 \cdot 8} = 63096$

5

(i) $0 \cdot 19953 = 10^{-1} \times 1 \cdot 9953 = 10^{-1} \times 10^{0 \cdot 3} = 10^{-0 \cdot 7}$
and
$0 \cdot 31623 = 10^{-1} \times 3 \cdot 1623 = 10^{-1} \times 10^{0 \cdot 5} = 10^{-0 \cdot 5}.$
$0 \cdot 19953 \times 0 \cdot 31623 = 10^{-0 \cdot 7} \times 10^{-0 \cdot 5} = 10^{-1 \cdot 2}$
$= 10^{-2} \times 10^{0 \cdot 8} = 0 \cdot 063096$

(ii) $0 \cdot 050119 \times 0 \cdot 63096 = 10^{-1 \cdot 3} \times 10^{-0 \cdot 2} = 10^{-1 \cdot 5}$
$= 10^{-2} \times 10^{0 \cdot 5} = 0 \cdot 031623$

(iii) $0 \cdot 079433 \times 0 \cdot 12589 \times 1 \cdot 9953 = 10^{-1 \cdot 7}$
$= 10^{-2} \times 10^{0 \cdot 3} = 0 \cdot 019953$

6

(i) $0 \cdot 19953 = 10^{-1} \times 10^{0 \cdot 3} = 10^{-0 \cdot 7},$
$794 \cdot 33 = 10^{2 \cdot 9}$ and $630 \cdot 96 = 10^{2 \cdot 8}$
$0 \cdot 19953 \times 794 \cdot 33 \div 630 \cdot 96$
$= 10^{-0 \cdot 7} \times 10^{2 \cdot 9} \div 10^{2 \cdot 8}$
$= 10^{-0 \cdot 7 + 2 \cdot 9 - 2 \cdot 8}$
$= 10^{-0 \cdot 6} = 10^{-1} \times 10^{0 \cdot 4} = 0 \cdot 25119.$

(ii) $0 \cdot 25119 = 10^{-1} \times 2 \cdot 5119 = 10^{-0 \cdot 6}$
$0 \cdot 25119 \div 7 \cdot 9433 \times 63 \cdot 096$
$= 10^{-0 \cdot 6} \div 10^{0 \cdot 9} \times 10^{1 \cdot 8}$
$= 10^{-0 \cdot 6 - 0 \cdot 9 + 1 \cdot 8}$
$= 10^{0 \cdot 3} = 1 \cdot 9953$

(iii) $0 \cdot 012589 = 10^{-2} \times 1 \cdot 2589 = 10^{-1 \cdot 9}$
$251 \cdot 19 \div 7943 \cdot 3 \times 0 \cdot 012589$
$= 10^{2 \cdot 4} \div 10^{3 \cdot 9} \times 10^{-1 \cdot 9}$
$= 10^{2 \cdot 4 - 3 \cdot 9 - 1 \cdot 9}$
$= 10^{-3 \cdot 4} = 10^{-4} \times 10^{0 \cdot 6} = 0 \cdot 00039811$

(iv) $31 \cdot 623 \div 63 \cdot 096 \div 0 \cdot 15849$
$= 10^{1 \cdot 5} \div 10^{1 \cdot 8} \div 10^{-0 \cdot 8}$
$= 10^{1 \cdot 5 - 1 \cdot 8 - (-0 \cdot 8)} = 10^{0 \cdot 5} = 3 \cdot 1623$

7

(i)   (a) $30 = 10^1 \times 3,$
so $\log_{10} 30 = 1 + \log_{10} 3 = 1 \cdot 4771.$
(b) $3000 = 10^3 \times 3,$
so $\log_{10} 3000 = 3 + \log_{10} 3 = 3 \cdot 4771.$
(c) $0 \cdot 03 = 10^{-2} \times 3,$ so $\log_{10} 0 \cdot 03$
$= -2 + \log_{10} 3 = -2 + 0 \cdot 4771 = -1 \cdot 5229.$
(d) $0 \cdot 00003 = 10^{-5} \times 3,$ so $\log_{10} 0 \cdot 00003$
$= -5 + \log_{10} 3 = -4 \cdot 5229.$

(ii)   (a) $2 \cdot 4771 = 2 + 0 \cdot 4771,$ so antilog $2 \cdot 4771$
$= 10^2 \times$ (antilog $0 \cdot 4771) = 10^2 \times 3 = 300.$
(b) $4 \cdot 4771 = 4 + 0 \cdot 4771,$
so antilog $4 \cdot 4771 = 10^4 \times 3 = 30\,000.$
(c) $-3 \cdot 5229 = -4 + 0 \cdot 4771,$
so antilog $-3 \cdot 5229 = 10^{-4} \times 3 = 0 \cdot 0003.$

8

(i) $\log_{10} 57 \cdot 6 - \log_{10} 28 \cdot 4 = 1 \cdot 7604 - 1 \cdot 4533$
$= 0 \cdot 3071$
so $57 \cdot 6 \div 28 \cdot 4 =$ antilog $0 \cdot 3071 = 2 \cdot 0282.$
(You should be able to evaluate this without
writing down any intermediate steps. Check
with the maker's handbook.)

(ii) $\log_{10} 17 \cdot 6 + \log_{10} 4 \cdot 3 = 1 \cdot 2455 + 0 \cdot 6335$
$= 1 \cdot 8790$
so $17 \cdot 6 \times 4 \cdot 3 =$ antilog $1 \cdot 8790 = 75 \cdot 68.$

(iii) $\log_{10} 0 \cdot 023 + \log_{10} 14 \cdot 17 - \log_{10} 0 \cdot 142$
$= -1 \cdot 6383 + 1 \cdot 1514 - (-0 \cdot 8477) = 0 \cdot 3608$
so $0 \cdot 023 \times 14 \cdot 17 \div 0 \cdot 142 =$ antilog $0 \cdot 3608$
$= 2 \cdot 2951.$

9

(i) $\log_{10} 2 + \log_{10} 6 = \log_{10} (2 \times 6) = \log_{10} 12$

(ii) $\log_{10} 12 - \log_{10} 4 = \log_{10} \left(\frac{12}{4}\right) = \log_{10} 3$

(iii) $1 - \log_{10} 2 + \log_{10} 3$
$= \log_{10} 10 - \log_{10} 2 + \log_{10} 3$
$= \log_{10} \frac{(10 \times 3)}{2} = \log_{10} 15$
(Notice that $\log_{10} = 1$ since $10 = 10^1.$)

(iv) $3 \log_{10} 2 - 2 \log_{10} 4 = \log_{10} (2^3) - \log_{10} (4^2)$
$= \log_{10} 8 - \log_{10} 16$
$= \log_{10} \left(\frac{8}{16}\right) = \log_{10} \left(\frac{1}{2}\right)$
Notice that $\log_{10} \left(\frac{1}{2}\right)$ can be written as $-\log_{10} 2,$
since $\log_{10} \left(\frac{1}{2}\right) = \log_{10} 1 - \log_{10} 2 = 0 - \log_{10} 2.$
(Notice that $\log_{10} 1 = 0$ since $1 = 10^0.$)

(v) $2 \log_{10} a - \log_{10} b = \log_{10} a^2 - \log_{10} b$
$= \log_{10} \left(\frac{a^2}{b}\right)$

10

(i) $125 = 5^3,$ so $\log_5 125 = 3.$

(ii) $9 = 3^2,$ so $\log_3 9 = 2.$

(iii) $64 = 4^3,$ so $\log_4 64 = 3.$

(iv) $\left(\frac{1}{9}\right) = 3^{-2},$ so $\log_3 \left(\frac{1}{9}\right) = -2.$

(v) $\left(\frac{1}{32}\right) = 2^{-5},$ so $\log_2 \left(\frac{1}{32}\right) = -5.$

(vi) $3 = 3^1,$ so $\log_3 (3) = 1.$

(vii) $1 = 3^0,$ so $\log_3 (1) = 0.$
Parts (vi) and (vii) illustrate that for any $a,$
$\log_a (a) = 1$ since $a = a^1$ for any a and
$\log_a (1) = 0,$ since $1 = a^0$ for any $a.$

Solutions

11

(i) (a) 0·0079433 (b) 0·0039811
(c) 0·31623 (d) 2·5119

(ii) (a) 1·6021 (b) 2·6021 (c) −0·3979
(d) −2·3979 (e) 4000 (f) 0·004

(iii) (a) $\log_{10} 20$ (b) $\log_{10} 1 = 0$
(c) $\log_{10} 32$ (d) $\log_{10} 60$

Section 9.3 Solutions

1

(i) $\sqrt{18} = \sqrt{9 \times 2} = 3\sqrt{2}$

(ii) $\sqrt{27} = \sqrt{9 \times 3} = 3\sqrt{3}$

(iii) $\sqrt{80} = \sqrt{16 \times 5} = 4\sqrt{5}$

(iv) $\sqrt{32} = \sqrt{16 \times 2} = 4\sqrt{2}$

(v) $\sqrt{300} = \sqrt{100 \times 3} = 10\sqrt{3}$

(vi) $\sqrt{576} = \sqrt{24 \times 24} = 24$

2

(i) $y = \dfrac{1 \pm \sqrt{1 + 4}}{2} = \dfrac{1 \pm \sqrt{5}}{2}$

(ii) $z = \dfrac{4 \pm \sqrt{16 + 4(2)(4)}}{4} = \dfrac{4 \pm \sqrt{48}}{4}$

$\quad = \dfrac{4\sqrt{3}}{4} = 1 \pm \sqrt{3}$

(iii) $x = \dfrac{6 \pm \sqrt{36 + 24}}{2} = \dfrac{6 \pm \sqrt{60}}{2}$

$\quad = \dfrac{6 \pm 2\sqrt{15}}{2} = 3 \pm \sqrt{15}$

3

(i) $3\sqrt{5} - 2\sqrt{7} + 7\sqrt{5} - 3\sqrt{7} = 10\sqrt{5} - 5\sqrt{7}$

(ii) $\sqrt{32} + \sqrt{18} = 4\sqrt{2} + 3\sqrt{2} = 7\sqrt{2}$

(iii) $2\sqrt{75} - 3\sqrt{48} = 10\sqrt{3} - 12\sqrt{3} = -2\sqrt{3}$

(iv) $\sqrt{27} + 2\sqrt{48} + 2\sqrt{20} - \sqrt{12} - \sqrt{45}$
$= 3\sqrt{3} + 8\sqrt{3} + 4\sqrt{5} - 2\sqrt{3} - 3\sqrt{5}$
$= 9\sqrt{3} + \sqrt{5}$

4

(i) $\sqrt{6} \times \sqrt{3} = \sqrt{6 \times 3} = \sqrt{18} = 3\sqrt{2}$

(ii) $2\sqrt{15} \times 3\sqrt{5} = 6\sqrt{15 \times 5} = 30\sqrt{3}$

(iii) $\sqrt{20} \times \sqrt{12} \times \sqrt{45} = 2\sqrt{5} \times 2\sqrt{3} \times 3\sqrt{5}$
$\qquad = 12\sqrt{5 \times 3 \times 5} = 60\sqrt{3}$

(iv) $\sqrt{2}(\sqrt{6} + 3\sqrt{3}) = \sqrt{12} + 3\sqrt{6}$
$\qquad = 2\sqrt{3} + 3\sqrt{6}$

(v) $\sqrt{3}(2\sqrt{2} - 4\sqrt{6} + \sqrt{18})$
$= 2\sqrt{6} - 4\sqrt{18} + \sqrt{54}$
$= 2\sqrt{6} - 12\sqrt{2} + 3\sqrt{6}$
$= 5\sqrt{6} - 12\sqrt{2}$

5

(i) $(1 + \sqrt{2})(1 + 2\sqrt{2})$
$= 1 + 2\sqrt{2} + \sqrt{2} + (\sqrt{2} \times 2\sqrt{2})$
$= 1 + 3\sqrt{2} + 4$
$= 5 + 3\sqrt{2}$

(ii) $(1 + \sqrt{2})(2 + \sqrt{3}) = 2 + \sqrt{3} + 2\sqrt{2} + \sqrt{6}$

(iii) $(\sqrt{5} + \sqrt{2})(\sqrt{10} - 2\sqrt{2})$
$= \sqrt{50} - 2\sqrt{10} + \sqrt{20} - 4$
$= 5\sqrt{2} - 2\sqrt{10} + 2\sqrt{5} - 4$

(iv) $(\sqrt{3} - \sqrt{2})(\sqrt{3} + \sqrt{2})$
$= (\sqrt{3} \times \sqrt{3}) + (\sqrt{3} \times \sqrt{2}) - (\sqrt{2} \times \sqrt{3})$
$\qquad\qquad\qquad\qquad - (\sqrt{2} \times \sqrt{2})$
$= 3 + \sqrt{6} - \sqrt{6} - 2$
$= 1$

6

(i) $\dfrac{10}{\sqrt{12}} = \dfrac{10}{\sqrt{12}} \cdot \dfrac{\sqrt{12}}{\sqrt{12}} = \dfrac{10\sqrt{12}}{12}$

$\quad = \dfrac{10 \times 2\sqrt{3}}{12} = \dfrac{5\sqrt{3}}{3}$

(ii) $\dfrac{\sqrt{5}}{\sqrt{2}} = \dfrac{\sqrt{5}}{\sqrt{2}} \times \dfrac{\sqrt{2}}{\sqrt{2}} = \dfrac{\sqrt{10}}{2}$

(iii) $5\sqrt{2} + \dfrac{2}{\sqrt{2}} = 5\sqrt{2} + \dfrac{2}{\sqrt{2}} \times \dfrac{\sqrt{2}}{\sqrt{2}}$

$\qquad = 5\sqrt{2} + 2 = 6\sqrt{2}$

(iv) Notice here that a suitable common denominator is $2\sqrt{5}$, since $\sqrt{20} = \sqrt{4 \times 5} = 2\sqrt{5}$. Of course you may have chosen another common denominator. Alternatively you may have rationalised each fraction separately.

$\dfrac{1}{\sqrt{5}} + \dfrac{1}{\sqrt{20}} = \dfrac{1}{\sqrt{5}} + \dfrac{1}{2\sqrt{5}} = \dfrac{2+1}{2\sqrt{5}} = \dfrac{3}{2\sqrt{5}}$

$\qquad = \dfrac{3}{2\sqrt{5}} \times \dfrac{\sqrt{5}}{\sqrt{5}} = \dfrac{3\sqrt{5}}{10}$

7

(i) $\dfrac{\sqrt{2}}{\sqrt{3} - \sqrt{2}} = \dfrac{\sqrt{2}}{(\sqrt{3} - \sqrt{2})} \times \dfrac{(\sqrt{3} + \sqrt{2})}{(\sqrt{3} + \sqrt{2})}$

$\qquad = \dfrac{\sqrt{2}(\sqrt{3} + \sqrt{2})}{1} = \sqrt{6} + 2$

(ii) $\dfrac{21}{\sqrt{18} + \sqrt{11}} = \dfrac{21}{\sqrt{18} + \sqrt{11}} \times \dfrac{(\sqrt{18} - \sqrt{11})}{(\sqrt{18} - \sqrt{11})}$

$\qquad = \dfrac{21(\sqrt{18} - \sqrt{11})}{18 - 11}$

$\qquad = \dfrac{21(\sqrt{18} - \sqrt{11})}{7}$

$\qquad = 3(3\sqrt{2} - \sqrt{11})$

$\qquad = 9\sqrt{2} - 3\sqrt{11}$

(iii) $\dfrac{2\sqrt{5}-\sqrt{2}}{\sqrt{5}-\sqrt{2}} = \dfrac{(2\sqrt{5}-\sqrt{2})}{(\sqrt{5}-\sqrt{2})} \times \dfrac{(\sqrt{5}+\sqrt{2})}{(\sqrt{5}+\sqrt{2})}$

$= \dfrac{(2\sqrt{5}-\sqrt{2})(\sqrt{5}+\sqrt{2})}{5-2}$

$= \dfrac{10+2\sqrt{10}-\sqrt{10}-2}{3}$

$= \dfrac{8+\sqrt{10}}{3}$

(iv) $\dfrac{19-7\sqrt{10}}{3\sqrt{5}-\sqrt{2}} = \dfrac{(19-7\sqrt{10})}{(3\sqrt{5}-\sqrt{2})} \times \dfrac{(3\sqrt{5}+\sqrt{2})}{(3\sqrt{5}+\sqrt{2})}$

$= \dfrac{(19-7\sqrt{10})(3\sqrt{5}+\sqrt{2})}{45-2}$

$= \dfrac{57\sqrt{5}+19\sqrt{2}-21\sqrt{50}-7\sqrt{20}}{43}$

$= \dfrac{57\sqrt{5}+19\sqrt{2}-105\sqrt{2}-14\sqrt{5}}{43}$

$= \dfrac{43\sqrt{5}-86\sqrt{2}}{43}$

$= \sqrt{5}-2\sqrt{2}$

8
(i) (a) $2\sqrt{15}$ (b) $4\sqrt{10}$ (c) $12\sqrt{3}$

(ii) (a) $x = \dfrac{1\pm\sqrt{5}}{4}$ (b) $y = -4\pm2\sqrt{5}$

(c) $c = \dfrac{-1\pm\sqrt{3}}{2}$

(iii) (a) $2\sqrt{3}$ (b) $4\sqrt{2}$ (c) $6\sqrt{3}+6$
(d) $2\sqrt{10}+\sqrt{2}-\sqrt{5}-10$ (e) $1+\sqrt{15}$

(iv) (a) $\dfrac{3\sqrt{2}+\sqrt{6}}{2}$ (b) $-3-\sqrt{6}$
(c) $\dfrac{21-7\sqrt{5}}{4}$ (d) $\dfrac{-9-\sqrt{15}}{2}$

Section 9.4 Solutions

1
(i) (a) $(a^2)^5 = a^{2\times5} = a^{10}$
(b) $(x^{-4})^3 = x^{(-4)\times3} = x^{-12}$
(c) $(z^{-2})^{-3} = z^{(-2)\times(-3)} = z^6$

(ii) (a) $(x^2y)^3 = ((x^2)^3)y^3 = x^6y^3$
(b) $(3xz^{-1})^{-1} = (3^{-1})(x^{-1})((z^{-1})^{-1}) = 3^{-1}x^{-1}z = \dfrac{z}{3x}$
(c) $\left(\dfrac{a}{b}\right)^{-2} = (ab^{-1})^{-2} = (a^{-2})((b^{-1})^{-2}) = a^{-2}b^2 = \dfrac{b^2}{a^2}$
(d) $\left(\dfrac{ab^2}{c^3}\right)^2 = (ab^2c^{-3})^2 = (a^2)(b^4)(c^{-6}) = \dfrac{a^2b^4}{c^6}$
(e) $\left(\dfrac{3x^{-1}}{x^2}\right)^2 = (3x^{-1}x^{-2})^2 = (3x^{-3})^2 = (3^2)(x^{-6})$
$= \dfrac{9}{x^6}$

2
(i) (a) $16^{1/2}\times16^{1/4} = 16^{1/2+1/4} = 16^{3/4} = (2^4)^{3/4}$
$= 2^3 = 8$
(b) $9^{1/2}\times9^{-1/4} = 9^{1/2-1/4} = 9^{1/4} = (3^2)^{1/4}$
$= 3^{1/2} = \sqrt{3}$
(c) $a^{1/5}a^{1/6} = a^{1/5+1/6} = a^{11/30}$
(d) $\dfrac{a^{1/4}}{a^{1/2}} = a^{1/4}\times a^{-1/2} = a^{1/4-1/2} = a^{-1/4}$

(ii) (a) $(4^{1/2})^{1/3} = (4)^{1/2\times1/3} = 4^{1/6} = (2^2)^{1/6} = 2^{1/3}$
(b) $(b^{1/3})^{-1/4} = b^{1/3\times(-1/4)} = b^{-1/12}$
(c) $(c^{-1/3})^{3/2} = c^{(-1/3)\times3/2} = c^{-1/2}$

3
(i) $(a^3x^{-3}y^{-1})^2 = (a^3)^2(x^{-3})^2(y^{-1})^2 = a^6x^{-6}y^{-2}$
$(yx^3)^3 = y^3(x^3)^3 = y^3x^9$
So $(a^3x^{-3}y^{-1})^2 \times (yx^3)^3 = a^6x^{-6}y^{-2}y^3x^9$
$= a^6x^{-6}x^9y^{-2}y^3 = a^6x^3y.$

(ii) $(a^{1/3}b^{2/3})^2 = (a^{1/3})^2(b^{2/3})^2 = a^{2/3}b^{4/3}$
$(a^4b^{-1})^{1/3} = a^{4/3}b^{-1/3}$
So $(a^{1/3}b^{2/3})^2 \times (a^4b^{-1})^{1/3} = a^{2/3}b^{4/3}a^{4/3}b^{-1/3}$
$= a^{2/3}a^{4/3}b^{4/3}b^{-1/3}$
$= a^2b.$

(iii) $(x^{2/3}y^{-1/2})^{3/4} = (x^{2/3})^{3/4}(y^{-1/2})^{3/4} = x^{1/2}y^{-3/8}$
$(x^{2/3}y^{3/4})^{1/2} = (x^{2/3})^{1/2}(y^{3/4})^{1/2} = x^{1/3}y^{3/8}$
$(x^{2/3}y^{-1/2})^{3/4} \times (x^{2/3}y^{3/4})^{1/2} = x^{1/2}y^{-3/8}x^{1/3}y^{3/8}$
$= x^{1/2}x^{1/3}y^{-3/8}y^{3/8}$
$= x^{5/6}y^0 = x^{5/6}$

(iv) $(16a^2)^{-1/4} \times (27a^3)^{1/3}$
$= (2^4a^2)^{-1/4}(3^3a^3)^{1/3}$
$= (2^4)^{-1/4}(a^2)^{-1/4}(3^3)^{1/3}(a^3)^{1/3}$
$= 2^{-1}a^{-1/2}3a^1 = \tfrac{3}{2}a^{-1/2}a$
$= \dfrac{3}{2}a^{1/2}$

Solutions

4

(i) $\left(\dfrac{1}{ab}\right)^{-2} = ((ab)^{-1})^{-2}$ (since $\dfrac{1}{ab} = (ab)^{-1}$)

$= (ab)^2 = a^2b^2.$

(ii) $\dfrac{(3x^{-1})^2}{x} = (3x^{-1})^2 \times x^{-1}$ (since $\dfrac{1}{x} = x^{-1}$)

$= 3^2x^{-2}x^{-1} = 9x^{-3} = \dfrac{9}{x^3}.$

(iii) $\dfrac{(3x^{-1})^2}{(x^2)^{-1}} = (3x^{-1})^2 \times (x^2)$ (since $x^2 = \dfrac{1}{(x^2)^{-1}}$)

$= 9x^{-2}x^2 = 9.$

(iv) $\dfrac{a^{1/2}a^{1/3}}{(a^{1/2})^{1/3}} = (a^{1/2}a^{1/3}) \times (a^{1/2})^{-1/3}$

$= a^{1/2}a^{1/3}a^{-1/6} = a^{1/2 + 1/3 - 1/6} = a^{2/3}$

(v) $\dfrac{(8x^2y)^{1/3}}{(16x^{1/3}y)^{1/2}} = (8x^2y)^{1/3} \times (16x^{1/3}y)^{-1/2}$

$= 2x^{2/3}y^{1/3}2^{-2}x^{-1/6}y^{-1/2}$

$= 2^{-1}x^{1/2}y^{-1/6} = \dfrac{x^{1/2}}{2y^{1/6}}$

(vi) $\dfrac{(a^2b^{-3/2})^3(a^{-2}b^6)^{1/2}}{(a^4b)^{1/2}}$

$= (a^2b^{-3/2})^3 \times (a^{-2}b^6)^{1/2} \times (a^4b)^{-1/2}$

$= (a^2)^3(b^{-3/2})^3(a^{-2})^{1/2}(b^6)^{1/2}(a^4)^{-1/2}(b)^{-1/2}$

$= a^6b^{-9/2}a^{-1}b^3a^{-2}b^{-1/2}$

$= a^{6 - 1 - 2}b^{-9/2 + 3 - 1/2} = a^3b^{-2} = \dfrac{a^3}{b^2}$

5

(i) (a) $\sqrt{x^2yz^2} = xz\sqrt{y}$

(b) $\sqrt{r}(\sqrt{r} + \sqrt{rs}) = (\sqrt{r} \times \sqrt{r}) + (\sqrt{r} \times \sqrt{rs})$

$= \sqrt{r^2} + \sqrt{r^2s}$

$= r + r\sqrt{s}$ or $r(1 + \sqrt{s})$

(c) $(1 + \sqrt{b})(3 - \sqrt{b}) = 3 - \sqrt{b} + 3\sqrt{b} - b$

$= 3 + 2\sqrt{b} - b$

(d) $(2\sqrt{c} + \sqrt{d})(\sqrt{c} - 3\sqrt{d})$

$= 2\sqrt{c^2} - 6\sqrt{cd} + \sqrt{cd} - 3\sqrt{d^2}$

$= 2c - 5\sqrt{cd} - 3d$

(ii) (a) $\dfrac{x}{\sqrt{2y}} = \dfrac{x}{\sqrt{2y}} \times \dfrac{\sqrt{2y}}{\sqrt{2y}} = \dfrac{x\sqrt{2y}}{2y}$

(b) $\dfrac{1}{\sqrt{a} - \sqrt{b}} = \dfrac{1}{(\sqrt{a} - \sqrt{b})} \times \dfrac{(\sqrt{a} + \sqrt{b})}{(\sqrt{a} + \sqrt{b})}$

$= \dfrac{\sqrt{a} + \sqrt{b}}{a - b}$

(c) $\dfrac{3\sqrt{m} + 2\sqrt{n}}{\sqrt{m} - 3\sqrt{n}}$

$= \dfrac{(3\sqrt{m} + 2\sqrt{n})}{(\sqrt{m} - 3\sqrt{n})} \times \dfrac{(\sqrt{m} + 3\sqrt{n})}{(\sqrt{m} + 3\sqrt{n})}$

$= \dfrac{(3\sqrt{m} + 2\sqrt{n})(\sqrt{m} + 3\sqrt{n})}{m - 9n}$

$= \dfrac{3m + 9\sqrt{m}\sqrt{n} + 2\sqrt{m}\sqrt{n} + 6n}{m - 9n}$

$= \dfrac{3m + 11\sqrt{mn} + 6n}{m - 9n}$

6

(i) (a) $2x^2y = 2(2a)^2(5a)$

$= 2(4a^2)5a$

$= 40a^3$

(b) $2x + 8y^2 + 3xy = 2(2a) + 8(5a)^2 + 3(2a)(5a)$

$= 4a + 8(25a^2) + 30a^2$

$= 4a + 200a^2 + 30a^2$

$= 230a^2 + 4a$

(c) $(3x^2)^2 - (2y^2)^3 = 3^2(x^2)^2 - (2)^3(y^2)^3$

$= 9x^4 - 8y^6$

$= 9(2a)^4 - 8(5a)^6$

$= 9(16a^4) - 8(15\ 625a^6)$

$= 144a^4 - 125\ 000a^6$

(ii) (a) $(4ab)^2 = 16a^2b^2$

$= 16(2t^2)^2(4s^3)^2$

$= 16(4t^4)(16s^6)$

$= 1024s^6t^4$

(b) $a^2 + 2ab + b^2 = (2t^2)^2 + 2(2t^2)(4s^3) + (4s^3)^2$

$= 4t^4 + 16s^3t^2 + 16s^6$

(c) $2a^2b + 3ab^2 + (ab)^2$

$= 2a^2b + 3ab^2 + a^2b^2$

$= 2(2t^2)^2(4s^3) + 3(2t^2)(4s^3)^2 + (2t^2)^2(4s^3)^2$

$= 2(4t^4)(4s^3) + 3(2t^2)(16s^6) + (4t^4)(16s^6)$

$= 32s^3t^4 + 96s^6t^2 + 64s^6t^4$

(iii) (a) Put $a = x$, $b = 2y$.

Then $(x + 2y)^2 = x^2 + 2(x)(2y) + (2y)^2$

$= x^2 + 4xy + 4y^2.$

(b) Put $a = v^2w$, $b = 3v$.

Then $(v^2w + 3v)^2 = (v^2w)^2 + 2(v^2w)(3v) + (3v)^2$

$= v^4w^2 + 6v^3w + 9v^2.$

(c) Put $a = 3x^2$, $b = 2y^2$.

Then $(3x^2 + 2y^2)^2$

$= (3x^2)^2 + 2(3x^2)(2y^2) + (2y^2)^2$

$= 9x^4 + 12x^2y^2 + 4y^4.$

7

(i) $(q^2 + 3r^2)(4q + 5r^4)$

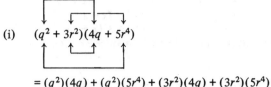

$$= (q^2)(4q) + (q^2)(5r^4) + (3r^2)(4q) + (3r^2)(5r^4)$$
$$= 4q^3 + 5q^2r^4 + 12qr^2 + 15r^6$$

(ii)

$(4p^4 + pq^2)(p^3 + 2q^2)$

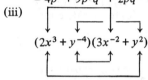

$$= (4p^4)(p^3) + (4p^4)(2q^2) + (pq^2)(p^3) + (pq^2)(2q^2)$$
$$= 4p^7 + 8p^4q^2 + p^4q^2 + 2pq^4$$
$$= 4p^7 + 9p^4q^2 + 2pq^4$$

(iii)

$(2x^3 + y^{-4})(3x^{-2} + y^2)$

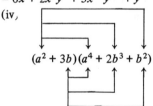

$$= (2x^3)(3x^{-2}) + (2x^3)(y^2) + (y^{-4})(3x^{-2}) + (y^{-4})(y^2)$$
$$= 6x + 2x^3y^2 + 3x^{-2}y^{-4} + y^{-2}$$

(iv,

$(a^2 + 3b)(a^4 + 2b^3 + b^2)$

$$= a^2a^4 + a^2(2b^3) + a^2b^2 + 3ba^4 + 3b(2b^3) + (3b)(b^2)$$
$$= a^6 + 2a^2b^3 + a^2b^2 + 3a^4b + 6b^4 + 3b^3$$

8

(i)   (a) p^8q^{12} (b) $p^{3/2}q^{9/4}$ (c) $c^{16}d$

(ii)   (a) ab^3 (b) $18a^2b^6$ (c) $\dfrac{16y^{5/3}}{x^{4/3}}$ (d) $\dfrac{9}{4xy^5}$

(iii)   (a) $\dfrac{2a + 5\sqrt{a} + 2}{4a - 1}$ (b) $\dfrac{3 + 4\sqrt{a} - 4a}{9 - 4a}$

        (c) $\dfrac{6a + 7\sqrt{ab} + 2b}{b - 4a}$

(iv)   (a) $9x^8 - 12x^4y^2 + 4y^4$ (b) $4y^8 - 9y^4$
        (c) $18x^4 + 30x^2y^3 + 8y^6$
        (d) $2 + 2a + 3a^3 + 5a^4 + 3a^7$

Section 9.5 Solutions

1
(i) $25 - t^2 = (5 - t)(5 + t)$
(ii) $9x^2 - 4y^2 = (3x - 2y)(3x + 2y)$
(iii) $64 - p^4 = (8 - p^2)(8 + p^2)$
(iv) $a^4 - 16b^6 = (a^2 - 4b^3)(a^2 + 4b^3)$
(v) $(x + y)^2 - (x - y)^2$
        $= ((x + y) - (x - y))((x + y) + (x - y))$
        $= (2y)(2x)$
        $= 4xy$

2
(i) $18 - 2y^2 = 2(9 - y^2) = 2(3 - y)(3 + y)$
(ii) $a^3 - 4a = a(a^2 - 4) = a(a - 2)(a + 2)$
(iii) $3bx^2 - 12b = 3b(x^2 - 4) = 3b(x - 2)(x + 2)$
(iv) $5(x + y)^2 - 5 = 5((x + y)^2 - 1)$
        $\qquad\qquad = 5(x + y - 1)(x + y + 1)$
(v) $12y^5 - 3y^3 = 3y^3(4y^2 - 1) = 3y^3(2y - 1)(2y + 1)$

3
(i)   Yes.
(ii)   Yes. The coefficient of xy is zero.
(iii)   No. There is an extra term, 1.
(iv)   No. The last term involves b, not b^2.

4   (i) $(a + 2b)(a + b)$ (ii) $(5x + y)(x + y)$
        (iii) $(p + 4q)(p + q)$ (iv) $(10b + c)(3b + c)$
        If you found these exercises hard, try putting
        one of the symbols equal to one. This converts
        each expression to a quadratic in one symbol
        and you can factorise using the methods
        discussed in Module 6.

5   (i) $(a - 2b)(a + b)$ (ii) $(x - 2y)(x - y)$
        (iii) $(b - 8c)(b + c)$ (iv) $(b - 2c)^2$

6
(i) $4b^2 + 8bc + 3c^2$
        Look at the coefficients. We need to find two
        numbers which multiply together to give
        $4 \times 3 = 12$ and whose sum is 8. The numbers
        are 6 and 2.
        Consider (4, 6) and (4, 2). These reduce to
        (2, 3) and (2, 1).
        Hence $4b^2 + 8bc + 3c^2 = (2b + 3c)(2b + c)$.
(ii) $2p^2 - 5pq - 12q^2$
        We need to find two numbers which multiply
        together to give $2 \times (-12) = -24$ and whose
        sum is -5. The numbers are -8 and 3.
        Consider (2, -8) and (2, 3). These reduce to
        (1, -4) and (2, 3).
        Hence $2p^2 - 5pq - 12q^2 = (p - 4q)(2p + 3q)$.

Solutions

(iii) $6a^2 - 7ab + 2b^2$
We need to find two numbers which multiply together to give $6 \times 2 = 12$ and whose sum is -7. The numbers are -3 and -4. Consider $(6, -3)$ and $(6, -4)$. These reduce to $(2, -1)$ and $(3, -2)$.
Hence $6a^2 - 7ab + 2b^2 = (2a - b)(3a - 2b)$.

7

(i) Putting $t = ab$ gives $2t^2 + 3t - 2$, which factorises into $(2t - 1)(t + 2)$.
Hence $2a^2b^2 + 3ab - 2 = (2ab - 1)(ab + 2)$.

(ii) Putting $t = xy$ gives $t^2 + 7t + 12$, which factorises into $(t + 4)(t + 3)$.
Hence $x^2y^2 + 7xy + 12 = (xy + 3)(xy + 4)$.

(iii) Putting $t = a^2b$ gives $t^2 - 4t - 12$, which factorises into $(t - 6)(t + 2)$.
Hence $a^4b^2 - 4a^2b - 12 = (a^2b - 6)(a^2b + 2)$.

8

(i) $x^2y^2 - 8x^2y - 20x^2 = x^2(y^2 - 8y - 20)$
$= x^2(y - 10)(y + 2)$

(ii) $a^2x^2 - 2a^2x + a^2 = a^2(x^2 - 2x + 1)$
$= a^2(x - 1)^2$

(iii) $a^2 - 2a^3b + a^4b^2 = a^2(1 - 2ab + a^2b^2)$
$= a^2(a^2b^2 - 2ab + 1)$
$= a^2(ab - 1)^2$

9

(i) $x(x + 1) + 6(x + 2) = x^2 + x + 6x + 12$
$= x^2 + 7x + 12$
$= (x + 3)(x + 4)$

(ii) $3x(x + 1) - 2(3x + 3) = 3x^2 + 3x - 6x - 6$
$= 3x^2 - 3x - 6$
$= 3(x - 2)(x + 1)$

(iii) $xy(4x + 3y) + x(y^2 + x^2) = x(y(4x + 3y) + y^2 + x^2)$
$= x(4xy + 3y^2 + y^2 + x^2)$
$= x(x^2 + 4xy + 4y^2)$
$= x(x + 2y)^2$

10

(i) (a) $a^2(a - 1)(a + 1)$ (b) $y(4x + 5y)$
(c) $(y - 1)(2x - 3y - 1)$

(ii) (a) $(a - 4b)(a - b)$ (b) $(x + 4y)(x - 2y)$
(c) $(y - 8z)(y - 2z)$ (d) $(a + 6b)(a - 2b)$
(e) $(y - 4z)(y + 3z)$ (f) $(a - 5b)(a - 4b)$

(iii) (a) $(x + m)(x + n)$ (b) $(ax + 1)(bx + 1)$
(c) $(ax + c)(bx + c)$

(iv) (a) $(4y - 3x)(4y + x)$ (b) $(y - 5z)(4y - z)$
(c) $(3a + 2b)(2a + 3b)$

(v) (a) $t^2(t - 7)(t + 2)$ (b) $k(p - 6)(p + 2)$
(c) $xy(x - 2y)(y - 2x)$
(d) $2b^2(2a + b)(a - 2b)$

(vi) (a) $(x + 3y)(2x + y)$ (b) $(3x + 5y)(x + y)$
(c) $p(1 + 2pq)(2 - pq)$